EUCLIDEAN GEOMETRY AND CONVEXITY

RUSSELL V. BENSON

California State College at Fullerton

EUCLIDEAN
GEOMETRY
AND CONVEXITY

McGRAW-HILL BOOK COMPANY

New York   St. Louis   San Francisco   Toronto   London   Sydney

EUCLIDEAN GEOMETRY AND CONVEXITY

Library of Congress Catalog Card Number 65-28585

04770

1234567890 MP 7321069876

TO BETTY

PREFACE

This text is intended to be used for an upper-division course in geometry suitable for any mathematics major whether he intends to teach, to work in industry, or to do graduate work in mathematics. In order to be of use to all three of these groups such a course must help train high school teachers, prepare students for further study in mathematics, and develop the student's geometric intuition. It is the author's contention that a course in euclidean geometry centered around the theory of convex sets is admirably suited to meet these objectives.

The text can be used roughly in any one of four ways:

a. All six chapters can be covered in two semesters of three units each.

b. If a three-unit course with emphasis on convexity is desired, Chaps. 2 and 4 can be covered along with selected topics from Chaps. 3 and 6.

c. If a three-unit course with emphasis on euclidean geometry is desired, Chaps. 1, 3, and 5 can be covered along with selected topics from Chap. 6.

d. Many sections are sufficiently self-contained that sections from each chapter could be covered in three units. For example, Secs. 1, 5, 6, 7, 8, 11, 12, 14, 17, 18, 20, 23, 24, 28, and 29 could be covered in a three-unit course.

Length, area, and volume are topics which are always covered in high school geometry courses. They are also topics which are almost always omitted from college geometry courses. The first chapter is an

vii

attempt to take these notions as presented in high school and reconcile them with the usual treatment given in elementary calculus. For example, Jordan plane measure is defined and shown to be an extension of the high school definition of the area of a circular region as well as a generalization of the integral definition of area. In Chap. 2 the basic properties of convex bodies are presented. The student is required to use indirect proofs a great deal in this chapter, and he is introduced to them by means of a number of short proofs. These proofs characterize convex bodies in terms of convex combinations of two points, the intersection of the boundary with lines through an interior point, supporting lines, and convex combinations of n points. Conjectures are easily made by the student in this chapter, but unfortunately their proofs (or disproofs) are often "loose," to say the least. Whenever there is a strong analogy between the proofs of two theorems, or whenever the proof of a theorem in E^n can be easily followed to give the proof of a similar theorem in E^m, $m \neq n$, then the second proof is left as a problem for the student. In this way it is hoped that the student will be able to produce "rigid" proofs and will appreciate the need for rigor as well as the need for conjecture.

Transformation theory is developed in Chap. 3 in a manner similar to that often given in college geometry texts, except that continuous transformations and vector set addition are also discussed. Properties of motions, dissections, set addition, and convex bodies are all tied together in a natural way through the concept of G-equidecomposable sets.

All the results of the first three chapters are used to some extent in the solution of extremum problems in Chap. 4. Sections 18 and 19 are probably the most difficult sections in the text. However, the author feels that a thorough discussion of Blaschke's selection theorem and the problem of surface area will be extremely helpful to the student. The selection theorem will give the student new insight into the limit concept, which will be helpful in future analysis and geometry courses and will also introduce him in a natural way to the important idea of a metric space different from euclidean space. The discussion of surface area should point out clearly to the student that this is far from being a closed subject and that there are many problems left to be answered.

The purpose of Chap. 5 is to introduce the student to n-dimensional euclidean space E^n and to extend much of the preceding work to E^n. The student reexamines the fundamental notions of length, area, volume, angle, etc., in 3-space and is made to appreciate the power of analytic methods when generalizing to E^n.

The final chapter is a short introduction to metric spaces, with most of the chapter devoted to geometric properties of n-dimensional Banach spaces (Minkowski spaces) $\mathfrak{M}^n$, $n = 2$ and 3.

Since euclidean geometry is a special kind of Minkowski geometry, properties of $\mathfrak{M}^n$ can often be conjectured from similar properties in E^n. This helps the student to give some "body" to his knowledge of metric spaces and at the same time highlights those properties which are unique to E^n and which are not general metric properties. In this way the student's knowledge of euclidean geometry is also enriched.

Consider now our three objectives. Clearly the combination of convexity, topological, and transformation properties used throughout the text will help to develop geometric intuition. The high school geometry teacher is asked to present material on length, area, volume, congruence, similarity, etc., all of which are covered here in depth. The theory of convex bodies is an active field of research today in many branches of mathematics, not only in geometry but in such fields as linear programming and the theory of games. It is the author's sincere hope that by meeting these objectives this text will serve in some small way to bring euclidean geometry back into the mainstream of the college mathematics curriculum.

The main sources of material on the theory of convex sets are "Theorie der Konvexen Körper" by Bonneson and Fenchel, "Convexity" by Eggleston, and "Convex Figures" by Yaglom and Boltyanskii. The first two books are at the graduate level, and an attempt has been made to select material from them suitable for upper-division students. The material in "Convex Figures" is all done in the plane, and we have generalized much of it to 3-space in Chaps. 2, 3, and 4.

Another source frequently used is "Vorlesungen über Inhalt, Oberfläche und Isoperimetrie" by Hadwiger. The blend of dissection theory and convexity developed by Hadwiger enables us to present material in Chaps. 1 and 3 which should easily convince students to discard the mistaken idea that all of euclidean geometry was completed 2,000 years ago.

The main reference for Chap. 6 is "Projective Geometry and Projective Metrics" by Busemann and Kelly. Other books referred to not so frequently will be found in the bibliography.

All the material has been used in the classroom, and we are indebted to the many students who patiently helped pick out inevitable errors. The author is particularly indebted to his teacher, Prof. Herbert Busemann, who first acquainted him with much of the enjoyment and fascination of geometry. Also, many thanks are due Miss Helen Kuntz, secretary to the mathematics department of California State College at Long Beach, for doing an excellent job of typing the manuscript.

Russell V. Benson

TO THE INSTRUCTOR

Since notation for lines, segments, and other geometric objects is not standard, Sec. 1 is devoted to explaining the notation we use. Other notation used in calculus and set theory, however, is assumed known. For example, "iff" is used for "if and only if," "sup" for "least upper bound," and "$\cap$" for "intersection." This is not meant to be a self-contained text, and notation and results from analytic geometry and calculus are used throughout. This applies to the postulates in Appendix 1 as well. The postulates are included as a pedagogic device only, and the text material is not developed in an axiomatic manner from these postulates. The proofs of theorems, however, are supposed to be rigorous, and any statement used in a proof should follow easily from known results in previous course work. If a student is not sure of the validity of some statement, he is urged to prove it from the given postulates. This gives a common frame of reference for all students regardless of background.

There has been a tendency in recent years to squeeze solid or three-dimensional euclidean geometry out of the mathematics curriculum. Material is either presented entirely in 2-space and later generalized directly to n-space or is presented entirely in n-space to begin with. Of course the student is urged to specialize (or generalize) this material to 3-space provided he has time. It is the author's contention that time should be taken to develop the student's knowledge of 3-space; therefore theorems and proofs are presented here which seem to be particularly suited to 3-space. For example, the proof of Helly's theorem in n-space (Theorem 25.9) is much shorter and more elegant than the proof of Helly's theorem in 3-space (Theorem 9.2). The latter proof, however, uses properties of 3-space the student might never become acquainted with if the shorter proof were used. It is for the same reason that we have purposely placed Chap. 5 after our development of 3-space. In this way we hope to ensure that properties of 3-space will not be slighted.

Much of the material (especially in Chaps. 2, 3, and 4) is presented here for the first time at this level in English. Since there are so few references for the student to use, each section includes more material than is needed to get the main concepts across. It is hoped that the instructor will judiciously move on to new material before the student becomes oversaturated. In general, the last few theorems of any section can be omitted without disrupting the continuity of the text. Chapter 1 is meant to be introductory in nature, and a large part of it can be omitted if the student has a strong background in high school geometry and calculus. It is possible to begin with Chap. 2 and thereafter refer to Chap. 1 only when the need arises.

There are a great many unsolved problems in the theory of convex sets and related material. Many of these can be stated in extremely elementary language, which adds greatly to their interest. "Convex Sets" by Valentine[1] is an excellent source of unsolved problems. Another is "Convexity," vol. 7, Proceedings of Symposia in Pure Mathematics, American Mathematical Society, 1963.

[1] F. A. Valentine, "Convex Sets," part 13, McGraw-Hill Book Company, New York, 1964.

CONTENTS

xiii

EUCLIDEAN GEOMETRY AND CONVEXITY

INTRODUCTION

1

BASIC CONCEPTS

In this chapter we present the notation and terminology which will be used throughout the text. We assume that the reader is familiar with set notation and the limit concepts used in a standard calculus course. However, the basic concepts of euclidean geometry are presented in various ways at the high school level. To avoid confusion we consistently refer to one set of axioms, namely those due to Birkhoff (see Appendix 1). A preliminary discussion of length, area, and volume is given, and some properties of equidecomposable sets are developed. Then the notion of interior and exterior is defined. We conclude this chapter with a proof of the Jordan-curve theorem for polygons.

1

1 NOTATION AND TERMINOLOGY

The following notation will be used throughout the text.

1.1 Capital letters $\{P,Q,R, \ldots\}$ will stand for points.
Small letters $\{p,q,r, \ldots\}$ will stand for lines.
Small Greek letters $\{\pi,\rho,\sigma, \ldots\}$ will stand for planes.

1.2 $S(A,B)$ will stand for the line segment joining points A and B excluding A and B.
$S(A,B] = S(A,B) \cup \{B\}$.
$S[A,B) = S(A,B) \cup \{A\}$.
$S[A,B] = S(A,B) \cup \{A,B\}$.

1.3 $L(A,B)$ will stand for the line through points A and B.

1.4 $R(A,B)$ will stand for the ray from A through B not including A.
$R[A,B) = R(A,B) \cup \{A\}$.

1.5 $H(l,P)$ will stand for the half plane containing point P with boundary line l.
$H[l,P) = H(l,P) \cup l$.
$H(\pi,P)$ will stand for the half space containing point P with boundary plane π.
$H[\pi,P) = H(\pi,P) \cup \pi$.

It will be convenient to define an addition of points and a scalar multiplication. Coordinates will always refer to one fixed rectangular coordinate system unless otherwise stated.

1.6 If point A has coordinates (a_1,a_2,a_3), B has coordinates (b_1,b_2,b_3), and k is a real number, then the **sum of points A and B**, $A + B$, is the point with coordinates $(a_1 + b_1, a_2 + b_2, a_3 + b_3)$ and the **product of k and point A**, kA, is the point with coordinates (ka_1,ka_2,ka_3).

With this terminology the following definitions agree with the usual ones given in analytic geometry.

1.7 Let $X = (1 - t)A + tB$, $-\infty < t < +\infty$, be parametric equations of a line. The **line segment** $S[A,B] = \{X|X = (1 - t)A + tB, 0 \leq t \leq 1\}$. The **ray** $R[A,B) = \{X|X = (1 - t)A + tB, 0 \leq t\}$.

There are various ways to define an angle and convexity. We shall use the following.

1.8 An **angle** is the union of two rays $R[A,B)$ and $R[A,C)$ having the same initial point. If we designate one ray as the **initial side** and the other ray as the **terminal side** we call the angle a **signed angle**.

1.9 A **convex set** is a set of points K such that A, $B \varepsilon K$ implies $S(A,B) \subset K$.

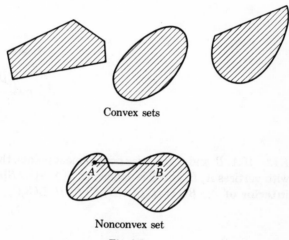

Convex sets

Nonconvex set

Fig. 1.1

In Appendix 1 we have listed a set of axioms for euclidean geometry which was first presented by Birkhoff. These are not as well known as Hilbert's axioms, for example, but their emphasis on metric and convexity properties are in the spirit of this text, so we use them. We need the separation axiom, Postulate 9, to define a half line.

1.10 Let l be a line lying in plane π. By the plane-separation axiom, $\pi - l$ is the union of two convex sets H_1 and H_2 such that whenever $P \varepsilon H_1$ and $Q \varepsilon H_2$, then $S(P,Q) \cap l$ is not empty. We call H_1 and H_2 **half planes** with boundary l.

Let $\angle ABC$ lie in plane π and have positive measure less than 180°. If B is the vertex, A lies on the initial side, and C lies on the terminal side, then we define

1.11 The **interior of** $\angle$ **ABC** $= H(L(A,B),C) \cap H(L(C,B),A)$. If the measure of $\angle ABC$ is between 180° and 360°, we define its interior to be all points of π not in the interior of $\angle CBA$ and not on $R[B,A)$ or $R[B,C)$.

We shall distinguish between a triangle and a triangular region.

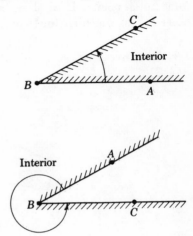

Fig. 1.2

1.12   If A, B, and C are three noncollinear points, then the **triangle** $\triangle ABC$ with vertices A, B, and C is defined as $S[A,B] \cup S[B,C] \cup S[C,A]$, and the **interior of** $\triangle ABC$ is $H(L(A,B),C) \cap H(L(B,C),A) \cap H(L(C,A),B)$.

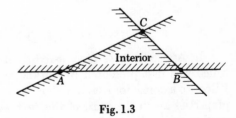

Fig. 1.3

1.13   A **triangular region** is the union of a triangle with its interior.

Besides the plane-separation axiom we need a corresponding axiom for space.   We shall often refer to the euclidean plane as two-dimensional euclidean space, or 2-space, and to euclidean space as three-dimensional euclidean space, or just 3-space.

1.14   Let π be a plane in 3-space E.   By the space separation axiom, $E - \pi$ is the union of two convex sets H_1 and H_2 such that whenever $P \in H_1$ and $Q \in H_2$, then $S(P,Q) \cap \pi$ is not empty.   We call H_1 and H_2 **half spaces** with boundary plane π.

In the future we shall use freely the usual results of a course in high school geometry and a course in analytic geometry.   However, the separation properties, as well as a few others, are sometimes not stressed in these courses, so we shall occasionally refer to postulates in Appendix 1 for use in a proof.

Exercises

1.1 Show that the origin O together with points A, B and $A + B$ are the vertices of a parallelogram.

1.2 If (x_1, y_1), (x_2, y_2), and (x, y) are the coordinates of points A, B, and X respectively, show that an equation of the line through A and B is $X = (1 - t)A + tB$. Can you describe the position of X in terms of t?

1.3 Find the direction cosines of line l if l contains two points with coordinates (a) $(2,4,6)$ and $(-1,-2,-3)$; (b) $(3,-1,2)$ and $(5,8,2)$.

1.4 Find an equation for a line in terms of a point on the line and the direction cosines of the line.

1.5 Show that each of the following is a convex set: (a) a single point; (b) a line; (c) a plane; (d) a ray.

1.6 Prove that the nonempty intersection of any number of convex sets is again a convex set. Do you think we should call the empty set convex? Why?

1.7 Let $x + y = 1$ be the equation of a line in the plane. If $(\bar{x}, \bar{y})$ are the coordinates of point P, show that each of the following sets is convex (sketch each set): (a) $\{P | \bar{x} + \bar{y} \geq 1\}$; (b) $\{P | \bar{x} + \bar{y} > 1\}$; (c) $\{P | \bar{x} + \bar{y} \leq 1\}$; (d) $\{P | \bar{x} + \bar{y} < 1\}$.

1.8 If line l has equation $2x + 3y = 1$ and $(\bar{x}, \bar{y})$ are the coordinates of point P, show that $H_1 = \{P | 2\bar{x} + 3\bar{y} < 1\}$ and $H_2 = \{P | 2\bar{x} + 3\bar{y} > 1\}$ are the half planes bounded by line l.

1.9 Let $x + 2y - z = 1$ be the equation of a plane in 3-space. If $(\bar{x}, \bar{y}, \bar{z})$ are the coordinates of point P, show that each of the following sets is convex: (a) $\{P | \bar{x} + 2\bar{y} - \bar{z} \geq 1\}$; (b) $\{P | \bar{x} + 2\bar{y} - \bar{z} > 1\}$; (c) $\{P | \bar{x} + 2\bar{y} - \bar{z} \leq 1\}$; (d) $\{P | \bar{x} + 2\bar{y} - \bar{z} < 1\}$.

1.10 If plane π has equation $ax + by + cz = 1$ and $(\bar{x}, \bar{y}, \bar{z})$ are the coordinates of point P, show that $H_1 = \{P | a\bar{x} + b\bar{y} + c\bar{z} < 1\}$ and $H_2 = \{P | a\bar{x} + b\bar{y} + c\bar{z} > 1\}$ are the half spaces bounded by plane π.

1.11 Show that each of the following is a convex set: (a) the interior of an angle with measure less than $180°$; (b) a triangular region; (c) all points in the plane whose coordinates satisfy the inequality $y \geq x^2$.

1.12 Show that the solid right circular cone $K = \{P$ with coordinates (x,y,z) $|z \geq x^2 + y^2\}$ is a convex set. Hence show that a parabola, an ellipse, and the branch of a hyperbola each bound a planar convex set.

2 LENGTH OF A CURVE

In the next few sections we attempt a brief reconciliation of the treatment of length, area, and volume in the calculus with the treatment in high school geometry. First we need a precise definition of a curve.

2.1   Let Γ be a continuous function whose domain is an interval $[a,b]$ of the real numbers (we include all the reals as a possible domain) and whose range is a set of points in space. We call Γ a **curve** and call its range the **trace of the curve** Γ. If the function is one-to-one, except possibly at its end points, we call Γ a **simple curve**. If $\Gamma(a) = \Gamma(b)$, we call Γ a **closed** curve.

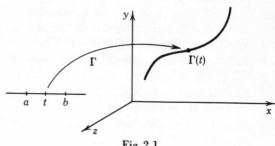

Fig. 2.1

Most of the curves we shall be concerned with will be simple curves, and we shall often use the word "curve" to mean the trace of a curve when there is no danger of confusion. If the trace of Γ lies in a plane, we call Γ a plane curve. If Γ lies in 3-space, we call Γ a space curve. A curve is ordinarily determined by parametric equations or a vector equation. If the trace of Γ lies in 3-space, we write

$$\overrightarrow{\Gamma}(t) = (x(t), y(t), z(t))$$

where $\overrightarrow{\Gamma}(t)$ is the position vector of the point $\Gamma(t)$ with coordinates $(x(t), y(t), z(t))$ and $a \leq t \leq b$.

Let $P_0, P_1, \ldots, P_n$ be $n + 1$ points in 3-space. We define a curve Π passing through these points as follows: $\Pi(i) = P_i$, $i = 0, \ldots, n$; if $i \leq t \leq i + 1$, then we define $\Pi(t)$ by $\Pi(t) = (1 - t + i)P_i + (t - i)P_{i+1}$.

2.2 Π is called the **polygonal curve** with **vertices** $P_0, P_1, \ldots, P_n$. The segments $S[P_i, P_{i+1}]$ are called the **sides of the polygonal curve.** A closed polygonal curve of n sides lying in the plane is sometimes called an *n*-**gon,** or simply a polygon.

We note that the order of the vertices is very important. In Fig 2.2, for example, Π_1 with vertices $ABCD$ is quite different from Π_2 with vertices $ACBD$, even though they have the same set of vertices. We shall occasionally refer to a polygonal curve by giving its vertices in the appropriate order. For example, we shall refer to Π_1 as the polygonal curve $ABCD$.

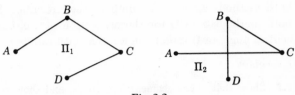

Fig. 2.2

2.3 The **length of polygonal curve** $P_0, P_1, \ldots, P_n$ is defined to be $\sum_{i=0}^{n-1} |P_i P_{i+1}|$, where $|P_i P_{i+1}|$ is the distance between points P_i and P_{i+1}.

We are now in a position to define the length of a curve. Let $P = (t_0, t_1, \ldots, t_n)$ be any partition of $[a,b]$, that is, $a = t_0 < t_1 < \cdots < t_{n-1} < t_n = b$, and let Γ be a curve from $[a,b]$ into 3-space.

2.4 The **length of** Γ is the least upper bound (supremum) of the lengths of the polygonal curves $\Gamma(t_0) \Gamma(t_1) \cdots \Gamma(t_n)$, for all partitions P of $[a,b]$.

We shall use the abbreviation **sup** for the least upper bound.

The following theorem, proved in the calculus, furnishes us with a convenient way to find the lengths of a large class of curves.

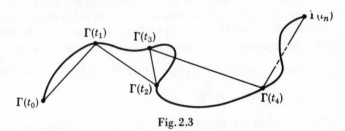

Fig. 2.3

2.5 *Theorem* Let Γ be a curve whose coordinate functions have continuous derivatives in the interval $[a,b]$. In other words if $\overrightarrow{\Gamma'}(t) = (x'(t), y'(t), z'(t))$, then the derivatives $x'(t)$, $y'(t)$, and $z'(t)$ are all continuous for $a \leq t \leq b$. The length L of Γ is given by

2.6 $$L = \int_a^b |\overrightarrow{\Gamma'}(t)| \, dt = \int_a^b |(x'(t), y'(t), z'(t))| \, dt$$

In high school geometry the only curve other than a polygonal curve for which length is usually defined is the circular arc. Essentially the same procedure as above is used, but the distance between any two successive vertices is kept constant for a given inscribed polygon. In other words, regular polygonal curves only are used. The easiest way to make sure both methods agree is to compare their results. Fortunately we get by both methods $s = r\Theta$ for the arc length of a circular arc subtended by a central angle of Θ radians in a circle with radius r.

Exercises

2.1 Show that a line segment is a curve, and show that the length of $S[A,B]$ equals the distance between A and B.

2.2 Show that of all curves joining two points A and B in 3-space the segment $S[A,B]$ has the shortest length.

2.3 Let $\overrightarrow{\Gamma}(t) = (r \cos t, r \sin t)$, $0 \le t \le 2\pi$, be a vector equation of a circle. Compute the length of a circular arc using Eq. 2.6.

2.4 Find a formula for the length L_n of a regular n-gon inscribed to a given circle of radius r. Show that $L_n < L_{n+1}$ for large n. (Hint: Compute the derivative of L_n with respect to n, and use the fact that $x < \tan x$ for $0 < x < \pi/2$.)

2.5 With the same notation as in Exercise 2.4, show that $\lim\limits_{n \to \infty} L_n = 2\pi r$. Use the fact that L_n is increasing for large n to show that $\sup\limits_n L_n = 2\pi r$.

2.6 Use the method of Exercises 2.4 and 2.5 to find the length of a circular arc.

2.7 Let $\overrightarrow{\Gamma}(t) = (t, t^k)$, $0 \le t \le 1$, $0 < k$, be the vector equation of a curve for some fixed k. Show that an arbitrary polygon inscribed to Γ has length less than 2. (Hint: Project the inscripture onto the x and y axes and use the fact that the sum of two sides of a triangle is greater than the third.)

2.8 The diameter of a simple closed curve Γ is defined to be the $\sup\limits_{A,B \varepsilon \Gamma} |AB|$. Show that the length of Γ is greater than or equal to twice its diameter.

3 PLANE AREA

The situation for plane area is not quite as simple as that for arc length. The method of computing areas in high school geometry is quite different from the methods of the calculus. In high school the area of a triangle or rectangle is postulated or defined to give us the standard formulas in terms of base and altitude. Then polygonal regions are subdivided into triangular regions, and the area of the region is defined as the sum of the areas of the triangles. So that there will be no confusion, we make the following definition:

3.1 A **polygonal region** is the union of a closed simple polygon with its interior.

In Sec. 5 we give a rigorous description of the interior of a polygon. We let our intuition serve until then.

An obvious question is to ask if it is always possible to triangulate a polygonal region.

3.2 Theorem Any polygonal region Π can be expressed as the union of a finite number of triangles which intersect only on their sides if they intersect at all.

PROOF We use induction on the number of sides of Π. The theorem is true for a triangle. Suppose it is true for all polygonal regions with less than n sides, and let $\Pi = P_0 P_1 \cdots P_{n-1} P_0$ be a polygonal region with n sides. We assume that the vertices have been labeled so that P_1 has a minimum y coordinate among all vertices. If no vertex of Π lies inside $\triangle P_0 P_1 P_2$, then $\Pi = \triangle P_0 P_1 P_2 \cup \Pi'$, where $\Pi' = P_0 P_2 \cdots P_{n-1} P_0$. Π' has $n - 1$ sides; therefore, by the induction hypothesis, Π' can be triangulated. It follows that Π can also be triangulated. Suppose $\triangle P_0 P_1 P_2$ contains vertices of Π in its interior and let P_j be such that $m \angle P_j P_0 P_2$ is a maximum for these vertices. If $P_1' = R[P_0, P_j] \cap S(P_1 P_2)$, then $\Pi = \triangle P_0 P_1 P_1' \cup \Pi' \cup \Pi''$, where $\Pi' = P_j P_1' P_2 \cdots P_{j-1} P_j$ and $\Pi'' = P_0 P_j P_{j+1} \cdots P_{n-1} P_0$. Π' and Π'' each have less than n sides. By the induction hypothesis Π' and Π'' can both be triangulated. Therefore Π can be triangulated, and our proof is complete.

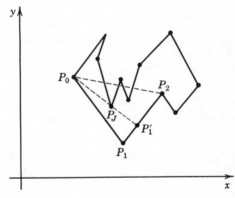

Fig. 3.1

Although the area of a rectangle is postulated in Appendix 1, we begin with the area of a triangle as one half the base times the altitude and define the area of an arbitrary polygonal region in terms of its triangulations.

We now ask the following question. If we triangulate a polygonal region Π in two different ways, and if we sum the areas of the triangles in the first triangulation, will we get the same result summing the areas of the triangles in the second triangulation? In order to answer this question we make the following definitions.

3.3   Polygonal region Π is **decomposed** into polygonal regions $\Pi_1, \ldots,$
Π_k iff $\Pi = \overset{k}{\underset{i=1}{\bigcup}} \Pi_i$ and Π_i and Π_j, $i \neq j$, intersect only on their boundaries.
Π and Π' are called **equidecomposable** iff there is a decomposition $\Pi_1,$
$\ldots, \Pi_k$ of Π and a decomposition $\Pi_1', \ldots, \Pi_k'$ of Π' such that Π_i is
congruent to Π_i' for $i = 1, \ldots, k$.

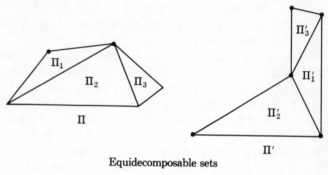

Equidecomposable sets

Fig. 3.2

In Chap. 3 we shall develop a precise notion of congruence for arbitrary
sets.   Until then we can use Postulate 15 of Appendix 1 to define congruent
triangles and let the intuitive notion of "superposition" serve to define
congruent nontriangular regions.

3.4   Theorem   Let $S[A,B]$ be a longest side of triangle ABC and construct a rectangle $ABXY$ of equal area so that $D = L(X,Y) \cap S[A,C]$ and
$E = L(X,Y) \cap S[B,C]$. $\triangle ABC$ is equidecomposable with $ABXY$.

   PROOF   Let H be the foot of the perpendicular from C onto $L(X,Y)$.
Then $\triangle AYD \cong \triangle CHD$ and $\triangle BXE \cong \triangle CHE$.

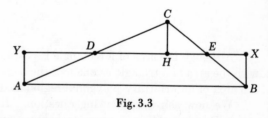

Fig. 3.3

3.5   Theorem   If two rectangles have equal base times altitude, then
they are equidecomposable.

   PROOF   First we assert that a rectangle and parallelogram having
equal base times altitude and also having an equal side are equidecom-

posable. Let S be the length of the equal sides, and lay off collinear points A, B, and C on a line l so that $|AB| = |BC| = S$. Draw a line m parallel to l a distance from l equal to the altitude of the rectangle. Let D, E, F, and G be chosen on m so that $ABED$ is congruent to the rectangle and $BCGF$ is congruent to the parallelogram, also so they do not overlap. Suppose the line through C perpendicular to l intersects $S[F,G]$ in a point X. Then the line through A parallel to $L(C,G)$ intersects $S[D,F]$ in a point Y, and $\triangle DAY \cong \triangle XCG$. We also have $AYEB \cong BFXC$. Therefore $ABED$ is equidecomposable with $BCGF$. Now suppose the line through C intersects $S[B,F]$ in point X and let the line through X parallel to l intersect $L(A,D)$, $L(B,E)$, and $L(C,G)$ in A', B', and C' respectively. Since $\triangle AA'B'' \cong' \triangle B'BA \cong \triangle XCB \cong \triangle CXC'$, it remains to show that $A'B'ED$ is equidecomposable with $XC'GF$. If the line through C' perpendicular to l does not intersect $S[F,G]$, we can repeat the preceding construction until it does. This reduces the second case to the first case and proves the assertion.

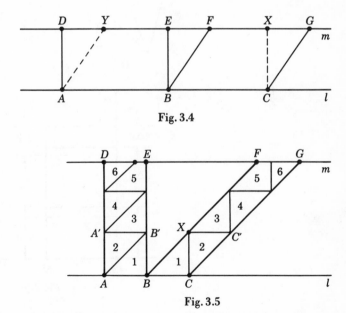

Fig. 3.4

Fig. 3.5

Now consider two rectangles of equal base times altitude, $\Pi = ABCD$ and $\Pi' = PQRS$, and suppose $|PQ|$ is the largest of the four side lengths. Let $\Pi'' = ABXY$ be a parallelogram with $|BX| = |PQ|$ and $|XY| = |AB|$. According to our assertion Π'' is equidecomposable with Π and also with Π'. Therefore Π is equidecomposable with Π', and we have finished.

We are now in a position to prove an important property of polygons.

3.6   Theorem   Let Π and Π' be two polygonal regions, and let $\triangle_1, \ldots, \triangle_k$ and $\triangle_1', \ldots, \triangle_l'$ be triangular decompositions of Π and Π' respectively.   If $|S|$ stands for the area of set S and if $\sum_{i=1}^{k} |\triangle_i| = \sum_{i=1}^{l} |\triangle_i'|$, then Π and Π' are equidecomposable.

PROOF   Let $P_0 QXY$ be a given rectangle with $|P_0 Q| = 1$ and $L(P_0, Y)$ perpendicular to $L(P,Q)$.   On ray $R[P,Y)$ lay off successively $P_1, \ldots, P_k$ so that $|P_{i-1}P_i| = |\triangle_i|$.   If Σ is the rectangle with P_0, Q, and P_k for vertices, it follows from Theorems 3.4 and 3.5 that Σ is equidecomposable with Π.   If we lay off $P_1', \ldots, P_l'$ on $R[P,Y)$ so that $|P_{i-1}'P_i'| = |\overline{\triangle_i'}|$, then $P_l' = P_k$ and Σ is equidecomposable with Π'.   Therefore Π is equidecomposable with Π'.

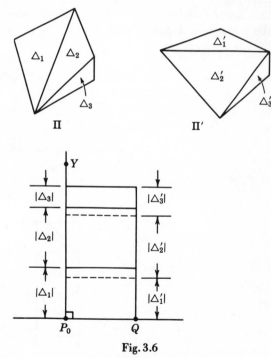

Fig. 3.6

The following two theorems are not only useful in computations but will also be needed to prove the converse of Theorem 3.6.

3.7   Theorem   Let $A_1 A_2 A_3$ be an arbitrary triangle in the plane and let U_i be the point on the unit circle with center at the origin O such that $\overrightarrow{OU_i}$ is the exterior normal vector to the side $S[A_j, A_k]$, $i \neq j, k$.   If Z is an arbitrary point and if X_i is any point on $L(A_j, A_k)$, $i \neq j, k$, then

$$2|\triangle A_1A_2A_3| = |A_1A_2|U_3 \cdot (X_3 - Z)$$
$$+ |A_2A_3|U_1 \cdot (X_1 - Z) + |A_3A_1|U_2 \cdot (X_2 - Z)$$

PROOF   Suppose Z lies on $L(A_1,A_2)$ and let

$$K = |A_1A_2|U_3 \cdot (X_3 - Z) + |A_2A_3|U_1 \cdot (X_1 - Z) + |A_3A_1|U_2 \cdot (X_2 - Z)$$

Since $U_3 \cdot (X_3 - Z) = 0$, we have

$$K = |A_2A_3|U_1 \cdot (X_1 - Z) + |A_3A_1|U_2 \cdot (X_2 - Z).$$

If $A_2 \varepsilon S[A_1,Z]$, then

$$K = 2|\triangle A_1ZA_3| - 2|\triangle A_2ZA_3| = 2|\triangle A_1A_2A_3|$$

If $Z \varepsilon S[A_1, A_2]$, then

$$K = 2|\triangle A_1ZA_3| + 2|\triangle A_2ZA_3| = 2|\triangle A_1A_2A_3|$$

Similarly, if $A_1 \varepsilon S[Z,A_2]$, then

$$K = 2|\triangle A_1A_2A_3|$$

The same technique shows that the theorem holds whenever Z is a point collinear with any two of the vertices $A_1A_2A_3$.

Let α be the angle formed by the rays opposite to $R[A_1,A_2)$ and $R[A_1,A_3)$, and suppose Z lies on the interior of α or the interior of $\angle A_2A_1A_3$. Let $P = L(A_1.Z) \cap S[A_2,A_3]$.   We now apply the preceding part to $\triangle PA_3A_1$ and $\triangle PA_2A_1$ to get

$$2|\triangle PA_3A_1| = |A_1P|U \cdot (P - Z)$$
$$+ |PA_3|U_1 \cdot (X_1 - Z) + |A_3A_1|U_2 \cdot (X_2 - Z)$$

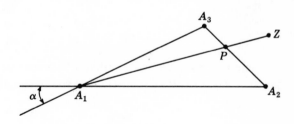

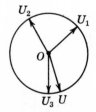

Fig. 3.7

$$2|\triangle PA_2A_1| = |A_1P|(-U) \cdot (P - Z)$$
$$+ |PA_2|U_1 \cdot (X_1 - Z) + |A_2A_1|U_3 \cdot (X_3 - Z)$$

where $\overrightarrow{OU}$ is the unit normal vector to $S[A_1,P]$ exterior to $\triangle A_1PA_3$. Therefore $2|\triangle A_1A_2A_3| = |A_2A_3|U_1 \cdot (X_1 - Z) + |A_3A_1|U_2 \cdot (X_2 - Z) + |A_1A_2|U_3 \cdot (X_3 - Z)$. Since the preceding does not depend on the angle whose interior contains Z, our proof is complete.

3.8 Theorem If $\triangle_1, \ldots, \triangle_k$ is any triangular decomposition of the polygonal region $\Pi = P_0P_1 \ldots P_nP_0$, then

$$2 \sum_{i=1}^{k} |\triangle_i| = |P_0P_1|U_{01} \cdot (X_{01} - Z)$$
$$+ |P_1P_2|U_{12} \cdot (X_{12} - Z) + \cdots + |P_nP_0|U_{n0} \cdot (X_{n0} - Z)$$

where Z is an arbitrary point, $\overrightarrow{OU}_{ij}$ is the unit exterior normal to $S[P_i,P_j]$, and $X_{ij} \in L(P_i,P_j)$.

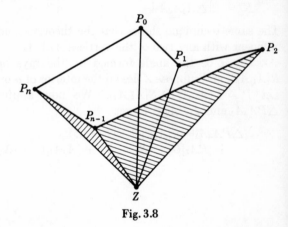

Fig. 3.8

PROOF   We may assume that whenever two triangles of the decomposition intersect, they intersect at a common vertex or in a common edge.

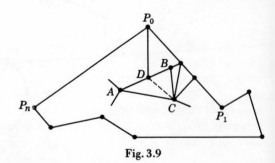

Fig. 3.9

For if $\triangle_i = \triangle ABC$ and a vertex D of $\triangle_j$ lies on $S[A,B]$, then, if we replace $\triangle ABC$ by $\triangle ADC$ and $\triangle BDC$, the sum of the areas of the triangles is unchanged. Consider any side $S[A,B]$ of any triangle in the decomposition. If either A or B is an interior point of Π, then $S[A,B]$ must be common to two triangles of the decomposition, say $\triangle_1$ and $\triangle_2$. If we use Theorem 3.7 to sum up all the areas of the triangles, the part of the sum due to $S[A,B]$ will be zero, since the unit normal to $S[A,B]$ exterior to $\triangle_1$ is equal and opposite to the unit normal to $S[A,B]$ exterior to $\triangle_2$. The remaining parts of the sum add up to precisely the right-hand side of the above equation, and our theorem is proved.

Since the above formula for $\sum_{i=1}^{k} |\triangle_i|$ is independent of the triangulation used, we are now in a position to define the area of a polygonal region in an unambiguous manner.

3.9 If $\triangle_1, \ldots, \triangle_k$ is a triangular decomposition of polygonal region Π, then $A(\Pi) = \sum_{i=1}^{k} |\triangle_i|$ is called the **area of** Π.

3.10 Theorem If Π and Π' are equidecomposable, then $A(\Pi) = A(\Pi')$.

PROOF Let $\Pi_1, \ldots, \Pi_k$ and $\Pi_1', \ldots, \Pi_k'$ be decompositions of Π and Π' respectively such that Π_i is congruent to Π_i'. Let each Π_i be triangulated to form a triangular decomposition $\triangle_1, \ldots, \triangle_n$ of Π. Then $A(\Pi) = \sum_{i=1}^{n} |\triangle_i| = \sum_{i=1}^{k} A(\Pi_i)$. Similarly we get $A(\Pi') = \sum_{i=1}^{k} A(\Pi_i')$. Since $\Pi_i \cong \Pi_i'$, we have $A(\Pi_i) = A(\Pi_i')$, and our theorem is proved.

Besides the areas of polygonal regions the only other areas usually computed in high school geometry are those of circular sectors and segments. The area of a circular sector is defined by dividing the arc into n equal parts with end points P_i, joining these points with the center to form triangular regions whose total area is A_n, and then finding the limit of A_n as n increases beyond bounds.

In the calculus, of course, area is defined in terms of integrals. It is not difficult to show that the area of a triangle, rectangle, or polygonal region computed by integrals gives exactly the same results as in high school geometry. A problem related to congruent figures is not so easy to solve. One of the most intuitively desirable properties of area is that congruent sets of points have the same area. This is usually postulated for triangular regions. For the more general regions discussed in the calculus it is rather difficult to show that congruent figures have the same area. The problem is equivalent to showing that the same area is obtained for a set of points regardless of what coordinate system is used to perform the integration.

Rather than pursue this line of reasoning it is more convenient for us to extend our definition of area from polygonal regions to more general regions in the way we obtain the area of circular regions in high school. We will then show that the calculus definition of area is included as a special case. The extension we use is called Jordan measure.

Any reasonable definition of plane area should at least agree with our preceding definitions for the area of polygonal and circular regions. The following satisfies this requirement and also extends our class of sets having area. In order to simplify matters we extend our definition of a polygonal region for the rest of this section to include the union of a finite number of polygonal regions which intersect at their edges, if they intersect at all. The area of a polygonal region is then defined to be the sum of the areas of all its parts.

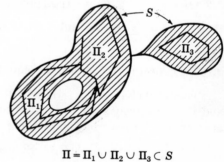

$$\Pi = \Pi_1 \cup \Pi_2 \cup \Pi_3 \subset S$$
$$A(\Pi) = A(\Pi_1) + A(\Pi_2) + A(\Pi_3)$$

Fig. 3.10

3.11 Let A be a set of points in the plane. If there is no polygonal region Π such that $\Pi \subset A$, then we define $m_i(A) = 0$. Otherwise we let $m_i(A) = \sup_{\Pi \subset A} A(\Pi)$. $m_i(A)$ is called the **inner measure** of A. Similarly, if there is no polygonal region Π such that $A \subset \Pi$, then $m_0(A)$ is undefined. Otherwise we let $m_0(A) = \inf_{A \subset \Pi} A(\Pi)$ and call $m_0(A)$ the **outer measure** of A. If $m_0(A) = m_i(A)$, we denote the common value by $|A|_J$ and call it the **Jordan measure** or area of A.

If Π_1 and Π_2 are distinct polygonal regions with Π_1 contained in Π_2, then by introducing appropriate cuts, if necessary, the region $\Pi_2 - \Pi_1$ becomes a union of polygonal regions having positive area. For example, the cut $S[P,Q]$, as shown in Fig. 3.11, transforms $\Pi_2 - \Pi_1$ into a union of two polygonal regions. It follows that the area of Π_2 is greater than the area of Π_1, and we have the following useful property.

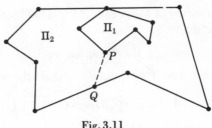

Fig. 3.11

3.12 Theorem If Π_1 and Π_2 are polygonal regions with $\Pi_1 \subset \Pi_2$, then $A(\Pi_1) \leq A(\Pi_2)$.

Two results are immediately obtained.

3.13 Theorem Every polygonal region has Jordan measure equal to its area.

PROOF For a given polygonal region Π we let P denote the set of all polygonal regions contained in Π and Q the set of all polygonal regions containing Π. Since $\Pi \subset \Pi$, we have $\Pi \, \varepsilon \, P$ and $\Pi \, \varepsilon \, Q$. It follows that $A(\Pi_1) \leq A(\Pi)$ for every $\Pi_1 \, \varepsilon \, P$. Therefore $m_i(\Pi) = A(\Pi)$. Similarly $A(\Pi) = m_0(\Pi)$, and the proof is complete.

3.14 Theorem For any set R having outer measure, $m_i(R) \leq m_0(R)$.

PROOF Let P be the set of all polygonal regions contained in R and Q the set of all polygonal regions containing R. If $\Pi \, \varepsilon \, P$ and $\Sigma \, \varepsilon \, Q$, then $m(\Pi) \leq m(\Sigma)$. Since Π is an arbitrary member of P, it follows that $m_i(R) \leq m(\Sigma)$. Since Σ is an arbitrary member of Q, it follows that $m_i(R) \leq m_0(R)$.

We now recall the definition of the definite integral of a continuous function. If $P = (x_0, x_1, \ldots , x_n)$ is any partition of the interval $[a,b]$ and f is a function continuous on $[a,b]$, we define the lower sum $S_p = \sum_{i=1}^{n} f(u_i) \, \Delta x_i$, where $f(u_i)$ is the minimum value of f on the ith interval of P. Similarly we define the upper sum $T_p = \sum_{i=1}^{n} f(v_i) \, \Delta x_i$, where $f(v_i)$ is the maximum value of f on the ith interval of P. We define the lower integral $\underline{\int_a^b} f = \sup S_p$ and the upper integral $\overline{\int_a^b} f = \inf T_p$. If $\underline{\int_a^b} f = \overline{\int_a^b} f$, we call the common value the definite integral of f over the interval $[a,b]$ and denote it by $\int_a^b f$.

3.15 Theorem If $f(x) \geq 0$ on $[a,b]$, then $\int_a^b f$ is equal to the Jordan measure of the region R bounded by the graphs of $y = f(x)$, $y = 0$, $x = a$, and $x = b$.

PROOF   By definition we have $S_p \leq m_i(R)$ for any partition P, and therefore $\int_a^b f \leq m_i(R)$. Similarly $m_0(R) \leq \overline{\int_a^b} f$. By Theorem 3.14 we have $m_i(R) \leq m_0(R)$. Therefore $\int_a^b f \leq m_i(R) \leq m_0(R) \leq \overline{\int_a^b} f$. If $\int_a^b f$ exists, then $\int_a^b f = \overline{\int_a^b} f$, equality must hold throughout, and the theorem is proved.

Exercises

3.1   Show that whenever Π_1 is equidecomposable with Π_2 and Π_2 is equidecomposable with Π_3, then Π_1 is equidecomposable with Π_3.

3.2   Show that trapezoid $ABCD$ with $L(A,B)$ parallel to $L(C,D)$ is equidecomposable with a triange having the same altitude and area and whose base lies on $L(A,B)$.

3.3   Use equidecomposable figures to prove the Pythagorean theorem.

3.4   Modify the proof of Theorem 3.2 to show that any polygonal region Π can be decomposed into triangles whose vertices lie only at the vertices of Π.

3.5   Use Exercise 3.4 to prove that the sum of the radian measure of the interior angles of a polygon of n sides equals $(n - 2)\pi$.

3.6   Dissect a regular hexagon by straight cuts into six pieces which can be reassembled to form an equilateral triangle.

3.7   Use properties of trigonometric functions to show that half the base times the altitude is the same for any given triangle regardless of which base and corresponding altitude are used.

3.8   Use Theorem 3.7 to compute the areas of the following triangles: (**a**) (2,1), (2,2), (3,1); (**b**) (2,2), (3,1), (5,1); (**c**) (2,2), (2,1), (5,1).

3.9   If moving from A to B then to C along $\triangle ABC$ we traverse in a counterclockwise sense, we say that $\triangle ABC$ is positively oriented. Let the oriented area $|\overrightarrow{ABC}| = + \, |\triangle ABC|$ if the orientation is positive, and let $|\overrightarrow{ABC}| = -|\triangle ABC|$ otherwise. Show that Theorem 3.7 is equivalent to the following statement:

$$|\overrightarrow{A_1A_2A_3}| = |\overrightarrow{ZA_1A_2}| + |\overrightarrow{ZA_2A_3}| + |\overrightarrow{ZA_3A_1}|$$

3.10   Show that the area of a triangle $P_1P_2P_3$ with $P_i = (x_i, y_i)$, $i = 1, 2$, and 3, is given by the absolute value of

$$\frac{1}{2} \begin{vmatrix} x_1 & y_1 & 1 \\ x_2 & y_2 & 1 \\ x_3 & y_3 & 1 \end{vmatrix}$$

3.11   If Exercise 3.10 is used to define the area of a triangle, show that the area of a triangle is independent of the coordinate system used. (Hint: Use the fact that any pair of perpendicular lines can be transformed into any other such pair by a combination of a translation and rotation.)

3.12 If the point Z is moved a great distance from π in Theorem 3.8, the lines $L(Z,P_i)$ come close to being parallel to each other. State and prove a theorem similar to Theorem 3.8 using parallel lines.

3.13 Show that the Jordan measure of a finite number of points is zero.

3.14 Show that the Jordan measure of a finite number of line segments is zero.

3.15 Show that every nonempty subset of a set having Jordan measure equal to zero also has measure equal to zero.

3.16 Given a circular arc $\overset{\frown}{AB}$ with radius r and center C, let $P_0P_1 \cdots P_n$ be a polygonal curve inscribed to $\overset{\frown}{AB}$ with $|P_{i-1}P_i| = b_i$ for $i = 1, \ldots, n$, and let h_i be the altitude of $\Delta P_{i-1}P_iC$. Find an expression for the area of the inscribed polygonal region and take the limit as n approaches infinity. Show that this limit is the inner measure of the circular sector CAB.

3.17 Use the same notation as in Exercise 3.16. Let π_n be the polygon circumscribed to sector CAB bounded by the tangents to $\overset{\frown}{AB}$ at P_i, $i = 0, \ldots, n$, and by $L(O,A)$ and $L(O,B)$. Find an expression for $A(\pi_n)$. Show that $\lim A(\pi_n)$ is the outer measure of the sector and that the Jordan measure of the sector exists.

3.18 Prove that $|A|_J$ exists iff for each $\epsilon > 0$ there exist polygonal regions $\pi_i(\epsilon) \subset A \subset \pi_0(\epsilon)$ such that $A[\pi_0(\epsilon)] - A[\pi_i(\epsilon)] < \epsilon$.

4 SURFACE AREA AND VOLUME

There are certain inherent difficulties involved in extending the ideas of the preceding section to 3-space. The greatest difficulty arises when one attempts to give a definition of surface area which will work for a large class of surfaces.

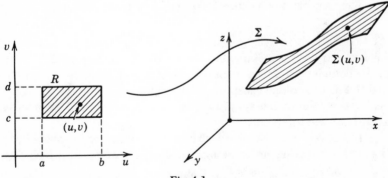

Fig. 4.1

4.1 A **surface** Σ is a continuous function whose domain is a rectangle R in the plane (we also allow the domain to be the whole plane) and whose range is in 3-space. The image of Σ is called its trace, and just as for a curve we often refer to the trace of a surface as the surface itself when there is no danger of confusion.

Analogous to Sec. 2 we might attempt the following definition. Let P be an arbitrary triangular decomposition of the domain of surface Σ. The vertices of each triangle $\triangle$ are mapped by Σ onto the vertices of a triangle $\triangle'$ (which may be degenerate) in 3-space. Let $A(P)$ be the sum of the areas of all the triangles $\triangle'$. The area of Σ is tentatively defined as the sup $A(P)$ over all triangulations of Σ. Unfortunately, many surfaces whose areas are found by elementary means will not have any area according to this definition. For example, a sequence of triangulations P_i can be inscribed to a right circular cylindrical surface[1] in such a manner that $\lim A(P_i) = \infty$.

There is a technique, however, which gives a workable definition for a wide class of surfaces. We will develop this in more detail in Sec. 19. For the time being we illustrate the method with the following example. Consider a right circular cone with radius r and altitude h. If we increase r by ϵ and h by δ so that the generator of the cone remains parallel to its original position, we obtain two cones with the same axis and with bases in the same plane. Let ζ be the perpendicular distance between the two conical lateral surfaces. We define the lateral surface area S of the original cone as

$$S = \lim_{\zeta \to +0} \frac{1}{\zeta} [\tfrac{1}{3}\pi(r + \epsilon)^2(h + \delta) - \tfrac{1}{3}\pi r^2 h] = \pi r \sqrt{r^2 + h^2}$$

We notice that this agrees with the results obtained in the calculus treating a conical surface as a surface of revolution.

The treatment of volume follows that of plane area quite closely.

4.2 Given a surface Σ, we call the curve Γ obtained by restricting Σ to the boundary of the rectangular domain the **boundary of** Σ. If the trace of the boundary of Σ is a point or is the trace of a simple curve in 3-space, and if Σ is one-to-one except on its boundary and if every small ball with center at a point of Σ is split into two disjoint pieces by Σ, then we call Σ a **simple closed surface.**

Intuitively a simple closed surface is obtained from a sphere by stretching without tearing or breaking. A simple surface in which $\Sigma(a,y) =$

---

[1] See T. Rado, "Length and Area," p. 6, American Mathematical Society, New York, 1948.

$\Sigma(b,y)$ for $c \leq y \leq d$ and $\Sigma(x,c) = \Sigma(x,d)$ for $a \leq x \leq b$ is called a torus. A torus is sometimes called a simple closed surface in other texts, but it is not a simple closed surface here. If we cut the torus as shown in Fig. 4.2, however, and add the cross sections, we obtain two simple closed surfaces which, for example, have the same total volume as the original torus. For our purposes the simplicity obtained using the above definition more than offsets the added restrictions. We now make the following definitions.

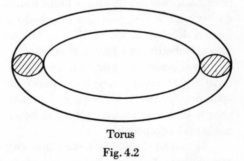

Torus

Fig. 4.2

4.3 A simple closed surface Σ which is the union of a finite number of polygonal regions Π_i is called a **polyhedron**, and each Π_i is called a **face** of Σ. The union of a polyhedron and its interior is called a **polyhedral region.**

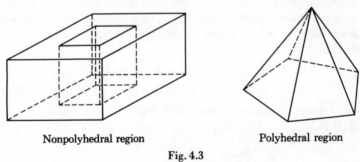

Nonpolyhedral region   Polyhedral region

Fig. 4.3

Most of the results of the preceding section can be generalized to 3-space.

4.4   Theorem   Any polyhedral region Π can be expressed as the union of a finite number of tetrahedra which intersect only at their faces if they intersect at all.

PROOF   Consider the set of all half spaces whose boundary planes contain some face of Π. Π is decomposed by these half spaces into a finite number of convex sets Π_i each of which is the intersection of a finite number of half spaces. Each face of Π_i is a polygonal region since it is convex and bounded by the union of straight line segments. Therefore Π_i is a convex polyhedral region (see Theorem 11.9). We assert that any convex polyhedral region Π' can be decomposed into a finite number of tetrahedra. To see this let Z be any point in the interior of Π' and decompose each face of Π' into a finite number of triangles. Each triangle together with Z determines a tetrahedron, and all these tetrahedra together form a decomposition of Π'. It follows that each Π_i can be decomposed into tetrahedra and therefore so can Π.

In the preceding section we saw that whenever two polygonal regions have equal areas, they are equidecomposable. Surprisingly, the corresponding property in 3-space does not always hold. In fact, it can be shown that a cube and a regular tetrahedron with the same volume are not equidecomposable.[1]

It can be shown, however, that any two equidecomposable polyhedral regions have the same value for their volume regardless of the decomposition used for its computation. We define the volume of a tetrahedron to be one-third the area of its base times its altitude.

4.5   Theorem   Let $T = P_1P_2P_3P_4$ be an arbitrary tetrahedron and let U_i be the point on the unit sphere with center at the origin O such that $\overrightarrow{OU_i}$ is the exterior normal vector to the face opposite P_i. If Z is an arbitrary point and X_i is any point on the plane containing the face opposite to P_i, then

$$3|T| = A(P_1P_2P_3)U_4 \cdot (X_4 - Z) + A(P_2P_3P_4)U_1$$
$$\cdot (X_1 - Z) + A(P_3P_4P_1)U_2 \cdot (X_2 - Z) + A(P_4P_1P_2)U_3 \cdot (X_3 - Z)$$

PROOF   Suppose Z lies on $L(P_1P_2)$ and $P_2 \varepsilon S[P_1,Z]$. Let $K = A(P_1P_2P_3)U_4 \cdot (X_4 - Z) + \cdots + A(P_4P_1P_2)U_3 \cdot (X_3 - Z)$. Then $U_3 \cdot$

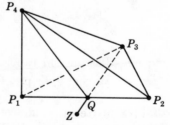
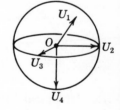

Fig. 4.4

[1] See V. G. Boltyanskii, "Equivalent and Equidecomposable Figures," p. 43, D. C. Heath and Company, Boston, 1963.

$(X_3 - Z) = U_4 \cdot (X_4 - Z) = 0$, and $K = A(P_2P_3P_4)U_1 \cdot (X_1 - Z) + A(OP_3P_4P_1)U_2 \cdot (X_2 - Z) = -3|ZP_2P_3P_4| + 3|ZP_3P_4P_1| = |T|$. In a similar manner we see that the theorem holds whenever Z is collinear with any two vertices of T. Now suppose Z lies on the plane containing $P_1P_2P_3$ and $L(Z,P_3)$ intersects $S[P_1,P_2]$ in a point Q. Since $Q \, \varepsilon \, L(Z,P_3)$ we can apply the preceding part twice to get

$$3|QP_3P_4P_1| = A(P_1QP_3)U_4 \cdot (X_4 - Z) + A(QP_3P_4)U$$
$$\cdot (Q - Z) + A(P_3P_4P_1)U_2 \cdot (X_2 - Z) + A(P_4P_1Q)U_3 \cdot (X_3 - Z)$$

$$3|QP_2P_3P_4| = A(QP_2P_3)U_4 \cdot (X_4 - Z) + A(P_2P_3P_4)U_1$$
$$\cdot (X_1 - Z) + A(P_3P_4Q)(-U) \cdot (Q - Z) + A(P_4QP_2)U_3 \cdot (X_3 - Z)$$

where $\overrightarrow{OU}$ is the unit vector normal to $\triangle QP_3P_4$ and exterior to $QP_3P_4P_1$. Therefore $3|T| = 3|QP_3P_4P_1| + 3|QP_2P_3P_4| = K$. Similarly, the theorem holds whenever Z is coplanar with any one of the faces of T. Now suppose that Z is not coplanar with any face of T and suppose $L(Z,P_4)$ intersects $\triangle P_1P_2P_3$ in a point of Q. In the same manner as above we can apply the preceding part three times to get

$$3|T| = 3|P_1P_2P_4Q| + 3|P_2P_3P_4Q| + 3|P_3P_4P_1Q| = K$$

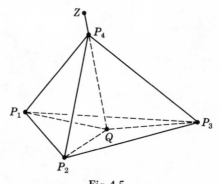

Fig. 4.5

The part of the sum due to the three pairs of coincident faces is zero, since, for example, the unit normal to $\triangle QP_3P_4$ exterior to $P_1QP_3P_4$ is equal and opposite to the unit normal to $\triangle QP_3P_4$ exterior to $P_2QP_3P_4$. Since every point not coplanar with a face of T lies interior to one of the trihedral angles of T or lies interior to its vertical angle, our proof is complete.

4.6   Theorem   If $T_1, \ldots , T_k$ is any tetrahedral decomposition of the polyhedral region Π, and if the faces of Π are $F_1, \ldots , F_n$, then $3 \sum\limits_{i=1}^{k} |T_i| = A(F_1)U_1 \cdot (X_1 - Z) + \cdots + A(F_n)U_n \cdot (X_n - Z)$ where Z is an arbitrary point, $\overrightarrow{OU}_i$ is the unit exterior normal to face F_i, and X_i is any point on the plane containing F_i.

PROOF   We may assume that any two intersecting tetrahedra of the decomposition intersect at a common vertex, edge, or face.   For if $T_i = ABCD$, $T_j = A'B'C'D'$, and $D' = T_i \cap T_j$ is a vertex of T_j which lies on $\triangle ABC$ but does not coincide with A, B, or C, then we may replace T_i by $AD'CD$, $D'BCD$ and $ABD'D$ without affecting the sum of the volumes. If $T_i \cap T_j = S[X,D']$, $X \in S[A,B]$, and $S[X,D'] \subset \triangle ABC$, then we can further replace $ABD'D$ by $AXD'D$ and $XBD'D$ and replace T_j by $A'B'C'X$ and $XB'C'D'$ without affecting the sum of the volumes.   A similar argument shows that the assertion also holds when $T_i \cap T_j$ is a polygonal region.   Consider any face $\triangle ABC$ of any tetrahedron in the decomposition.   If a vertex of $\triangle ABC$ lies inside Π, then $\triangle ABC$ is the common face of two tetrahedra, say T_i and T_j.   If we use Theorem 4.5 to sum up all the volumes of the tetrahedra, the part of the sum due to $\triangle ABC$ will be zero, since the unit normal to $\triangle ABC$ exterior to T_i is equal and opposite to the unit normal to $\triangle ABC$ exterior to T_j.   The rest of the sum is the right-hand side of the above equation, and our proof is complete.

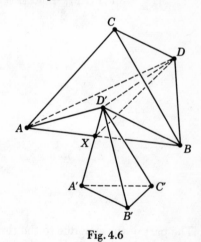

Fig. 4.6

4.7   If $T_1, \ldots, T_k$ is a tetrahedral decomposition of polyhedral region Π, then $V(\Pi) = \sum_{i=1}^{k} |T_i|$ is called the **volume of** Π.

We leave the proof of the following theorem to the reader.

4.8   Theorem   If Π and Π' are equidecomposable polyhedral regions, then $V(\Pi) = V(\Pi')$.

Now we extend our class of sets having volume by introducing three-dimensional Jordan measure.

4.9 Let A be a set of points in 3-space. If there is no finite union of nonoverlapping polyhedral regions Π such that $\Pi \subset A$, then we define $m_i(A) = 0$. Otherwise we let $m_i(A) = \sup_{\Pi \subset A} V\ (\Pi)$. $m_i(A)$ is called the **inner measure** of A. Similarly, if there is no finite union of nonoverlapping polyhedral regions Π such that $A \subset \Pi$, then $m_0(A)$ is undefined. Otherwise we let $m_0(A) = \inf_{A \subset \Pi} V\ (\Pi)$ and call $m_0(A)$ the **outer measure** of A. If $m_0(A) = m_i(A)$, we denote the common value by $|A|_J^3$ and call it the three-dimensional Jordan measure or volume of A.

We have used the notion of "inside" and "outside" in an intuitive manner up to now. In the next section we will make these ideas more precise.

Exercises

4.1 Use the method described in this section to find the surface area of (a) a sphere, (b) a right circular cylinder.

4.2 If we use the method described in this section to compute surface area, show that the surface area of a polyhedral region is equal to the sum of the areas of its faces.

4.3 Use the method of proof in Theorem 4.4 to prove Theorem 3.2.

4.4 Let ABC be an equilateral triangle. Rotate ABC through 30° in its plane and then translate a fixed distance in a direction perpendicular to ABC to get $A'B'C'$. Let Π be the polyhedron with faces ABC, $A'B'C'$, $AA'C'$, $CC'B$, $BB'A$, $AA'B$, $BB'C'$, and $CC'A'$. Show that Π cannot be decomposed into tetrahedra whose vertices lie only at the vertices of Π. Hence show that Exercise 3.4 cannot be generalized to 3-space.

4.5 Show that any two right prisms which have equal altitudes and bases of equal area are equidecomposable.

4.6 Show that any oblique prism with lateral edge length S is equidecomposable with a right prism of equal volume which has lateral edge length S.

4.7 Use Exercise 4.6 to show that every prism is equidecomposable with a rectangular parallelepiped of the same volume.

4.8 Use Theorem 4.5 to compute the volume of the following tetrahedra:

  a. (0,1,1), (0,2,1), (−1,1,1), (0,1,2)
  b. (0,2,1), (−1,2,1), (0,2,2), (−1,1,2)

4.9 Use properties of the vector cross and dot products to show that one-third the area of the base times the altitude is the same for a given tetrahedron regardless of which base and corresponding altitude are used.

4.10   Extend Exercise 3.10 to 3-space.

4.11   Extend Exercise 3.12 to 3-space.

4.12   Prove Theorem 4.8.

4.13   Extend Theorems 3.12 to 3.14 to 3-space.

4.14   State and prove a theorem analogous to Theorem 3.15 for a function of two variables.

4.15   Show that the three-dimensional Jordan measure of a plane polygonal region is zero.

4.16   Extend Exercise 3.15 to 3-space.

5   ELEMENTARY TOPOLOGY

In this section we introduce the topological ideas needed in the sequel. Let P be an arbitrary point and r a positive real number.

5.1   The **spherical neighborhood** (or simply **neighborhood**) of P with radius r is the set of points $N(P,r) = \{Q| \ |PQ| < r\}$.

If we restrict our points to lie in a plane, then $N(P,r)$ is called an **open disk**.   In 3-space $N(P,r)$ is called an **open ball**.

5.2   The **closed spherical neighborhood** (or simply **closed neighborhood**) of P with radius r is the set of points $\bar{N}(P,r) = \{Q| \ |PQ| \leq r\}$.

In the plane $\bar{N}(P,r)$ is called a **closed disk**.   In space $\bar{N}(P,r)$ is called a **closed ball**.

5.3   We call P an **interior point** of the set S iff there is a positive ϵ such that $N(P,\epsilon) \subset S$.

5.4   Let $\sim S$ stand for the complement of set S.   If Q is a point such that there is a positive number δ with $N(Q,\delta) \subset \sim S$, then we call Q an **exterior point** of S.

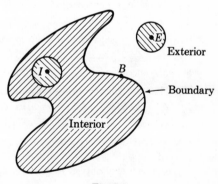

Fig. 5.1

5.5   If every neighborhood of point B contains both points of S and of $\sim S$, then we call B a **boundary point** of S.

5.6   The set of all interior (exterior) points of S is called the **interior (exterior)** of S.   The set of all boundary points of S is called the **boundary** of S.

For centuries geometers used the intuitively obvious fact that a simple closed curve in the plane partitions the plane into three mutually disjoint connected sets of points.   It was not until the last century that they thought it necessary to prove such a statement.   Surprisingly, the proof was quite difficult and challenged mathematicians for many years.   The proof is too long to present here, but if we restrict ourselves to polygons, the solution of the problem is quite easy.

5.7   The Jordan-curve theorem for simple closed polygons.   Any simple closed polygon Π in the plane partitions the plane into three disjoint connected sets Π, A, and B such that Π is the boundary of both A and B. A set S is called **connected** iff any two points of S can be joined by a curve contained in S.

PROOF   We say that $R[A,B)$ and $R[C,D)$ have the same direction iff $ABDCA$ is a trapezoid or $A'B'DCA'$ is a trapezoid for some translation $S[A',B']$ of $S[A,B]$.   In Fig. 5.2, for example, $R[A,B)$ and $R[C,D)$ have

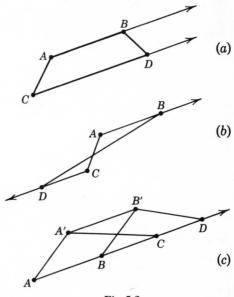

Fig. 5.2

the same direction in (a) and (c) but have opposite directions in (b). Let R be a fixed ray in the plane not parallel to any side of Π. Beginning at each point P in the plane there is a unique ray $R(P)$ having the same direction as R. Let $\sigma(P)$ be the number of points in which $R(P)$ intersects Π, with the following restriction. If $R(P)$ intersects Π in a vertex V, then V is not counted in $\sigma(P)$ if the sides of Π adjacent to V lie on the same side of $R(P)$. Otherwise V is counted. For example, in Fig. 5.3 $\sigma(P) = 3$ and $\sigma(P') = 1$. We now define A to be the set of all points P in the plane not on Π such that $\sigma(P)$ is odd and B as all points Q not on Π for which $\sigma(Q)$ is even.

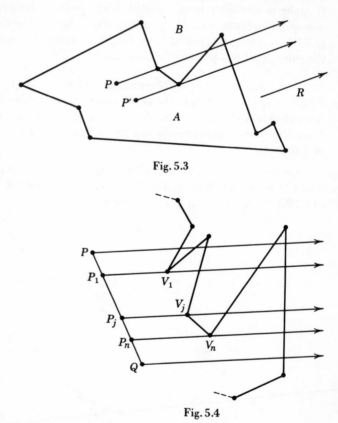

Fig. 5.3

Fig. 5.4

Now let $S[P,Q]$ be any line segment not intersecting Π. We assert that $S[P,Q]$ lies entirely in A or entirely in B. To see this consider the set $V_1, \ldots, V_n$ of all vertices of Π which lie in the convex region bounded by $R(P)$, $R(Q)$, and $S[P,Q]$. Let $P_1, P_2, \ldots, P_n$ be the points of $S[P,Q]$ such that $R[P_i, V_i]$ have the same direction as R, and suppose that the subscripts are chosen so that P, P_1, P_2, $\ldots$, P_n, Q is the natural order on $S[P,Q]$. By definition σ is the same for all points of $S(P,P_1)$, and it follows that $\sigma(P)$ differs from $\sigma(P_1)$ by an even number. Similarly $\sigma(P_i)$ differs from $\sigma(P_{i+1})$ by an even number for $i = 1, \ldots, n$, and $\sigma(P_n)$ differs from $\sigma(Q)$ by an even number. It follows that $S[P, Q]$ lies entirely in A or entirely in B. An immediate result is that if Π' is any polygon beginning in A and ending in B, then Π' must intersect Π.

We now show that any two points of the same set, A or B, can be joined by a polygonal curve which does not intersect Π. Let $P, Q \in A$. If $S[P,Q]$ does not intersect Π, we have finished. Otherwise let P' be the point of $\Pi \cap S[P,Q]$ closest to P and Q' be the point of $\Pi \cap S[P,Q]$ closest to Q. Let P'' be a point of $S(P,P')$ close to P' and trace a polygonal path Π beginning at P'' with sides close to those of Π until a point Q'' of $S(P,Q)$ near Q' is reached. If Q' lies between Q'' and Q, then $\sigma(Q'')$ and $\sigma(Q)$ differ by 1, and Q and Q'' do not both belong to A. But Q'' belongs to A by construction of Π', and Q belongs to A by assumption. It follows that Q'' lies between Q' and Q. The polygonal curve from P to P'', along Π' to Q'' and thence to Q, joins P to Q and lies entirely in A.

The argument just completed for set A also holds for set B. Since A and B are disjoint by construction, it remains only to show that Π is the boundary of A and B. But, as above, if P is any point of Π, then there are points P' and P'' arbitrarily close to P, with P between them, such that $\sigma(P')$ and $\sigma(P'')$ differ by 1. This implies that every neighborhood of P contains points of A and points of B so that P is a boundary point of both A and B.

Since a closed simple polygon is bounded, there are points in the plane with σ equal to zero. These belong to B. Consequently we call B the exterior of Π and A the interior of Π. The union of Π and A is the polygonal region bounded by Π.

The preceding discussion in the plane has its analog in 3-space. We present the results without proof.[1]

5.8   The Jordan theorem in 3-space   Any simple closed surface Σ in 3-space partitions space into three disjoint connected sets Σ, A, and B such that Σ is the boundary of both A and B. One of the sets is unbounded. If B is the unbounded set, we call B the exterior of Σ and A the interior of Σ.

We conclude this section with two properties of simple closed surfaces which are frequently called upon.

[1] See D. W. Hall and G. L. Spencer, "Elementary Topology," John Wiley & Sons, Inc., New York, 1955.

5.9   Theorem   Let Σ be a simple closed surface in 3-space (or a simple closed curve in the plane) with interior A and exterior B. If $P \varepsilon A$ and $Q \varepsilon B$, then $S(P,Q) \cap \Sigma$ is not empty.

PROOF   Since P is not a boundary point, there must be at least one neighborhood $N(P,\epsilon)$ contained in A. Let $R = \{|PX| \, | S(P,X) \subset A$ and $X \varepsilon S(P,Q)\}$. R is bounded from above by $|PQ|$, therefore $\alpha = \sup R$ exists and $\alpha \geq \epsilon > 0$. Let X be the point on $S[P,Q]$ such that $|PX| = \alpha$. We assert that $X \varepsilon \Sigma$. For if $N(X,\delta)$ is an arbitrary neighborhood of X, then at least one point of $N(X,\delta)$ belongs to the complement of A, otherwise $\sup R \geq \alpha + \delta > \alpha$, contrary to assumption. On the other hand, at least one point of $N(X,\delta)$ belongs to A, otherwise $\sup R < \alpha$, contrary to assumption. Therefore X is a boundary point of A and $X \varepsilon \Sigma \cap S(P,Q)$.

5.10   Theorem   If P lies in the interior of a simple closed surface Σ in 3-space, or a simple closed curve in the plane, then every ray R beginning at P intersects Σ.

PROOF   Since Σ is bounded, at least one point Q of R belongs to the exterior of Σ. But then $S(P,Q)$ intersects Σ in a point on R.

Exercises

5.1   Show that every point which is not an exterior or interior point of set S is a boundary point of S.

5.2   Prove that the interior A of a closed simple polygon Π, as defined in the proof of Theorem 5.7, is identical to the interior of $A \cup \Pi$ according to Definition 5.3. State and prove similar results for the exterior of a polygonal region.

5.3   Show that Definition 1.12 is in accord with the terminology of this section.

5.4   Show that the following sets are connected: (*a*) a curve; (*b*) a spherical neighborhood; (*c*) a closed spherical neighborhood; (*d*) the union of two intersecting connected sets; (*e*) a convex set.

5.5   Describe the interior, exterior, and boundary of the following sets:
a. $\{(x,y)$ in the plane $|x^2 + y^2 \leq 1\}$
b. $\{(x,y,0)$ in 3-space $|x^2 + y^2 \leq 1\}$
c. $\{(x,y)$ in the plane $|0 \leq x < 1$ and $0 < y \leq 1\}$
d. $\{(x,y,0)$ in 3-space $|0 \leq x < 1$ and $0 < y \leq 1\}$

5.6   Describe the interior, exterior, and boundary of the set
a. $\{(x,y)$ in the plane $|x$ and y are integers$\}$
b. $\{(x,y)$ in the plane $|x$ and y are rational$\}$

INTRODUCTION

2

CONVEX BODIES

The theory of convex bodies is the most modern branch of euclidean geometry. It had its start near the end of the last century and has been growing rapidly ever since. We devote this chapter to an introduction to this theory. First we characterize convex bodies in terms of their boundary points and then in terms of their supporting lines or supporting planes. In Secs. 7 and 8 we discuss the possibility of approximating convex bodies by means of circumscribed as well as inscribed polyhedra. Next we investigate various intersection and separation problems which are closely related to Helly's theorem. In the last section we introduce the ideas of diameter, width, insphere, and circumsphere and present some basic properties of sets of constant width.

6 BASIC PROPERTIES OF CONVEX BODIES

It turns out that there are a great many interesting properties of a certain class of convex sets which we call convex bodies. First we need the following.

6.1 A set S is called **open** iff every point of S is an interior point of S.

6.2 A set S is called **closed** iff S contains all its boundary points.

It should be noticed that there are sets which are neither open nor closed. For example, the open disk together with a point on its boundary forms such a set. This implies that a set which is not open is not necessarily closed. The whole plane is an example of a set which is both open and closed.

We need one more preliminary definition.

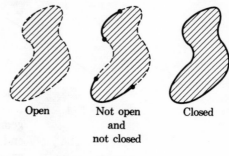

Open   Not open   Closed
and
not closed

Fig. 6.1

6.3 A set S is **bounded** iff there is a disk (or ball) which contains S.

The subject of this chapter can now be defined.

6.4 A convex set K which is closed, bounded, and nonempty is called a **convex body.**

It is important to realize that a set may have interior points when considered as a subset of one space and may not have interior points when considered as a subset of another. For example, an open line segment $S(A,B)$ consists entirely of interior points when considered as a subset of $L(A,B)$, but when considered as a subset of 2-space or 3-space $S(A,B)$ consists entirely of boundary points.

If a closed bounded convex set K contains interior points considered as a subset of n-space but does not contain interior points as a subset of $(n + 1)$-space, then we call K an n-**dimensional convex body** for $n = 0, 1, 2,$ or 3. A closed disk and triangular region are two-dimensional convex bodies, whereas a closed ball is a three-dimensional convex body.

We shall completely characterize convex bodies in the next few sections. First we give some preliminary properties of general convex sets.

6.5   Theorem   A convex polygonal region is the intersection of a finite number of closed half planes.   Conversely the intersection of a finite number of closed half planes is a closed convex set.

PROOF   Let Π be a convex polygonal region and P, Q, and R be any three consecutive vertices of Π. We assume for simplicity that no three successive vertices are collinear. We assert that $\Pi \subset H[L(P,Q),R]$. Suppose the contrary; then there is a point $A \in \Pi$ such that $A \notin H[L(P,Q),R]$. By the plane separation axiom, Theorem 1.10, $H[L(P,Q),A] \cup H[L(P,Q),R]$ is the whole plane, and the quadrilateral $\Pi' = PAQRP$ is a simple closed curve. This implies that $S(P,Q)$ consists entirely of points interior to Π'. However, Π is convex, so that $\Pi' \subset \Pi$ and $S(P,Q)$ consists of interior points of Π. This is impossible, since $S(P,Q)$ consists of boundary points of Π, which proves our assertion.

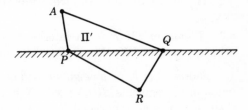

Fig. 6.2

Let $\Pi = P_0 P_1 \cdots P_n P_0$ and let $\Sigma = \bigcap_{i=0}^{n-1} H[L(P_i,P_{i+1}),P_{i+2}]$. We now have $\Pi \subset \Sigma$, and it remains to show that $\Sigma \subset \Pi$. Suppose $X \in \Sigma$ and $X \notin \Pi$. We shall show that this leads to a contradiction. Let F be the point of Π closest to X (see Appendix 2). If F is not a vertex and $S(P,Q)$ is the side of Π containing F, then the vertex R which follows P and Q must lie on the side of $L(P,Q)$ opposite from X. For if not, $\triangle PQR$ would intersect $S(X,F)$ in a point closer than F to X, contradicting the choice of F. It follows that $X \notin \Sigma$. If F is a vertex and P and Q are the vertices of Π adjacent to F, then $\angle XFP$ and $\angle XFQ$ must both be greater than or equal to $90°$. But then $X \notin H[L(P,F),Q)$, therefore $X \notin \Sigma$. It follows that $X \in \Pi$ and therefore $\Sigma \subset \Pi$.

The converse follows immediately from the fact that the intersection of any number of convex sets is again a convex set, together with Exercise 6.1.

The corresponding theorem in space also holds. The proof is left as an exercise.

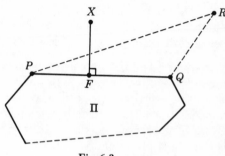

Fig. 6.3

6.6   Theorem   A convex polyhedral region is the intersection of a finite number of closed half spaces. Conversely the intersection of a finite number of closed half spaces is a closed convex set.

The next two properties will be quite useful in the sequel.

6.7   Theorem   If P is an interior point of convex set K and Q is an arbitrary point of K, then $S(P,Q)$ is contained in the interior of K.

PROOF   Let N be a neighborhood of P contained in K. Let C be the union of all segments $S(Q,X)$ with X in N. If Y is any point of $S(P,Q)$, then there is a neighborhood N' of Y contained in C. Since K is convex, C is contained in K. Therefore N' is contained in K and Y is an interior point of K.

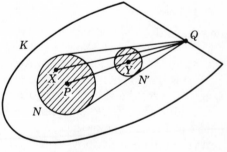

Fig. 6.4

6.8   Theorem   If P and Q are boundary points of convex set K, then either $S(P,Q)$ is in the interior of K or $S(P,Q)$ is in the boundary of K.

PROOF   Suppose $S(P,Q)$ contains an interior point X of K. By Theorem 6.7 $S(X,P)$ and $S(X,Q)$ consist of interior points. Therefore $S(P,Q)$ is in the interior of K. If $S(P,Q)$ contains no interior points, then it must lie in the boundary of K.

We now characterize a convex body in terms of its boundary points.

6.9   Theorem   A simple closed curve (surface) Γ bounds a convex body K iff every line through a point interior to Γ intersects Γ in exactly two points.

PROOF   Suppose that Γ bounds a convex body K and let P be an interior point of K. It follows from Exercise 6.4 that any ray R beginning at P must intersect K in a line segment $S[P,B]$. B must be a boundary point of K, otherwise we would have a segment of R properly containing $S[P,B]$ and lying in K. By Theorem 6.7 $S(P,B)$ consists of interior points of K. Therefore every line through P intersects Γ in exactly two points.

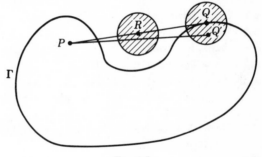

Fig. 6.5

Conversely, suppose that every line through an interior point of Γ intersects Γ in exactly two points and suppose that Γ bounds a nonconvex set K. We shall show that a line can be found which cuts Γ in more than two points, and this contradiction will imply the convexity of K. Since K is assumed not convex, there are points $P, Q \varepsilon K$ and a point $R \varepsilon S(P,Q)$ which is exterior to Γ. This implies that there is a neighborhood N of R lying entirely outside of Γ. We can assume that Q is an interior point of K since otherwise we could pick an interior point Q' close to Q so that $S(P,Q')$ intersects N in points exterior to Γ and then work with P and Q'. Let P_1 be a point of Γ on $S[P,R]$ and Q_1 a point of Γ on $S[R,Q]$. The ray through Q opposite to $R[Q,R)$ intersects Γ in a point B distinct from P and Q. Therefore line $L(P,Q)$ intersects Γ in at least three points P_1, Q_1, and B, and we have finished.

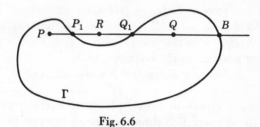

Fig. 6.6

A careful examination of the preceding proof will show that all steps are valid if Γ is a curve throughout or if Γ is a surface throughout.

In order to give a complete characterization of convex bodies in terms of boundary points, we need the fact that the boundary of a convex body is a simple closed curve in the plane and is a simple closed surface in space. This will be shown later in Sec. 11 (see Theorem 11.9).

Exercises

6.1   Prove that the intersection of any number of closed sets is a closed set.

6.2   Let K be a convex set and $\bar{K}$ the union of K and its boundary points. Show that $\bar{K}$ is convex.

6.3   Prove Theorem 6.6.

6.4   Prove that every one-dimensional convex set is either a line segment, a ray, or a line.   It follows that the only one-dimensional convex bodies are closed line segments.

6.5   Verify that the proof of Theorem 6.9 is still valid if the curve Γ is replaced by a surface Σ.

6.6   Give an example of a nonconvex set which has the property that every line cuts its boundary in no more than two points.

6.7   Prove that a closed neighborhood is a closed set and that an open neighborhood is an open set.

6.8   Prove that the complement of a closed set is open and that the complement of an open set is closed.

6.9   Which of the sets in Exercises 5.5 and 5.6 are open and which are closed?

6.10   Determine which of the following sets in the plane are open, closed, bounded, convex:

    a. $\{(x,y) \mid y > x^2\}$ *b.* $\{(x,y) \mid y \leq x^2\}$

    c. $\{(x,y) \mid x^{1/2} + y^{1/2} = 1\}$ *d.*   the whole plane

6.11   Determine which of the following sets in 3-space are open, closed, bounded, convex:

    a. $\{(x,y,z) \mid x^2/a^2 + y^2/b^2 + z^2/c^2 \leq 1\}$

    b. $\{(x,y,z) \mid y > |x| \text{ and } z < 1\}$

    c. $\{(x,y,z) \mid x^2/a^2 + y^2/b^2 < z \text{ and } z \leq 1\}$

7 PLANE CONVEX BODIES

In this section additional characteristic properties of plane convex bodies are developed which involve the important notion of a supporting line.

7.1 Let S be any plane set of points. Line l is called a **supporting line** of S iff l contains at least one boundary point of S and S lies entirely in one of the closed half planes bounded by l. The closed half plane bounded by l which contains S is called a **supporting half plane** of S.

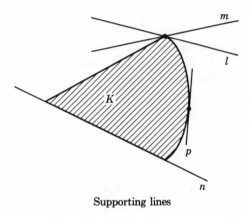

Supporting lines

Fig. 7.1

It is obvious that a supporting line of S can contain no interior points of S. As a matter of fact this property can be used as an alternate definition for two-dimensional convex sets.

7.2 Theorem l is a supporting line of the two-dimensional convex set K iff l contains boundary points but no interior points of K.

PROOF Suppose P is an interior point of K and let Q be a point of K separated from P by line l. It follows from Theorem 6.7 that $S(P,Q)$ intersects l in an interior point of K. Therefore, if l contains boundary points but no interior points of K, then l is a supporting line of K. The proof of the converse is left to the reader.

The notion of supporting line enables us to characterize the boundary of a convex set in a useful manner. First we need a few preliminaries.

7.3 Let B be a boundary point of the convex set K. The union of all rays beginning at B and passing through points of K, together with its boundary, is called the **tangent cone** of K at B.

The tangent cones of any plane convex set K are themselves convex sets (see Exercise 7.1). This implies that the angle containing K determined by the boundary of a tangent cone must have measure 180° or less. Also the boundary rays of the tangent cone at B lie on supporting lines of K through B.

7.4 The boundary rays of the tangent cone at boundary point B of convex set K are called the **semitangents** to K at B. If the semitangents at B are collinear, we call the union of the semitangents the **tangent line** to K at B.

7.5 A boundary point B of convex set K is called **regular** iff K has a tangent line at B. Otherwise B is called a **corner point** of K.

In Fig. 7.2, $R[B,X)$ and $R[B,Y)$ are the semitangents to K at B. In (a) B is a corner point. In (b) B is regular and $L(X,Y)$ is the tangent line to K at B.

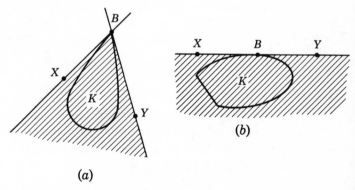

(a)

(b)

Fig. 7.2

It is easy to see that the vertices of a convex polygon Π are corner points of the polygonal region bounded by Π, whereas all other points of Π are regular.

We are now in a position to prove the following theorem, which is analogous to Theorem 6.9.

7.6 Theorem Let Γ be a simple curve which partitions the plane into three disjoint connected sets Γ, K, and K'. Γ bounds a plane convex set K iff through each point of Γ there passes at least one supporting line of K.

PROOF There are two possibilities. Either Γ is closed or Γ is unbounded. The following proof holds for both cases.

Suppose Γ bounds a convex set K and let R_1, R_2 be the semitangents to K at $B \varepsilon \Gamma$. The measure α of the angle bounded by R_1 and R_2 which contains K is less than or equal to 180°. If $\alpha = 180°$, then the tangent line at B is a supporting line of K. If $\alpha < 180°$, then the line containing R_1 (or R_2) is a supporting line of K.

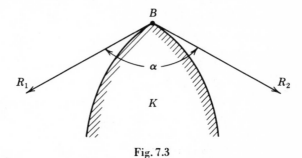

Fig. 7.3

On the other hand suppose that a set K bounded by Γ is not convex. Then we can find an interior point P and a point Q of K such that a boundary point B lies on $S(P,Q)$. Line $L(P,Q)$ is not a supporting line of K since P is an interior point of K. Any other line through B separates P from Q and cannot be a supporting line. Therefore there is no supporting line of K through B.

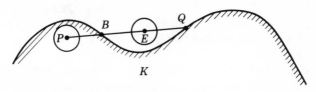

Fig. 7.4

The following property seems obvious but requires some proof.

7.7 Theorem   If K_1 is a closed convex set and K_2 is a convex body which does not intersect K_1, then there exists a line separating K_1 from K_2.

PROOF   Let P_1 and P_2 be points of K_1 and K_2 respectively which are a minimum distance apart, and construct lines l_1 and l_2 through P_1 and P_2 perpendicular to $L(P_1,P_2)$. According to Appendix 2 such points can always be found. We assert that l_i is a supporting line of K_i for $i = 1,2$. Suppose, for example, that l_1 is not a supporting line of K_1. Then there exists a point Q of K_1 on the same side of l_1 as P_2. Let F be the foot of the perpendicular from P_2 to the ray $R[P_1,Q)$. If F lies on $S(P_1,Q]$, then $|P_2F| < |P_2P_1|$. If Q lies on $S(P_1,F]$, then $|P_2Q| < |P_2P_1|$. Both possibilities contradict the choice of P_1 and P_2, which proves our assertion. Any line between l_1 and l_2 will separate K_1 from K_2.

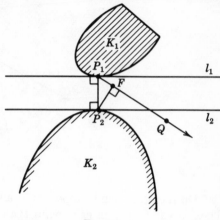

Fig. 7.5

If a finite set of supporting lines of a plane convex body K determine a convex polygon Π circumscribed to K, then the polygonal region bounded by Π can be considered as an approximation to K. If we add more supporting lines to form a new convex polygon Π' circumscribed to K, in general, Π' will determine a better approximation to K. The following theorem can be considered as a limiting case.

7.8   Theorem   A plane closed convex set (not the whole plane) is identical to the intersection of all its supporting half planes.

PROOF   By definition a convex set K is contained in the intersection Σ of its supporting half planes. On the other hand suppose that $P \notin K$. Let F be the point of K closest to P. As in the proof of Theorem 7.7, line l perpendicular to $L(P,F)$ at F is a supporting line of K at F. By Theorem 7.7, however, P does not belong to the supporting half plane of K bounded by l, therefore $P \notin \Sigma$. It follows that $\Sigma \subset K$, and the proof is complete.

We now investigate the possibility of approximating a two-dimensional convex body by inscribed convex polygonal regions.

7.9   Theorem   Let $\Pi = P_0P_1 \cdots P_NP_0$ be a closed polygonal curve inscribed to the boundary Γ of a two-dimensional convex body K. As we trace Γ in a given direction, starting with P_0, if the vertices occur on Γ in their natural order, then Π', the polygonal region bounded by Π, is convex.

PROOF   Let l be the line through two successive vertices P and Q of Π. Since K is convex, either $S(P,Q)$ is contained in Γ or $S(P,Q)$ is inside Γ. If $S[P,Q] \subset \Gamma$, then $l \cap \Gamma$ is a segment $S[P',Q']$ which contains $S[P,Q]$. Since l can contain no interior points of K, l is a supporting line of K. It follows that all points of Π' lie on the same side of l, and therefore l is a supporting line of Π'. On the other hand, if $S(P,Q)$ lies in the interior of Γ, then P and Q are the only points of Γ lying on l, and Γ is partitioned into two curves one on each side of l. Let H be the closed half plane bounded by l which contains all the vertices of Π. l is a supporting line of $H \cap K$, and since $\Pi' \subset H \cap K$, it follows that l is a supporting line of Π'. In either case through each point of $S[P,Q]$ there passes at least one supporting line of Π'. By Theorem 7.6, Π' is convex.

A converse of this theorem gives us another characterization of plane convex bodies.

7.10   Theorem   Let $\{P_0,P_1, \ldots ,P_n\}$ be any finite set of successive points on a simple closed curve Γ. If for every such set $\Pi = P_0P_1 \cdots P_nP_0$ is always a convex polygon, then Γ bounds a convex set.

PROOF   To prove this we need only show that if the set K bounded by Γ is not convex, then there is at least one quadrilateral region inscribed to Γ which is not convex. Suppose K is not convex; then we can find two points P and Q of Γ such that $S(P,Q)$ contains an exterior point E of K.

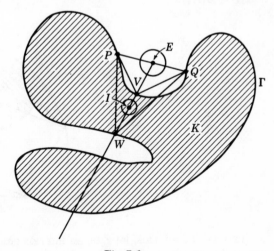

Fig. 7.6

Let I be any interior point of K not lying on $L(P,Q)$. Let S be the set of all points X on $L(E,I)$ such that $S[X,I]$ lies inside Γ. S is a bounded one-dimensional convex set and therefore must be a segment $S[V,W]$. Both V and W must lie on Γ, and one of them, say V, lies between E and I. It follows that V is an interior point of $\triangle PQW$. But then the quadrilateral region $PVQWP$ is not convex.

We conclude this section with a discussion of the comparative lengths of convex bodies. If Γ_1 and Γ_2 are arbitrary closed simple curves and Γ_1 is inside Γ_2, it is possible that the length of Γ_1 is greater than the length of Γ_2. For convex bodies, however, this is not possible. We let $L(K)$ stand for the length of the boundary of K.

7.11 Theorem If Π_1 and Π_2 are convex polygonal regions with $\Pi_1 \subset \Pi_2$, then $L(\Pi_1) \leq L(\Pi_2)$. If Π_1 is properly contained in Π_2, then $L(\Pi_1) < L(\Pi_2)$.

PROOF Let the vertices of Π_1 in order be $P_0, P_1, \ldots, P_n$ and let l_i, $i = 1, \ldots, n$ be the line through P_i and P_{i-1}. Let $S_0 = \Pi_2$ and $S_i = H_i \cap S_{i-1}$, $i = 1, \ldots, n$, where H_i is the supporting half plane of Π_1 bounded by l_i. Since a line segment has the shortest length of all curves between two points, for each i we have $L(S_i) \geq L(S_{i+1})$. It follows that $L(S_0) \geq L(S_n)$, or, since $S_n = \Pi_1$, that $L(\Pi_2) \geq L(\Pi_1)$. The equality can hold iff $S_i = S_{i+1}$ for all i. But then $\Pi_1 = \Pi_2$, contrary to assumption.

7.12 Theorem If K_1 and K_2 are two-dimensional convex bodies with $K_1 \subset K_2$, then $L(K_1) \leq L(K_2)$. If K_1 is properly contained in K_2, then $L(K_1) < L(K_2)$.

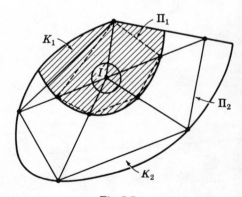

Fig. 7.7

PROOF To see this, let I be an interior point of K_1. Each ray beginning at I intersects the boundary of K_1 in exactly one point and the boundary of K_2 in exactly one point. This correspondence enables us to associate to each polygon Π_2 inscribed to K_2 a unique polygon Π_1 inscribed to K_1, and conversely. Since Π_2 contains Π_1, it follows from Theorem 7.11 that $L(\Pi_2) \geq L(\Pi_1)$, and therefore sup $L(\Pi_2) \geq$ sup $L(\Pi_1)$. Since K_2 is bounded, we can apply the preceding argument to K_2 and a rectangular region R containing K_2 to get sup $L(\Pi_2) \leq L(R)$. It follows that the sup $L(\Pi_2)$ is finite and $L(K_2) \geq L(K_1)$. The fact that equality cannot hold if K_1 is properly contained in K_2 is left as an exercise (see Exercise 7.4).

Exercises

7.1 Prove that the tangent cone to a convex set at a boundary point is itself a convex set. (Hint: Use Exercise 6.2.)

7.2 Let K be a two-dimensional convex set with boundary point B and let I be an interior point of K. Let $\alpha = $ sup $\{m \angle IBY | Y \in K$ and $S[X,I] \subset$ Interior $\angle IBY\}$, and let $\beta = $ sup $\{m \angle XBI | X \in K$ and $S[X,I] \subset$ Interior $\angle XBI\}$. If $m \angle XBI = \beta$ and $m \angle IBY = \alpha$, show that $\angle XBY$ and its interior form the tangent cone to K at B.

7.3 Give an example of two plane closed convex sets for which Theorem 7.7 does not hold.

7.4 Complete the proof of Theorem 7.12. [Hint: Let B be a boundary point of K_1 which is an interior point of K_2. Let H_1 be a supporting half plane of K_1 through B. Compare $L(H_1 \cap K_2)$ with $L(K_2)$.]

7.5 Show that a plane convex body K possesses a tangent line at boundary point B iff there is exactly one supporting line of K at B.

7.6 Let Γ be the graph of a function which has a derivative at point B on Γ. If the set K of points on and above Γ is convex, show that if the tangent line l to K at B exists (in the sense of Definition 7.4), then l is tangent to Γ at B according to the definition given in the calculus.

7.7 Prove that the line drawn perpendicular to $S[C,R]$ at point R is a supporting line of the disk with center C and radius $|CR|$.

8 CONVEX BODIES IN SPACE

The natural analog to a supporting line of a plane convex body is a supporting plane of a convex body in 3-space.

8.1 Let S be a set of points in space. Plane π is called a **supporting plane** of S iff π contains at least one boundary point of S and S lies entirely in one of the closed half spaces bounded by π. The closed half space bounded by π which contains S is called a **supporting half space** of S.

The proof of the following closely follows the proof of Theorem 7.2 and is left to the reader.

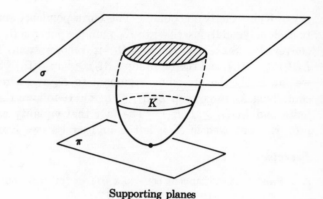

Supporting planes

Fig. 8.1

8.2   Theorem π is a supporting plane of the three-dimensional convex set K iff π contains boundary points but no interior points of K.

Definition 7.3 applies without change to 3-space, and we obtain the following analogy to 7.4.

8.3   If the boundary of the tangent cone at boundary point B of the convex set K is a plane π, then we call π the **tangent plane** to K at B.

It follows directly from the definition and the convexity of a tangent cone that a tangent plane is also a supporting plane.

Supporting lines can also be defined for three-dimensional convex sets, but a little care is necessary.   Obviously Definition 7.1 cannot be followed without some radical modification.   We can follow 7.2, however.

8.4 l is called a **supporting line** of the three-dimensional convex set K iff l contains boundary points but no interior points of K.

Consider the disk $x^2 + y^2 < 1$, $z = 0$.   In 3-space the z axis would be a supporting line of the disk if 8.4 were not restricted to three-dimensional convex bodies.   The restriction is purposely made to avoid such cases.

It is obvious that every line of a supporting plane of the three-dimensional convex set K which passes through a boundary point of K is a supporting line of K.   We also have the following.

8.5   Theorem   Let l be a supporting line of the three-dimensional convex body K and let π be the plane spanned by l and an interior point I of K.   Then $\pi \cap K$ is a two-dimensional convex body which has l as supporting line.

PROOF I is also an interior point of $\pi \cap K$, so that $\pi \cap K$ is a two-dimensional convex body. Suppose l is not a supporting line of $K \cap \pi$. Since B lies on l and B is a boundary point of $K \cap \pi$, it follows that l contains an interior point X of $K \cap \pi$ and there is a point Y of $K \cap \pi$ such that X lies between Y and I. Since I is an interior point of K and $Y \in K$, it follows that X is an interior point of K. But then l is not a supporting line of K, contrary to assumption.

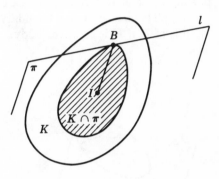

Fig. 8.2

The proof of the converse of Theorem 8.5 is left to the reader.

8.6 Theorem Let π be any plane through an interior point of a three-dimensional convex set K. If l is a supporting line of $K \cap \pi$, then l is a supporting line of K.

An immediate corollary is the following existence theorem.

8.7 Theorem Every boundary point B of a three-dimensional convex set K lies on a supporting line of K.

PROOF Let I be an interior point of K. Any plane through B and I intersects K in a two-dimensional convex body K'. By Theorem 8.6 any supporting line of K' through B will be a supporting line of K.

In Chap. 3 we shall study many different geometric mappings. One mapping of immediate use is the parallel projection.

8.8 The **projection of set A on plane π** parallel to line l is the intersection with π of all lines through points of A parallel to l.

The **projection of set A on line l** parallel to plane π is the intersection with l of all planes through points of A parallel to π.

8.9   Theorem   a. The projection of convex set K on line l parallel to plane π is a convex set P.

    b. The projection of convex set K on plane π' parallel to line l' is a convex set P'.

    c. An interior point of K is projected onto an interior point of P (or P').

    d. The plane through a boundary point of P parallel to π is a supporting plane of K if K is a convex body.

    e. The line through a boundary point of P' parallel to l' is a supporting line of K if K is a convex body.

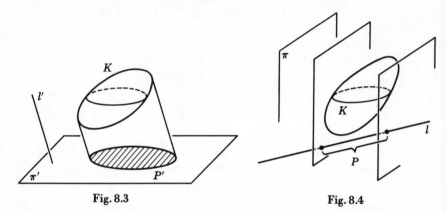

Fig. 8.3   Fig. 8.4

PROOF   We shall prove only parts (a) and (d). Let A and B be any two points of P and let A' and B' be points of K which project onto A and B respectively. Any point X of $S(A,B)$ lies on a plane ζ parallel to π. Since ζ separates A from B, it also separates A' from B' and $S(A',B')$ intersects ζ in a point X'. But $X' \varepsilon K$, since K is convex. Therefore $X \varepsilon P$, and P is convex. Now let D be a boundary point of P. If an interior point of K projects onto D, then D would be an interior point of P, which is impossible. Let π_D be the plane through D parallel to π. If $\pi_D \cap K = \varnothing$, then there is a positive distance δ between π_D and K. But then the distance between D and P is at least δ, and D cannot be a boundary point of P. Therefore π_D is a supporting plane of K.

The following theorem similar to 7.6 holds in space, but its proof requires some modification.

8.10   Theorem   Let Σ be a simple surface which partitions space into three disjoint connected sets. Σ bounds a convex set K iff through each point of Σ there passes at least one supporting plane of K.

PROOF   Suppose Σ bounds a convex set K with boundary point B. Let I be an interior point of K and let π and π' be any two planes through I and B. Let l be a supporting line of $K \cap \pi$ at B and project K onto π' parallel to l. Let l' be a supporting line of the projection P which passes through B. We assert that the plane ζ spanned by l and l' is a supporting plane of K. For if not, ζ would contain an interior point I' of K. But then the projection of I' on π' would be an interior point of P lying on l'. This contradicts the fact that l' is a supporting line of P, and our assertion is proved.

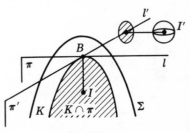

Fig. 8.5

On the other hand suppose that a set K bounded by Σ is not convex. Then we can find an interior point P and a point Q of K such that a boundary point B lies on $S(P,Q)$. No plane through P and Q can be a supporting plane of K, since P is an interior point of K. Any other plane through B separates P from Q and cannot be a supporting plane. Therefore there is no supporting plane of K through B.

If we use the three-dimensional analog of Theorem 7.7, then the proof of the following theorem is similar to the proof of Theorem 7.8.

8.11   Theorem   A three-dimensional closed convex set (not all of space) is identical to the intersection of all its supporting half spaces.

Continuing the pattern of Sec. 7, we now investigate the possibility of approximating a convex body by inscribed convex polyhedra. The notion of convex cover proves useful and also provides us with another characterization of convex polyhedra.

8.12   The **convex cover** of a set S is the smallest convex set containing S.
Obviously a convex set is its own convex cover. Conversely a set is convex if it is its own convex cover. In Fig. 8.6, K is the convex cover of S. In order to present the next theorem we need one more definition.

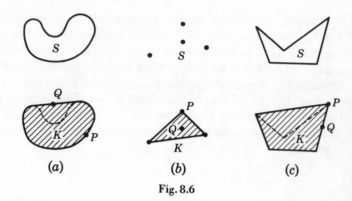

Fig. 8.6

8.13 A point E of convex set K is called an **extreme point** of K iff there are no two points P_1, P_2 of K such that E belongs to $S(P_1,P_2)$.

In Fig. 8.6, P is an extreme point of K, whereas Q is not.

8.14 Theorem A convex polyhedral region Π is the convex cover K of its extreme points.

PROOF   Obviously the extreme points of Π are the vertices of Π which do not lie in the interior of a face of Π.   Since each pair of extreme points belongs to K, each edge of Π joining extreme points belongs to K.   Since each face of Π is bounded by a polygon belonging to K, it follows that each face of Π belongs to K.   Any line through an interior point of Π intersects the surface of Π in two points belonging to K.   It follows that $\Pi \subset K$. Since K is the smallest convex set containing the vertices, we have $K \subset \Pi$ and therefore $\Pi = K$.

8.15 Theorem The convex cover of a finite number of points in space is a convex polyhedral region.

PROOF   Let K be the convex cover of the set of points $S = \{P_1, \ldots ,P_k\}$ lying in space.   If K is one-dimensional, then K is a line segment, and we have finished.   Suppose K is two-dimensional, and let us restrict the following discussion to the plane containing K and S. K is bounded and is therefore bounded by a simple closed curve Γ (see Theorem 11.9).   Let Π be the intersection of all half supporting planes of S whose boundaries contain at least two points of S.   Since S is finite, there are only a finite number of such half planes.   We denote them by $H_1, H_2, \ldots , H_N$.   Since Π is convex and $S \subset \Pi$, we have $K \subset \Pi$.   It remains to show that $\Pi \subset K$. Suppose $X \notin K$ and let F be the point of K a minimum distance from X.

The line l (in the plane of K) perpendicular to $L(X,F)$ at F is a supporting line of K at F. At least one point S_1 of S must lie on l, otherwise we could move l parallel to itself along $L(X,F)$ and cut off a proper convex subset of K which would contain S. Now rotate the half plane $H = H[l,X)$ about S_1, keeping X in H, until a second point S_2 of S is contained in l. The half plane H_i opposite to H will then be one of the defining half planes of Π, and since $X \notin H_i$, we have $X \notin \Pi$. It follows that $K = \Pi$ and the boundary of K consists of the union of line segments. Therefore K is a convex polygonal region.

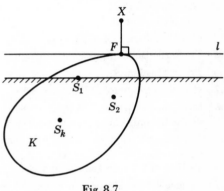

Fig. 8.7

If K is three-dimensional, we let Σ be the simple closed surface which bounds K and let Π be the intersection of all half supporting spaces of S whose boundaries contain at least three noncollinear points of S. The remainder of the proof is very similar to the two-dimensional case and is left as an exercise.

If the above set of points S lies on the boundary of a convex set, we obtain the following corollary.

8.16   Theorem   The convex cover Π of any finite set of points S lying on the boundary of convex body K is a convex polyhedral region contained in K. No point of S is an interior point of Π.

PROOF   By definition of convex cover, $\Pi \subset K$. Therefore all interior points of Π are also interior points of K.

We conclude this section with a converse to the preceding theorem.

8.17   Theorem   Let S be an arbitrary finite set of points on a simple closed surface Σ. If no point of S is an interior point of the convex cover of S for all such sets S, then Σ bounds a convex set.

PROOF   The proof is almost identical to the proof of Theorem 7.10. Let K be the region bounded by Σ and suppose K is not convex.   Let the points P, Q, E, I, V, and W be exactly as in Theorem 7.10, except that Σ takes the place of Γ.   Then V is an interior point of the convex cover of the set $\{P,Q,V,W\} \subset \Sigma$.

Exercises

8.1 Prove Theorem 8.2.

8.2 Prove Theorem 8.6.

8.3 Give examples which show that parts (**d**) and (**e**) of Theorem 8.9 are not true if K is not bounded.

8.4 Complete the proof of Theorem 8.9.

8.5 Prove the three-dimensional analog to Theorem 7.7.

8.6 Prove Theorem 8.11.

8.7 Complete the proof of Theorem 8.15.

8.8 Show that plane π is the tangent plane to convex set K at boundary point B iff π is the only supporting plane to K at B.

8.9 Prove that a polygonal region Π in the plane is convex iff all its interior angles have radian measure less than π.   (Hint: Show that the convex cover of the vertices of Π coincides with Π.)

8.10 Whenever possible give examples of the following:
  a. A regular point which is an extreme point.
  b. A corner point which is an extreme point.
  c. A regular point which is not an extreme point.
  d. A corner point which is not an extreme point.

8.11 Give examples which illustrate the fact that Theorem 8.14 does not hold in general for (**a**) unbounded convex sets, (**b**) bounded convex sets.

8.12 Show that a set of points may be closed and its convex cover not closed.

8.13 Prove that the convex cover of a finite set of points S is $\{\sum_{i=1}^{k} \alpha_i S_i | S_i \in S,\ \sum_{i=1}^{k} \alpha_i = 1, \alpha_i \geq 0, k = 1,2,3, \ldots\}$.

8.14 Show that Exercise 8.13 still holds if S is an arbitrary set.

8.15 Let S_0 be an arbitrary set of points and let $S_1 = \{X | X \in S[P,Q], P,Q \in S_0\}$, $S_2 = \{X | X \in S[P,Q], P,Q \in S_1\}$.   In general let $S_k = \{X | X \in S[P,Q], P,Q \in S^{k-1}\}$.   Show that the convex cover of S is $\bigcup_{i=0}^{\infty} S_i$.

8.16 Using the notation in Exercise 8.15, show that when S_0 is a finite set of points, the convex cover of S_0 is $S_0 \cup S_1 \cup S_2$.

9   HELLY'S THEOREM

We now turn our attention to some applications of the theory of convex bodies which center about a result known as Helly's theorem. The following theorem is of some interest in itself and will be needed in our proof of Helly's theorem.

9.1   Radon's theorem   Let $S = \{S_1, \ldots, S_N\}$ be a finite set of points lying in n-space, $n = 1, 2,$ or 3. If $N \geq n + 2$, then S can be partitioned into two sets whose convex covers intersect.

PROOF   For $n = 1$ we have $N \geq 3$, and all the points of S lie on a line. Let the points of S be numbered according to their order on the line. $S[S_1,S_{N-1}] \cap S[S_2,S_N] \neq \varnothing$, and the desired sets are $X = \{S_1,S_{N-1}\}$ and $Y = S - X$.

For $n = 2$ we have $N \geq 4$, and all the points of S lie on a plane. If some point P of S lies in the convex cover of the remaining points, then $X = \{P\}$ and $S - X$ are the desired sets. Assume the contrary; then S_1 does not lie in the convex cover K of $S - \{S_1\}$, and there is a line l which separates S_1 from K. Let $P_i, i = 2, \ldots, N$ be the intersection of $S(S_1,S_i)$ with l. The P_is are all distinct, otherwise S_1 would be collinear with two other points S_i and S_j, and if S_i were between S_1 and S_j, then S_i would lie in the convex cover of $S - \{S_i\}$, contrary to assumption. Suppose that P_3 lies between P_2 and P_4. Let α be the smaller angle bounded by rays $R[S_1,S_2)$ and $R[S_1,S_4)$. S_3 lies inside α. S_3 cannot lie in $\triangle S_1S_2S_4$ since then S_3 would lie in the convex cover of $S - \{S_3\}$. It follows that $S(S_1,S_3) \cap S(S_2,S_4) \neq \varnothing$, and $X' = \{S_1,S_3\}$ and $Y' = S - X'$ are the desired sets.

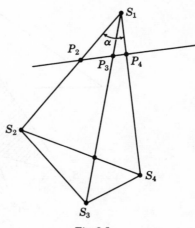

Fig. 9.1

When $n = 3$, we have $N \geq 5$. As in the preceding case we can assume that no point of S lies in the convex cover of the remaining points, and we can find a plane π which separates S_1 from the convex cover of the

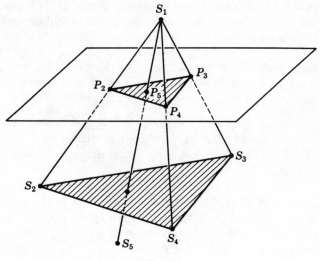

Fig. 9.2

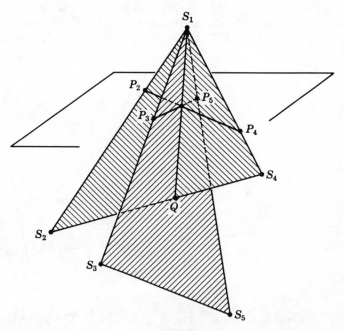

Fig. 9.3

remaining points. Also the points $P_i = \pi \cap S(S_1,S_i)$, $i = 2, \ldots, N$, form a set of $N - 1$ distinct points in π. According to the preceding part, $\{P_2,P_3,P_4,P_5\}$ can be partitioned into two sets X and Y whose convex covers intersect. There are two possibilities. Either one of the sets contains three points and the other one, or each contains two points.

Suppose X contains one point, say P_5. Then P_5 lies in the triangle $P_2P_3P_4$. Let α be the convex trihedral angular region bounded by the convex angular regions $\angle S_2S_1S_3$, $\angle S_3S_1S_4$, and $\angle S_4S_1S_2$. S_5 lies inside α but cannot lie in the tetrahedron $S_1S_2S_3S_4$ since then S_5 would lie in the convex cover of $S - \{S_5\}$. This argument is still valid if α degenerates into a plane angle. It follows that $S(S_1,S_5) \cap \triangle S_2S_3S_4$ is not empty, and $X' = \{S_1,S_5\}$ and $Y' = S - X'$ are the desired sets.

Suppose X and Y contain two points each. For definiteness let $X = \{P_2,P_4\}$ and $Y = \{P_3,P_5\}$. Since $S(P_2,P_4) \cap S(P_3,P_5) \neq \varnothing$, it follows that $\triangle S_1S_2S_4$ and $\triangle S_1S_3S_5$ intersect in a line segment with end points S_1 and Q. Q must lie either on $S(S_2,S_4)$ or on $S(S_3,S_5)$. If Q lies on $S(S_2,S_4)$, then $X' = \{S_2,S_4\}$ and $Y' = S - X'$ satisfy the requirements, and our proof is complete.

9.2 Helly's Theorem Let $K = \{K_1,K_2, \ldots,K_N\}$ be N convex sets, $N \geq n + 1$, lying in n-space, $n = 1, 2,$ or 3, having the property that every $n + 1$ of the sets have a nonempty intersection. Then the intersection of all the sets is not empty.

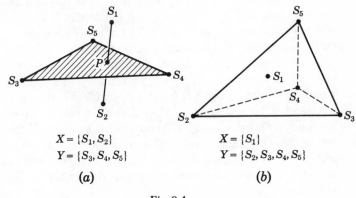

$$X = \{S_1, S_2\} \qquad\qquad X = \{S_1\}$$
$$Y = \{S_3, S_4, S_5\} \qquad\qquad Y = \{S_2, S_3, S_4, S_5\}$$

$$(a) \qquad\qquad\qquad (b)$$

Fig. 9.4

PROOF We shall prove the theorem only for $n = 3$. If $N = 4$, the theorem is trivially true. Suppose $N = 5$, let $S_i \in \bigcap\limits_{i \neq j} K_j$, and let $S = \{S_1, \ldots ,S_5\}$. According to Theorem 9.1, S can be partitioned into two sets X and Y whose convex covers intersect. We assert that any point P of this intersection belongs to all N of the convex sets. To see this we notice that there are two possibilities. Either S is partitioned into sets of three and two points or into sets of four and one points. By construction the convex cover of every four points of S lies entirely in one of the sets of K, and conversely. Suppose $X = \{S_1, S_2\}$ and $Y = \{S_3, S_4, S_5\}$. Then P lies in the convex cover of every subset of four points of S, and therefore P lies in all sets of K. On the other hand if $X = \{P\}$ and $Y = S - X$, then X is contained in the convex cover of Y, and P again lies in the convex cover of every subset of four points of S.

We complete the proof by induction on N. Assume the theorem true for m convex sets and let $K_1, \ldots, K_m, K_{m+1}$ be convex sets any four of which have a common point. Let $K = K_m \cap K_{m+1}$. From the preceding part for $N = 5$ it follows that K_m, K_{m+1} and any other three sets K_i, K_j, K_l have a point in common. Therefore $K_1, K_2, \ldots, K_{m-1}, K$ are m convex sets each four of which have a common point. By the induction hypothesis there is a point common to all these sets. This point is common to $K_1, \ldots, K_m, K_{m+1}$.

Helly's theorem does not hold for an infinite number of convex sets unless some restriction is made. For example, consider the set of all closed half spaces contained in a given closed half space. Any four of these sets have a common point, but there is no point common to all of them. In Exercise 18.7 and in Appendix 2 it is shown that Helly's theorem holds for an infinite number of closed convex sets provided at least one of them is bounded.

Helly's theorem also does not hold for nonconvex sets. The reader can easily construct a counter-example to show this.

Our first application of Helly's theorem tells us that for an arbitrary set there are points which behave approximately like a center of the set. If for each point P of a set S there is a point P' of S such that $S(P, P')$ is always bisected by the same point O then O is called the **center of S.** For example, a spherical neighborhood of a point P has P for center, and the intersection of the diagonals of a parallelogram is the center of the parallelogram. Using the calculus it is easy to see that any plane through the center of a set having volume partitions the set into two parts having equal volume.

9.3 Theorem Let $S = \{P_1, \ldots, P_n\}$ be any finite set of points in space. Then there is a point O such that every closed half space bounded by a plane through O contains at least $n/4$ points of S.

PROOF Since S is finite, there is a ball B which contains all the points P_i. Consider the set of all closed half spaces which contain more than

$3n/4$ points of S. We assert that every four of these sets have a common point. By intersecting these half spaces with B we can apply Helly's theorem to conclude that there is a point O common to all such half spaces. To prove our assertion let H_1, H_2, H_3, and H_4 be any four closed half spaces each containing more than $3n/4$ points of S. Let H' be the complement of H. From set theory we know that $(H_1 \cap H_2 \cap H_3 \cap H_4)' = H_1' \cup H_2' \cup H_3' \cup H_4'$. Since each H_i' contains less than $n/4$ points of S, it follows that $H_1' \cup H_2' \cup H_3' \cup H_4'$ contains less than n points of S and $H_1 \cap H_2 \cap H_3 \cap H_4$ contains at least one point of S. This proves our assertion.

We now show that the point O whose existence has just been shown is the desired point. Suppose the contrary. Then there is a plane π through O which bounds a closed half space containing less than $n/4$ points of S. The opposite open half space H will contain more than $3n/4$ points of S. Let π' be the plane parallel to π passing through the points of $S \cap H$ closest to π. The closed half space H' bounded by π' and lying in H contains more than $3n/4$ points of S, but H' does not contain O. This contradiction completes the proof.

9.4 Theorem Let S be a bounded set of points in space having volume V. Then there is a point O such that every closed half space through O intersects S in a set of volume at least $V/4$.

PROOF The proof closely follows the proof of Theorem 9.3. As before, we use Helly's theorem to obtain a point O which belongs to every closed half space intersecting S in a set of volume more than $3V/4$. Suppose that π is a plane through O which bounds a closed half space intersecting S in a set of volume less than $V/4$. The opposite closed half space H intersects S in a set of volume V' greater than $3V/4$. We can find a plane π' lying in H parallel to π such that the portion of S between π' and π has volume less than $V' - 3V/4$. The closed half space H' lying in H and bounded by π' intersects S in a set of volume greater than $3V/4$ and does not contain O. This gives us the desired contradiction.

The following theorem is a consequence of Helly's theorem which has applications to analysis.

9.5 Theorem Let S be any finite collection of parallel line segments lying in the plane. If for every three members of S there is a line which intersects all three, then there is a line which intersects all members of S.

PROOF Choose a coordinate system in the plane with the y axis parallel to the given segments. Let $P_i(x_i, y_i')$ and $Q_i(x_i, y_i'')$ be the end points of the ith segment where $y_i' < y_i''$. If the line $y = mx + b$ intersects the ith segment, we must have $y_i' \leq mx_i + b \leq y_i''$. Since every line l not parallel to the y axis is completely determined by its slope and y intercept, to each point (m,b) there corresponds a unique line l, and conversely. Consider the equation $b = -x_im + y_i'$ and $b = -x_im + y_i''$. These represent parallel lines in the mb plane, since they have the same slope $-x_i$. It follows from the above inequalities that the line l intersects the ith segment iff the point (m,b) corresponding to l lies in the strip S_i bounded by these parallel lines. By hypothesis each three segments are intersected by a line. Therefore each three of the corresponding strips contains a common point. By Helly's theorem there is a point (m_1,b_1) common to all the strips. The line $y = m_1x + b_1$ intersects all the segments.

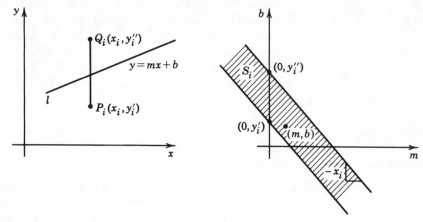

Fig. 9.5

To illustrate the use of this theorem consider a continuous function f defined on the interval $[a,b]$. We say that line $y = mx + b$ approximates the function f on the set S (contained in $[a,b]$) with exactness within $\epsilon > 0$ iff $|f(x) - (mx + b)| \leq \epsilon$ for every x in S. It follows from Theorem 9.5 that if for each three points of $[a,b]$ there is a line which approximates f within ϵ on the three points, then there is a line which approximates f within ϵ on any finite number of points of $[a,b]$. Together with the continuity of f this implies the existence of a line which approximates f within ϵ on the whole interval $[a,b]$.

In the proof of the preceding theorem we found it convenient to set up a duality between points in a plane and lines in a plane. The proof of the next theorem utilizes a duality between points of a plane and planes in 3-space.

Given a triangle $P_1P_2P_3$ and a point I in its interior, it is impossible to find a line in the plane of $P_1P_2P_3$ which will separate I from $\{P_1,P_2,P_3\}$.

We now look for conditions which will assure us that two sets of points can be separated.

9.6 Theorem Let S_1 and S_2 be two finite sets of points in the plane. Suppose that for every subset X of $S_1 \cup S_2$ consisting of four points there is a line l that strictly separates $X \cap S_1$ from $X \cap S_2$. Then there is a line which separates S_1 from S_2.

PROOF Let each point $P(x_1,y_1)$ of S_1 in the xy plane correspond to the open half space $ax_1 + by_1 + c > 0$ lying in abc-space and let each point $P(x_2,y_2)$ of S_2 correspond to the open half space $ax_2 + by_2 + c < 0$ lying in abc-space. Consider the collection of all such half spaces and select any four of them. Let $X = \{M,N,P,Q\}$ be the corresponding points of $S_1 \cup S_2$, and for definiteness suppose $M(x_1,y_1)$ belongs to S_1. By assumption there is a line $a'x + b'y + c' = 0$ which separates $X \cap S_1$ from $X \cap S_2$. If $a'x_1 + b'y_1 + c' > 0$, then the point $P(a',b',c')$ lies in all four half spaces. If $a'x_1 + b'y_1 + c' < 0$, then $P(-a',-b',-c')$ lies in all four half spaces. It follows from Helly's theorem that there is a point $P(\bar{a},\bar{b},\bar{c})$ lying in all the half spaces. The line $\bar{a}x + \bar{b}y + \bar{c} = 0$ will strictly separate S_1 from S_2.

We conclude this section with a theorem closely related to the results of the preceding section.

9.7 Carathéodory's theorem If X is any point of the convex cover K of a closed bounded set S in n-space, then there is a set of q points $P = \{P_1, \ldots ,P_q\}$, $P \subset S$, $q \leq n + 1$, such that X belongs to the convex cover of P.

PROOF Suppose $n = 1$. Then the convex cover K of set S is a line segment $S[P,Q]$, P, $Q \in S$, and every point of K belongs to the convex cover of P and Q.

Suppose that $n = 2$. We assert that $l \cap K$ is the convex cover K' of $l \cap S$ for every supporting line l of K. To see this suppose $X \in l \cap K$. Then, according to Exercise 8.13, there is a k such that $X = \sum_{i=1}^{k} \alpha_i S_i$, $\sum_{i=1}^{k} \alpha_i = 1$, $\alpha_i \geq 0$, $S_i \in S$. Choose a coordinate system in the plane so that l is the y axis and all points of S have nonnegative x coordinates. Since $X \in l$, all points $S_1, \ldots , S_k$ must have zero x coordinates, and $S_i \in l \cap S$, $i = 1, \ldots , k$. Therefore $X \in K'$. On the other hand, suppose $X \in K'$. Since $l \cap S \subset l \cap K$, we have $K' \subset l \cap K$ and $X \in l \cap K$. This proves the assertion. Now consider an arbitrary point X of K and let P be any point of S distinct from X. If X is a boundary point of K, then it lies on a supporting line l of K. From our assertion X lies on the convex cover of $l \cap S$. It follows from the case $n = 1$ that X lies on a line segment $S[Q,R]$ with Q, $R \in S$.   Therefore X belongs to the convex cover of $\{P,Q,R\}$.   If X' is an interior point of K, the ray $R[P,X')$ intersects the boundary of K in some point X.   But then X' lies on the convex cover of $\{P,Q,R\}$ just constructed.   This proves the theorem for $n = 2$.

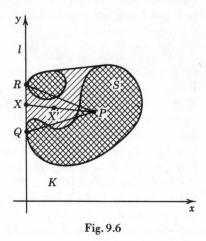

Fig. 9.6

If we use Exercise 9.8, the proof of the theorem for $n = 3$ follows the same pattern as for $n = 2$.   We leave the details to the reader.

Exercises

9.1 Prove Helly's theorem for $n = 1$ and $n = 2$ by following the proof of Theorem 9.2.

9.2 Prove Helly's theorem for $n = 1$ and $n = 2$ without using Theorem 9.1.

9.3 Construct four sets in the plane such that each three intersect while all four do not.

9.4 State and prove theorems analogous to Theorems 9.3 and 9.4 for sets lying in the plane.   Do the same thing for sets lying on a line.

9.5 Show that every supporting plane of the convex cover of a closed bounded set S contains at least one point of S.

9.6 Show that every supporting line of a plane convex body K contains at least one extreme point of K.

9.7 Prove that a convex body is the convex cover of its extreme points.

9.8 Let $\tilde{M}$ be the convex cover of set M.   Show that, for every closed bounded set S in space, if τ is a supporting plane of $\tilde{S}$, then $\tau \cap \tilde{S} = \tau \cap S$.

9.9 Give examples to show that the number q in Carathéodory's theorem cannot be decreased.

9.10 Use the equation $y = ax^2 + bx + c$ to establish a one-to-one correspondence between line segments in the xy plane parallel to the y axis and strips in abc-

space bounded by parallel planes. Then use Helly's theorem to prove the following: *Theorem* Let S be any finite collection of parallel line segments in the plane. If for every four members of S there is a parabola, with axis parallel to the y axis, which intersects all four, then there is a parabola which intersects all members of S.

9.11 Give examples to show that the number of points (four) in Theorem 9.6 cannot be reduced.

9.12 Use Carathéodory's theorem to prove that Exercise 8.16 still holds when S_0 is an arbitrary closed bounded set.

10 SETS OF CONSTANT WIDTH

So far the only numerical quantities we have used for the comparison of sets are the volume and surface area. We conclude this chapter by introducing a number of other numerical quantities associated with a given set.

10.1 The **diameter** of a set S is the least upper bound of the distances between any two points of S.

10.2 If l is a line perpendicular to two parallel supporting planes π and π' of a bounded set S, then we call the distance between $l \cap \pi$ and $l \cap \pi'$ the **width of S in the direction** l.

In Fig. 10.1 w is the width of K in the direction l.

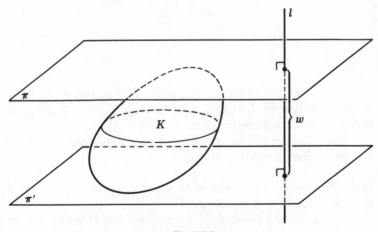

Fig. 10.1

If S lies entirely in a plane, then in the preceding definition we replace π and π' by parallel supporting lines. Exercise 10.1 assures us that π and π' exist, so that the width of a bounded set is a well-defined concept. The following theorem shows the close relationship between diameter and width.

10.3   Theorem   The diameter of a closed bounded set S is equal to the maximum width of S.

PROOF   To see this let d be the maximum width of S and let π_1 and π_2 be parallel supporting planes of S a distance d apart. If P_1 and P_2 are points of S lying on π_1 and π_2 respectively, we assert that $|P_1P_2| = d$. If $L(P_1,P_2)$ is perpendicular to π_1, our assertion obviously holds. Suppose $L(P_1,P_2)$ is not perpendicular to π_1, and let σ_1 and σ_2 be parallel supporting planes of S which are perpendicular to $L(P_1,P_2)$. If d' is the width of S in the direction of $L(P_1,P_2)$, we have $d < |P_1P_2| \leq d'$. This is impossible, since d is the maximum width. Therefore $d = |P_1P_2|$, which proves the assertion.

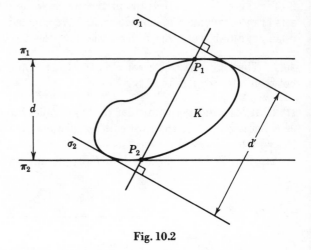

Fig. 10.2

Now let Q_1 and Q_2 be any two points of S and let d'' be the width of S in the direction of $L(Q_1,Q_2)$. We have $|P_1P_2| = d \geq d'' \geq |Q_1Q_2|$. By definition d is the diameter of K.

The following two propositions are easy consequences of Theorem 10.3, and their proofs are left to the reader.

10.4   Theorem   Let π and π' be supporting planes of a closed bounded set S in a direction of maximum width.

   a.   If P is any point of $S \cap \pi$, then the line l through P perpendicular to π intersects π' in a point P' belonging to S.

   b. $\pi \cap S$ ($\pi' \cap S$) consists of exactly one point $P(P')$. The line $L(P,P')$ is perpendicular to π and π'.

   It follows from Theorems 10.3 and 10.4 that a closed set K of constant width w has diameter w, every supporting plane π of K intersects K in a single point P, and if π' is a parallel supporting plane intersecting K in P', then $L(P,P')$ is perpendicular to π and π'. The converse is also true.

10.5   Theorem   If P and Q are any two points of a closed set K of constant width w, with $|PQ| = w$, then the planes perpendicular to $L(P,Q)$ at P and Q respectively are both supporting planes of K.

At first sight we might conjecture that the only convex sets of constant width are spherical neighborhoods. This is not the case, however. Let $\triangle ABC$ be equilateral with edge length w. With each vertex as center draw the smallest arc of radius w joining the other two vertices. The union of these three arcs bounds a set of constant width w called a **Reuleaux triangle.** The most striking difference between the disk and the Reuleaux triangle is that the latter has corner points. It is possible to modify the preceding construction to obtain a set of constant width, different from the disk, which has no corner points. Let ABC be an equilateral triangle of edge length d and extend each side a distance h in both directions (see Fig. 10.3). With each vertex as center and with radius h construct the arcs $A'A''$, $B'B''$, and $C'C''$. Then with each vertex as center and with radius $d + h$ construct the arcs $A''B'$, $B''C'$, and $C''A'$. The union of these six arcs bounds a set of constant width $d + 2h$.

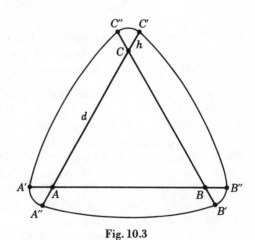

Fig. 10.3

If a plane set K of constant width w has an axis of symmetry l, then the three-dimensional set generated by rotating K about l is a set of constant width w.

The following theorems give us an equivalent definition for convex sets of constant width.

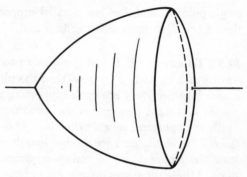

Fig. 10.4

10.6   Theorem   If K is a convex body of constant width and if $P \notin K$, then the diameter of K is less than the diameter of $K \cup \{P\}$.

PROOF   Suppose K has constant width w and suppose $P \notin K$.   Let X be a point of K closest to P and let π be the plane through X perpendicular to $L(P,X)$.   According to Exercise 8.5, π is a supporting plane of K.   It follows from Theorems 10.3 and 10.4 that the ray $R[P,X)$ intersects the boundary of K in a point X' such that $|XX'| = w$.   But then $|PX'| = |PX| + |XX'| > |XX'| = w$, and we have finished.

10.7   Theorem   If S is a closed bounded set and K is its convex cover, then (**a**) every supporting plane of S is a supporting plane of K and conversely (**b**) the diameter of K equals the diameter of S.

PROOF   Let σ be a supporting plane of K.   According to Exercise 9.5, σ contains at least one point P of S.   If P is an interior point of S, then P is an interior point of K and σ is not a supporting plane of K.   Therefore σ is a supporting plane of S.   On the other hand, suppose σ is a supporting plane of S and let H be the supporting half space of S bounded by σ. H is a convex set containing S, therefore $K \subset H$.   Since σ contains a point of S, and therefore a point of K, it follows that σ is a supporting plane of K.

The proof of part (**b**) now follows easily from the definition of width of a set and is left to the reader.

The following theorem is similar to Theorem 10.4.

10.8   Theorem   Let Δ be the minimum width of a three-dimensional convex body K and let π_1, π_2 be parallel supporting planes of K in a direction of width Δ.   Then there are points $P_1 \varepsilon \pi_1 \cap K$ and $P_2 \varepsilon \pi_2 \cap K$ such that $L(P_1,P_2)$ is perpendicular to π_1.

PROOF   Suppose the contrary.   Then the intersection of the orthogonal projection M of $\pi_1 \cap K$ onto π_2 with $\pi_2 \cap K$ is empty.   Let σ be a plane perpendicular to π_1 which separates $\pi_2 \cap K$ from M.   Rotate π_1 about $\pi_1 \cap \sigma$ to π_1', and rotate π_2' about $\pi_2 \cap \sigma$ to π_2' so that π_1' is parallel to π_2' and K lies within the strip bounded by π_1' and π_2'.   The width of K in a direction perpendicular to π_1' is less than or equal to the distance between π_1' and π_2', which in turn is less than Δ.   But this contradicts the definition of Δ and proves the theorem.

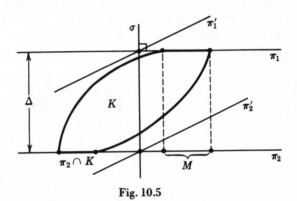

Fig. 10.5

10.9   Theorem   Let K be a convex body with the property that whenever $P \notin K$, then the diameter D of K is less than the diameter of $K \cup \{P\}$. Then K has constant width D.

PROOF   Let π_1, π_2 be parallel supporting planes of K such that $P_1 \varepsilon \pi_1 \cap K$, $P_2 \varepsilon \pi_2 \cap K$, $L(P_1,P_2)$ is perpendicular to π_1, and $|P_1P_2|$ is the minimum width of K.

We assert that there is at least one point $Q \varepsilon K$ such that $|P_1Q| = D$. Suppose the contrary; then there is a neighborhood N of P_1 and a point X in N, which does not belong to K, such that $|XQ| < D$ for all $Q \varepsilon K$.   But then K does not satisfy the hypothesis of our theorem, and the assertion is proved.

To complete our proof one more fact is needed.   We claim that for every two points of K any circular arc joining them with radius D smaller than a semicircle also belongs to K.   To see this we note that K is identical to the intersection S of all balls with center belonging to K and radius D. For, from the definition of diameter, it follows that $K \subset S$.   Let $P \varepsilon S$, then $|PQ| \leq D$ for all points $Q \varepsilon K$, and it follows from the hypothesis of the theorem that $P \varepsilon K$.   Therefore $S \subset K$ and $S = K$.   Now if X and Y are two arbitrary points, any arc of radius D, smaller than a semicircle, joining X to Y belongs to the intersection of all balls with radius D containing X and Y (see Exercise 10.11). In particular if X, $Y \in K$, any arc of radius D, smaller than a semicircle with radius D, joining X to Y belongs to $S = K$.

Now suppose the minimum width is $\Delta < D$, and let α be the smaller circular arc with center C and radius D lying in the plane of P_1, P_2, and Q which joins P_2 to Q. C does not lie on $L(P_1,P_2)$. For then $|QC| = |P_1C|$ and $m \angle QP_1C = m \angle P_1CQ$, which is impossible. Therefore α intersects π_2 in a point Q' distinct from Q and P_2. The subarc of α joining Q' to P_2 then lies outside the strip between π_1 and π_2. But this contradicts the fact that π_2 is a supporting plane of K, and therefore $\Delta = D$ and K has constant width D.

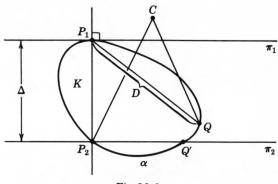

Fig. 10.6

Our next proposition is concerned with the following concepts.

10.10 A sphere of largest diameter which lies entirely inside a set S is called an **insphere** of S. The sphere of smallest diameter which can be circumscribed to S is called the **circumsphere** of S.

In general the insphere is not unique. The circumsphere, however, is always unique. The existence of an insphere and circumsphere for closed bounded sets will be shown in Sec. 18. If the set S lies in a plane, we speak of the incircle and circumcircle of S.

10.11 Theorem The insphere and circumsphere of a convex set of constant width w are concentric, and the sum of their radii equals w.

PROOF Let K have constant width w and let S be an insphere of K with center P and radius r. At least one boundary point X of K lies on S, otherwise a sphere of radius greater than r with center P would lie in K.

Let π be the plane through X perpendicular to $L(P,X)$. Every other plane through X contains interior points of S and therefore contains interior points of K. Since K is convex, every boundary point of K lies on a supporting plane of K, and π must be the supporting plane of K at X. Let Y be the point such that $|YX| = w$ and P lies between X and Y. Since K has constant width, it follows from Theorem 10.4 that Y is a boundary point of K. We now let S' be the sphere with center P and radius $R = w - r$.

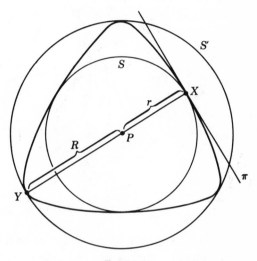

Fig. 10.7

Let Σ be the boundary of K and consider the set $S \cap \Sigma$. We assert that P is contained in the convex cover of $S \cap \Sigma$. Suppose the contrary; then there is a closed half space H whose boundary passes through P which does not contain $S \cap \Sigma$. Let 2δ be the smallest distance between $H \cap S$ and $H \cap \Sigma$. If P' is a point in H such that $L(P,P')$ is perpendicular to the boundary plane of H and $|PP'| = \delta$, then the sphere with center P' and radius $r' = \sqrt{r^2 + \delta^2} > r$ will lie inside K, contradicting the choice of S. According to Theorem 9.7 there is a set $U = \{X_1, \ldots, X_4\}$ of four or fewer points of $S \cap \Sigma$ such that P lies in the convex cover of U. Let $V = \{Y_1, \ldots, Y_4\}$, where $|X_iY_i| = w$ and P lies between X_i and Y_i. It follows from the preceding that $V \subset S' \cap K$. Consider the set W obtained by reflecting V about P. By construction the convex cover of W contains the convex cover of U and therefore contains the point P. It follows that the convex cover of V also contains P. Let P' be any point distinct from P and let σ be the plane through P perpendicular to $L(P,P')$.

At least one point Y_i of V must lie in the closed half space opposite to $H[\sigma,P')$, otherwise P would not lie in the convex cover of V. But then $|P'Y_i| > |PY_i| = R$. It follows that any sphere with center other than P cannot be the circumsphere of K. This leaves S' as the only possibility, and since a circumsphere of K exists, our proof is complete.

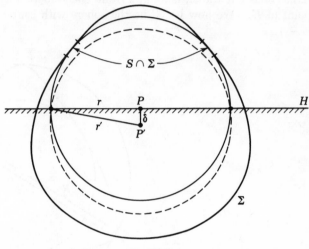

Fig. 10.8

If the insphere and circumsphere of a convex body K with constant width coincide, then K is a set with center (see the discussion preceding Theorem 9.3), namely a spherical neighborhood. The following is also true.

10.12 Theorem   The only three-dimensional convex bodies of constant width having a center are the closed spherical neighborhoods.

PROOF   Let C be the center of the convex body K of constant width w. If X is any point of K, then its reflection X' about P also belongs to K. It follows that $|XX'| \le w$ and $|CX| \le w/2$. The closed ball B with center C and radius $w/2$ contains the boundary of K and therefore contains all of K. It follows from Theorem 10.11 that the circumsphere must have radius greater than or equal to $w/2$. But then the boundary S of ball B must be the circumsphere of K, and since its radius is $w/2$ it must also be the insphere of K. Therefore $K = B$.

Exercises

10.1   Show that every closed bounded set S in space has the property that there are two supporting planes of S (which may degenerate to one) in a given direction. (Hint: Use Exercise 9.5 and Theorem 8.9.)

10.2 Prove Theorem 10.4.

10.3 Prove Theorem 10.5.

10.4 Use the method of constructing the Reuleaux triangle on the vertices of a regular polygon with an odd number of sides to construct a Reuleaux polygon of constant width.

10.5 Prove that a plane set of constant width w with an axis of symmetry l generates a set of constant width w when rotated about l.

10.6 Give an example which shows that the insphere of a set may not be unique.

10.7 Prove that the circumsphere of a set is always unique.

10.8 Show that the projection of a set of constant width w, parallel to a line l, onto a plane perpendicular to l, is a plane set of constant width w.

10.9 Prove part (**b**) of Theorem 10.7 using part (**a**).

10.10 Prove part (**b**) of Theorem 10.7 directly from the definition of diameter without using part (**a**).

10.11 Prove that if X and Y are two arbitrary points, any arc of radius D smaller than a semicircle joining X to Y belongs to the intersection of all balls with radius D containing X and Y. [Hint: Let X, $Y \in \bar{N}(P,D)$ and let Q be the center of the arc joining X to Y. Consider $\bar{N}(P,D) \cap \bar{N}(Q,D)$.]

10.12 Show that Theorems 10.11 and 10.12 hold equally well in the plane.

10.13 Find the minimum width, diameter, inradius, and circumradius of each of the following sets in the plane: (**a**) a rectangle with side lengths x and $2x$; (**b**) an equilateral triangle with edge length S; (**c**) a Reuleaux triangle with width r.

10.14 Give an example of a convex set K with exactly one insphere which is not concentric with the circumsphere of K.

10.15 Let $d(l)$ be the maximum length of all chords of a convex body K parallel to l. Show that $\min d(l)$, over all lines l, equals the minimum width of K. [Hint: If $S[A,B]$ is a chord of K of length equal to $\min d(l)$, show that there is a pair of parallel supporting planes of K through A and B.]

10.16 Find the minimum width, diameter, inradius, and circumradius of each of the following sets in 3-space: (**a**) a cube with edge length x; (**b**) a regular tetrahedron with edge length S; (**c**) the body of constant width obtained by rotating a Reuleaux triangle of constant width r about an axis of symmetry.

INTRODUCTION

3

TRANSFORMATIONS

This chapter is devoted to a discussion and classification of the principal transformations which are used in euclidean geometry. A transformation is first presented as a generalization of a real-valued function, and general properties are developed. The notion of a bicontinuous or topological transformation is given, along with a discussion of the bicontinuous image of a sphere.

We next give a complete description of the euclidean motions and similarities in terms of the fundamental transformations of translation, rotation, reflection, and homothety. Vector addition of sets is presented as a generalization of translation and homothety, and properties of the spherical neighborhood of a set are developed.

After showing that the vector sum of polyhedral regions is again a polyhedral region, we introduce the notion of G-equidecomposable sets for a group of motions G. The possibility of being G-equidecomposable is discussed for various subclasses of the class of all polyhedra, and decompositions of the vector sum of polyhedra are related to decompositions of the summands. The final section is devoted to topics associated with the polar dual of a set. The distance function, support function, and convex cones are all defined, and various properties are presented.

11   TRANSFORMATION GROUPS

In high school geometry texts one sometimes finds statements similar to the following: "Two figures are congruent iff it is possible to move one of them so as to become superimposed upon the other." Since geometric figures are not physical objects, the usual definition of "move" has no meaning for them, and this definition is highly unsatisfactory without some modification. An attempt to make the notion of congruence precise leads us to the following generalization of a function.

11.1   A **mapping** f of a set A onto a set B is a correspondence between elements of A and elements of B such that each element of A corresponds to exactly one element of B and each element of B is the correspondent of some element of A. If $P \varepsilon A$ and Q corresponds to P under f, we write $Q = f(P)$ and call Q the **image of P under f**. If A' is a subset of A, the union of all points, each of which is the image of a point of A', is called the **image of A' under f** and is denoted by $f(A')$.

Most of the mappings we shall be concerned with will be between two sets of points. However, it will sometimes be convenient to consider mappings between different kinds of objects. In Sec. 16, for example, we discuss mappings between a set of points and a set of half spaces.

If f is a mapping of A onto B, an element of $f(A)$ will in general be the image of more than one point. For example, let f be the projection of a ball B onto a plane π in a given direction. Any interior point of $f(B)$ is the image of a whole segment of points in B.

11.2   A mapping f of A onto B such that each element of B is the image of exactly one element of A is called a **one-to-one mapping** or a **transformation**.

We are now in a position to give a precise definition of congruence.

11.3   A set of points A is called **congruent** or **isometric** to a set of points B iff there is a transformation f of A onto B which preserves distances, that is, $|f(P)f(Q)| = |PQ|$ for any two points $P,Q \varepsilon A$. The transformation f is called an **isometry** of A onto B.

11.4   If f is an isometry of a set onto itself, then f is called a **motion** of the set. (Some texts refer to f as a rigid motion, but since we use no other kind of motion, the word "rigid" becomes redundant.)

It is conceivable that set A may be congruent to set B without B being congruent to A. This is not possible, however. Let f be an isometry of A onto B. If g is the correspondence which associates P with the point $f(P)$, then g is an isometry of B onto A, and by 11.3 B is congruent to A. We give a special name to g.

11.5 If f is a transformation from A onto B and g is a transformation from B onto C, then the **product** $h = gf$ is defined to be the transformation from A onto C such that $h(P) = g[f(P)]$ for each P in A. If h is the **identity mapping** which lets each point of A correspond to itself, then g is denoted by f^{-1} and is called the **inverse transformation** of f.

Let us designate the rotation of the plane about a point O through an angle α by $R(O,\alpha)$. In the next section we will show that $R(O,\alpha)$ is a motion of the plane. The inverse of $R(O,\alpha)$ is of course $R(O,-\alpha)$. Now consider the product of two such rotations. It is easy to see that $R(O,\alpha)R(O,\beta) = R(O,\alpha + \beta)$. We say that the set of rotations about a point O is closed under multiplication. There are many other sets which satisfy similar conditions. We call such a set a group of transformations.

11.6 A collection $G = \{f,g,h \ldots \}$ of transformations of a space onto itself is called a **group of transformations** iff

  a. $f \,\varepsilon\, G$ implies $f^{-1} \,\varepsilon\, G$,

  b. $f \,\varepsilon\, G$ and $g \,\varepsilon\, G$ implies $fg \,\varepsilon\, G$.

We see immediately that the identity transformation belongs to any group.

If f, $g \,\varepsilon\, G$, then $fg \,\varepsilon\, G$ and $gf \,\varepsilon\, G$. If $fg = gf$ for all elements of G, then we call the group **commutative** or **abelian**. The group of all rotations of the plane about the same point is abelian. It may happen, however, that $fg \neq gf$. Let S be a set of four points $\{1,2,3,4\}$ which are the vertices of a square. We use the symbol $\begin{pmatrix} a & b & c & d \\ e & f & g & h \end{pmatrix}$ to stand for the mapping F of S onto itself such that $F(a) = e$, $F(b) = f$, $F(c) = g$, and $F(d) = h$. Consider the following set G of transformations of S.

$$H = \begin{pmatrix} 1 & 2 & 3 & 4 \\ 4 & 3 & 2 & 1 \end{pmatrix} \qquad V = \begin{pmatrix} 1 & 2 & 3 & 4 \\ 2 & 1 & 4 & 3 \end{pmatrix} \qquad D_1 = \begin{pmatrix} 1 & 2 & 3 & 4 \\ 1 & 4 & 3 & 2 \end{pmatrix}$$

$$D_2 = \begin{pmatrix} 1 & 2 & 3 & 4 \\ 3 & 2 & 1 & 4 \end{pmatrix} \qquad R(90) = \begin{pmatrix} 1 & 2 & 3 & 4 \\ 2 & 3 & 4 & 1 \end{pmatrix} \qquad R(180) = \begin{pmatrix} 1 & 2 & 3 & 4 \\ 3 & 4 & 1 & 2 \end{pmatrix}$$

$$R(270) = \begin{pmatrix} 1 & 2 & 3 & 4 \\ 4 & 1 & 2 & 3 \end{pmatrix} \qquad I = \begin{pmatrix} 1 & 2 & 3 & 4 \\ 1 & 2 & 3 & 4 \end{pmatrix}$$

The reader can verify that G forms a group. This is called the group of symmetries of the square. These symmetries are easily visualized as follows. H and V are the reflections about horizontal and vertical axes through the center of the square, D_1 and D_2 are reflections about the diagonals, and $R(\alpha)$ is the rotation about the center through an angle of α degrees. This group, however, is not commutative. For example, $HD_1 \neq D_1H$.

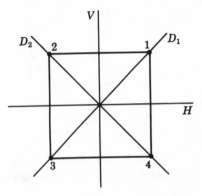

Fig. 11.1

Near the beginning of this century the geometer Felix Klein suggested that all geometries be classified according to groups of transformations. This was embodied in the so-called "Erlangen Program." The program considers a geometry as the study of those properties of a space which are invariant under a group of transformations. For example, we can speak of the geometry of rotations about a point in the plane. An invariant property is that the center O is a fixed point under every transformation in the group of rotations, that is, $f(O) = O$ for every such rotation f.

The set of all motions of a space forms a group. In this case we speak of the metric geometry of the space as the study of all those properties of the space which are invariant under motions of the space. For example, the study of congruent triangles belongs to plane metric geometry, whereas the study of parallel projections of a plane set onto a line does not belong to plane metric geometry. The group of rotations mentioned above is a subgroup of the group of plane motions. Any invariant property of plane metric geometry is therefore an invariant property of the rotation geometry. The converse, of course, is not true. For example, the common center of rotation is fixed under the rotations but is not fixed under an arbitrary motion.

Another group of transformations is the set of bicontinuous transformations of a space onto itself.

11.7   A transformation f of A onto B is called **continuous** iff for each point $f(P)$ and each positive number ϵ there is a positive number δ such that $f[N(P,\delta) \cap A] \subset N[f(P),\epsilon]$.

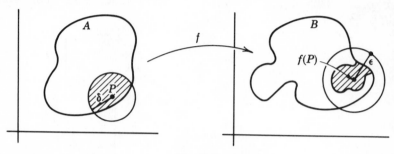

Fig. 11.2

If f is a real-valued function from a subset S of the x axis into the y axis, then this reduces to the usual $\epsilon - \delta$ definition of a function continuous on a set S.

11.8   A transformation f of A onto B is called **bicontinuous** iff both f and f^{-1} are continuous.

The geometry associated with the group of bicontinuous transformations of a space is called the topology of the space. We speak of plane topology and the topology of 3-space.   The Jordan-curve theorem is a property of plane topology.   Any motion of a space is obviously a bicontinuous transformation of the space, so that any property of plane topology is also a property of plane metric geometry.   Let β be a simple closed curve whose domain is the interval $[a,b]$ and whose range lies in the plane.   If α is any other simple closed curve lying in the same plane whose domain is also $[a,b]$ and if we restrict the domain of α and β to the half open interval $(a,b]$, then it can be shown[1] that $\gamma = \alpha\beta^{-1}$ is a bicontinuous transformation of the trace of β onto the trace of α.   It follows that any simple closed plane curve is the bicontinuous image of a circle, and conversely.   This is sometimes used to define a simple closed curve.

In Exercise 11.5 we show that a sphere is a simple closed surface.   It follows that every bicontinuous image of a sphere is also a simple closed surface.   This leads us to the following.

11.9   Theorem   The boundary Γ of a three-dimensional (two-dimensional) convex body K is the bicontinuous image of a sphere (circle) and therefore is a simple closed surface (curve).

[1] See J. Hocking and G. Young, "Topology," Addison-Wesley Publishing Company, Inc., Reading, Mass., 1961.

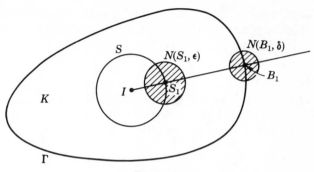

Fig. 11.3

PROOF   Since K is three-dimensional, it contains an interior point I. It follows that there is a sphere S with center I which is entirely contained inside Γ.   Each ray beginning at I intersects Γ and S in exactly one point each, and therefore there is a transformation f of Γ onto S.   Let S_i be a point on S and let B_i be the corresponding point on Γ.   If ϵ is any positive number and S_1 is any point of S, then by picking δ small enough the segment joining any point of $N(B_1,\delta)$ to I will intersect S in a point belonging to $N(S_1,\epsilon)$.   It follows that $f[N(B_1,\delta) \cap \Gamma] \subset N(S_1,\epsilon)$, and therefore f is continuous.

It remains to show that f^{-1} is continuous.   Let ϵ be any positive number and consider the neighborhood $N(B_1,\epsilon)$.   Since S_1 is an interior point of K, it is possible to find an exterior point P and an interior point Q lying on the ray $R[S_1,B_1]$ such that $N(P,r)$, consisting of exterior points of K, and $N(Q,s)$, consisting of interior points of K, are both contained in $N(B,\epsilon)$ for some positive numbers r and s.   Choose δ small enough so that every ray beginning at I and passing through a point of $N(S_1,\delta)$ intersects

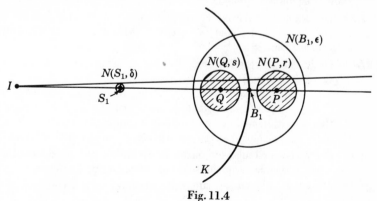

Fig. 11.4

$N(P,r)$ and $N(Q,s)$. Since these points are exterior and interior to K respectively, a boundary point of K lies between them and also lies in $N(B_1,\epsilon)$. It follows that $f^{-1}[N(S_1,\delta) \cap S] \subset N(B_1,\epsilon)$, and therefore f^{-1} is continuous.

Exercises

11.1 Let PFQ stand for Q corresponds to P under the correspondence F. A correspondence F between elements of a set S is called an equivalence relation on S iff for $P, Q, R \in S$ we have

a. PFP,

b. PFQ implies QFP,

c. PFQ and QFR implies PFR.

Show that the correspondence F of "being congruent" is an equivalence relation on the collection S of all sets of points in space.

11.2 Construct a multiplication table for the set of symmetries of an equilateral triangle. Is this set a group? Is it abelian?

11.3 Show that the collection of all motions of a space is a group.

11.4 Show that the collection of all bicontinuous transformations of a space onto itself is a group.

11.5 Let $\overrightarrow{\Gamma} (u,v) = (x,y,z)$ where $x = \cos u \sin v$, $y = \sin u \sin v$, and $z = \cos v$. Show that $\overrightarrow{\Gamma}$ is a continuous map of the rectangle $R = \{(u,v)|0 \leq u \leq 2\pi, 0 \leq v \leq \pi\}$ onto a sphere S in 3-space. Hence show that a sphere is a simple closed surface.

11.6 Show that a transformation group satisfies all the axioms of an abstract group.

11.7 Show that all the motions of a space S which map a fixed point P onto itself form a subgroup of the group of all motions of S.

11.8 Describe the subgroups of (**a**) the symmetries of a square, (**b**) the symmetries of an equilateral triangle.

11.9 Show that the following concepts are metric invariants but not topological invariants of the plane: (**a**) a circle, (**b**) a line, (**c**) a segment, (**d**) perpendicular lines.

11.10 In the calculus the following definition is often given. A real-valued function f of two real variables is continuous on $R = \{(x,y)|a \leq x \leq b, c \leq y \leq d\}$ iff at any point (x_0,y_0) of R, given $\epsilon > 0$, there is a $\delta > 0$ such that $|f(x,y) - f(x_0,y_0)| < \epsilon$ whenever $|x - x_0| < \delta$ and $|y - y_0| < \delta$. Show that a continuous function f induces a continuous map of R onto the graph of f. Hence show that the graph of a continuous function f is a surface.

11.11 Show that a circular arc, including its end points, which is not a complete circle, is the bicontinuous image of a straight line segment.

11.12 Show that an angle is the bicontinuous image of a straight line.

11.13 Use Exercises 11.11 and 11.12 to show that (**a**) any angle is the bicontinuous image of any other angle; (**b**) any circular arc is the bicontinuous image of any other circular arc.

12 EUCLIDEAN MOTIONS

The motions of 3-space and the motions of the plane are sometimes called euclidean motions. In this section we classify the euclidean motions and discuss some of their properties. First we consider the motions of the plane.

If we are given two congruent triangles ABC and $A'B'C'$ in the plane, then there is an isometry f of ABC onto $A'B'C'$. Intuitively we can think of f as the result of cutting $\triangle ABC$ from a sheet of paper and superimposing it upon $\triangle A'B'C'$. If the sheet of paper is transparent, we can also accomplish the same result by sliding the whole sheet of paper until $\triangle ABC$ is superimposed upon $\triangle A'B'C'$.

12.1 Theorem Let $\triangle ABC$ and $\triangle A'B'C'$ be in the plane and suppose f is an isometry of $\triangle ABC$ onto $\triangle A'B'C'$. There is exactly one motion of the plane which agrees with f on $\triangle ABC$.

PROOF Let $\triangle ABC$ be congruent to $\triangle A'B'C'$ under the mapping f and let X' stand for $f(X)$. Let $\angle XYZ$ be the signed angle from X at vertex Y to point Z and consider any point P in the plane distinct from A, B, and C. If $\angle CAB$ has the same sense and magnitude as $\angle C'A'B'$, we construct a unique point P' as follows. Construct an angle $\angle C'A'X$ equal in sense and magnitude to $\angle CAP$ and let P' be the point on the ray $R[A',X)$ such that $|A'P'| = |AP|$. This establishes a transformation F of the plane onto itself. Now let P and Q be any two points of the plane. $\triangle APQ$ is congruent to $\triangle A'P'Q'$ so that $|PQ| = |P'Q'|$ and F is a motion. Since, for given P, there is only one point R of the plane such that $|RA'| = |PA|$, $|RB'| = |PB|$, and $|RC'| = |PC|$ (see Exercise 12.1), it follows that

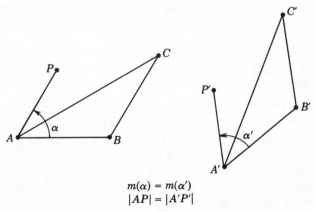

$$m(\alpha) = m(\alpha')$$
$$|AP| = |A'P'|$$

Fig. 12.1

$R = P$ and F is the only motion sending $\triangle ABC$ onto $\triangle A'B'C'$. If $\angle CAB$ has the sense opposite to $\angle C'A'B'$, we proceed as before, except that we construct $\angle C'A'X$ opposite in sense and equal in magnitude to $\angle CAP$. The rest of the proof is as before.

The following corollary is immediate.

12.2 Theorem   Any motion of the plane which has three or more non-collinear fixed points is the identity.

We now describe the different kinds of plane motions.

12.3   Let P be an arbitrary point in the plane.   The transformation T_P such that $T_P(X) = X + P$ is called the **translation** of the plane in the direction $\overrightarrow{OP}$.

12.4   Let O be a fixed point in the plane and let α be an arbitrary signed angle.   The **rotation** $R(O,\alpha)$ through α about O is defined to be the transformation which maps O onto O and maps any other point P onto the point P' such that $\angle POP' = \alpha$ and $|PO| = |P'O|$.

12.5   Let l be a fixed line in the plane.   The **reflection** R_l is defined to be the transformation which maps each point of l onto itself and maps any other point P onto the point P' such that l is the perpendicular bisector of $S[P,P']$.

The rotation $R(O,180°)$ is sometimes called the **reflection about** O or a **half-turn** about O.   If the reflection of a set S about the point O coincides with S, we say that S **has center** O (see pages 54 and 66).

12.6 Theorem   The translations, rotations, and reflections are all motions of the plane.

Actually any product of these motions can be reduced to products of reflections alone.   It follows that these motions form a group.

12.7 Theorem   Each translation and each rotation can be expressed as the product of two reflections, and conversely the product of any two reflections is either a translation or a rotation.

PROOF   Let l and l' be any two lines of the plane intersecting in the point O.   If the directed angle from l to l' is α, then $R(O,2\alpha) = R_{l'}R_l$.   Now let m and m' be any two parallel lines perpendicular to the vector $\overrightarrow{OP}$ and a distance $|OP|/2$ apart.   Then $T_P = R_{m'}R_m$.

It is a remarkable fact that every motion can be expressed as the product of reflections so that the group generated by reflections actually coincides with the group of plane motions.

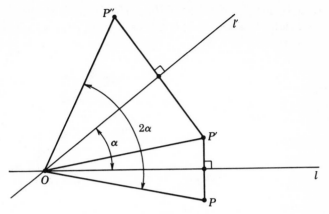

Fig. 12.2

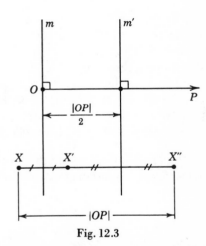

Fig. 12.3

12.8 Theorem Every plane motion is the product of three or fewer reflections. If the motion has a fixed point, then it is the product of two or fewer reflections.

PROOF Let f be an arbitrary plane motion. If f has three or more noncollinear fixed points, then f is the identity and $f = R_l R_l$ for any line l in the plane. If f has two or more fixed points all lying on line l, then $f = R_l$. For if A and B are fixed points of f lying on l and P lies on l, then P must also be a fixed point. If P does not lie on l, it cannot be a fixed point and must be mapped onto a point P' such that $\triangle ABP$ is congruent to $\triangle ABP'$. This can occur iff l is the perpendicular bisector of $S[P,P']$. If f has exactly one fixed point O and A, B, and O are distinct points, then either the rotation $R(O, \angle AOA')$ or the reflection about the perpendicular bisector of $S[A,A']$ maps $\triangle OAB$ onto $\triangle OA'B'$.

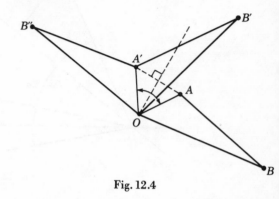

Fig. 12.4

If f has no fixed points, let ABC be any triangle in the plane and let l be the perpendicular bisector of $S[A,A']$. The image of $\triangle ABC$ under R_l is congruent to $\triangle A'B'C'$. By Theorem 12.1 there is exactly one motion M mapping this image onto $\triangle A'B'C'$ and $f = MR_l$. But M has A' for a fixed point so that M is the product of two or fewer reflections. Therefore f is the product of three or fewer reflections.

We have already discussed the product of two reflections. We now consider the product of three reflections.

12.9   Theorem   The product of three reflections in the plane is either a reflection or the product of a reflection and a translation.

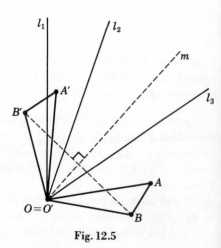

Fig. 12.5

PROOF   Suppose $f = R_{l_1}R_{l_2}R_{l_3}$. If $l_1 = l_2$, then $f = R_{l_3}$. If l_1 is parallel to l_2 and $\overrightarrow{OP}$ is the vector perpendicular to l_1 and l_2 with length twice the distance between l_1 and l_2, then $f = T_P R_{l_3}$.

It remains to consider the case in which l_1 intersects l_2 in a point O'. Let α be the directed angle from l_2 to l_1 so that $R(O',2\alpha) = R_{l_1}R_{l_2}$ and $f = R(O',2\alpha)R_{l_3}$. Let $f(O) = O'$ and consider the triangle OAB whose image under f is $\triangle O'A'B'$. If O lies on l_3 and m is the perpendicular bisector of the segment joining B' to the image of B under R_{l_3}, then $O = O'$, R_m maps $\triangle OAB$ onto $\triangle O'A'B'$, and $f = R_m$. If O does not lie on l_3, then $f = R_m T_P$, where the position vector of P equals $\overrightarrow{OO'}$.

We now carry out a characterization of the motions of 3-space. The results are very similar to the plane case, and their proofs require only slight modification of the preceding proofs.

12.10   Theorem   Let $ABCD$ and $A'B'C'D'$ be tetrahedra in 3-space and suppose f is an isometry of $ABCD$ onto $A'B'C'D'$. There is exactly one motion of 3-space which agrees with f on $ABCD$.

12.11   Theorem   Any motion of space which has four or more non-coplanar fixed points is the identity.

If we replace the word "plane" by "space" in Definition 12.3, we have defined a **translation** of 3-space. Rotations, however, require some modification.

12.12   Let l be a fixed line in space and let α be an arbitrary signed angle. The **rotation** $R(l,\alpha)$ through α about l is defined to be the transformation which maps each point of l onto itself and maps any other point P onto P'

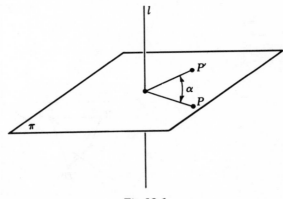

Fig. 12.6

as follows: If π is the plane through P perpendicular to l, then P' is obtained by rotating P about $\pi \cap l$, in π, through α.

If we replace the word "line" by "plane" in Definition 12.5, we have defined a **reflection** R_π of space about a plane π. The rotation about a line l through 180° is sometimes called the **reflection of space about line** l. We can also speak of the reflection of space about a point.

The proofs of the following three theorems closely follow the proofs of the corresponding plane theorems and are left to the reader.

12.13 Theorem   The translations, rotations, and reflections are all motions of space.

12.14 Theorem   Each translation and each rotation in space can be expressed as the product of two plane reflections, and, conversely, the product of any two plane reflections is either a translation or a rotation.

12.15 Theorem   Every motion of space is the product of four or fewer plane reflections.   If the motion has a fixed point, then it is the product of three or fewer reflections.

In order to categorize the motions of space it is convenient to classify them as direct or opposite.

12.16   A motion is called **direct** (**opposite**) iff it is the product of an even (odd) number of reflections.

Direct motions preserve the "sense" of a tetrahedron, whereas opposite motions reverse the "sense." For example, if we reflect about the three coordinate planes, the sense of a tetrahedron is reversed (see Fig. 12.7).

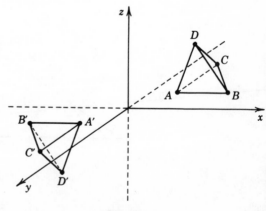

Fig. 12.7

12.17 Theorem Every direct motion with at least one invariant point is a rotation. Every opposite motion with at least one invariant point is the product of a reflection R_π and a rotation about a line perpendicular to π.

PROOF Suppose f is a direct motion with $f(O) = O$. Since f is direct, it is the product of two reflections $R(\pi)$ and $R(\pi')$. In order to be a fixed point, O must lie on both π and π'. By Theorem 12.14 f is a rotation.

Suppose f is an opposite motion with $f(O) = O$. Let T be the product of any three reflections about mutually perpendicular planes through O. This is equal to the reflection about point O. fT is a direct motion with fixed point O and therefore is a rotation $R(l,\alpha)$ about a line l through O. Since $TT = I$, we have $f = R(l,\alpha)T = R_{\pi_1}R_{\pi_2}R_{\pi_3}R_{\pi_4}R_{\pi_5}$. Choose planes π_3 and π_4 so that $l = \pi_3 \cap \pi_4$. $R_{\pi_1}R_{\pi_2}R_{\pi_3}R_{\pi_4}$ is a direct motion which keeps l pointwise fixed and therefore is a rotation $R(l,\beta)$. Since l is perpendicular to π_5, our proof is complete.

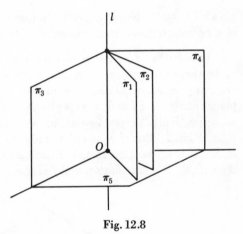

Fig. 12.8

12.18 Theorem Every direct motion is the product of two line reflections.

PROOF Let $A' = f(A) \neq A$ for a direct motion f. Let π_1 be the perpendicular bisector of $S(A,A')$. The product $R_{\pi_1} f$ is an opposite motion with A as a fixed point. Therefore $R_{\pi_1} f = R_{\pi_2}R_{\pi_3}R_{\pi_4}$, where $l = \pi_2 \cap \pi_3$ is perpendicular to π_4. Since $R_{\pi_1}R_{\pi_1} = I$, it follows that $f = R_{\pi_1}R_{\pi_2}R_{\pi_3}R_{\pi_4}$. Through any line we can always construct a plane perpendicular to a given plane, so that we can pick π_2 perpendicular to π_1. But then $f = R_{\pi_1 \cap \pi_2}R_{\pi_3 \cap \pi_4}$, and we have finished.

12.19 Theorem Every direct motion with no fixed points is either a translation or the product of a translation T_P and a rotation about an axis

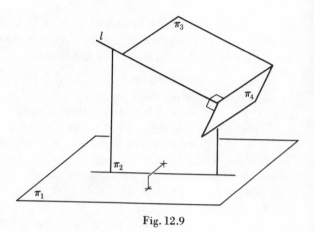

Fig. 12.9

parallel to $\overrightarrow{OP}$.   Every opposite motion with no fixed points is the product of a reflection and a translation.

PROOF   Let f be a direct motion with no fixed points.   By Theorem 12.18 there are two lines l and m such that $f = R_l R_m$. l and m must be skew or parallel, otherwise f would have a fixed point.   Let π_1, π_2 be parallel planes containing l and m respectively and let σ_1, σ_2 be planes through l and m respectively perpendicular to π_1 and π_2.   Then $f = R_{\sigma_1} R_{\pi_1} R_{\sigma_2} R_{\pi_2} = R_{\sigma_1} R_{\sigma_2} R_{\pi_1} R_{\pi_2}$.   But if σ_1 is not parallel to σ_2, then $R_{\sigma_1} R_{\sigma_2}$ is a rotation, and $R_{\pi_1} R_{\pi_2}$ is a translation in the direction of $\sigma_1 \cap \sigma_2$.   If σ_1 is parallel to σ_2, then $R_{\sigma_1} R_{\sigma_2}$ is a translation and f is also a translation.

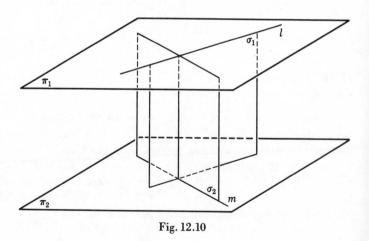

Fig. 12.10

Now let f be an opposite motion with no fixed points. f must be the product of three reflections $f = R_{\pi_1}R_{\pi_2}R_{\pi_3}$, where $\pi_1 \cap \pi_2 \cap \pi_3 = \varnothing$, otherwise f would have a fixed point. If all three planes are parallel, then f is a reflection times a translation. If π_2 intersects π_3 in a line l, then l must be parallel to π_1. We can choose π_2' and π_3' so that π_1 is parallel to π_2' and $f = R_{\pi_1}R_{\pi_2'}R_{\pi_3'}$. But then $R_{\pi_1}R_{\pi_2'}$ is a translation which completes our proof.

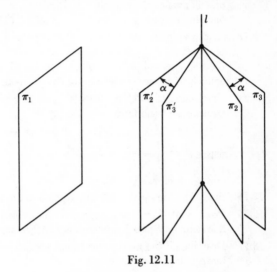

Fig. 12.11

Exercises

12.1 If $\triangle ABC$ is congruent to $\triangle A'B'C'$ and P is an arbitrary point of the plane, prove that there is exactly one point P' such that $|PA| = |P'A'|$, $|PB| = |P'B'|$, and $|PC| = |P'C'|$.

12.2 Prove Theorem 12.2.

12.3 What effect does a change of coordinates have on a translation T_P?

12.4 Prove Theorem 12.6.

12.5 Given any translation T and any line reflection R of the plane, show that there is a translation T' and a reflection R' such that $RT = T'R'$. What can be said about T and R if $RT = TR$?

12.6 Prove Theorems 12.10 and 12.11.

12.7 Prove Theorems 12.13 and 12.14.

12.8 Prove Theorem 12.15.

12.9 Show that in Theorem 12.9 the reflection R_l and translation T_P can always be chosen so that $\overrightarrow{OP}$ is parallel to l. (Hint: Write R_lT_P as the product of a reflection about a point and a reflection about a line.)

12.10 State and prove a result similar to Exercise 12.9 for the reflection and translation of Theorem 12.19.

12.11 Show that every translation T of the xy plane has equations of the form $x' = x + a$, $y' = y + b$, where $T(x,y) = (x',y')$, and conversely.

12.12 Show that every rotation R of the xy plane which leaves the origin fixed has equations of the form $x' = x \cos \alpha - y \sin \alpha$, $y' = x \sin \alpha + y \cos \alpha$, and conversely. Explain the difference between these formulas and the ones in analytic geometry for a rotation of the coordinate axes.

12.13 In the xy plane let m be the slope of the line l passing through the origin. Show that R_l has equations $x' = [(1 - m^2)x + 2my]/(1 + m^2)$, $y' = [2mx + (m^2 - 1)y]/(1 + m^2)$. Conversely, show that every such pair of equations defines a reflection of the plane about a line through the origin.

12.14 Use Exercises 12.11 to 12.13 to show that every motion of the xy plane has equations of the form

$$x' = a_{11}x + a_{12}y + b_1 \qquad y' = a_{21}x + a_{22}y + b_2$$

where $\begin{vmatrix} a_{11}a_{12} \\ a_{21}a_{22} \end{vmatrix} = \pm 1$

and $a_{11}^2 + a_{12}^2 = a_{21}^2 + a_{22}^2 = 1$

12.15 Prove the converse of the proposition in Exercise 12.14.

12.16 Prove that there are exactly four motions of the plane which map a given line segment $S[A,B]$ onto segment $S[C,D]$ where $|AB| = |CD|$.

12.17 Describe all the motions of 3-space which map a given line segment onto a line segment of equal length.

12.18 Prove that the product of any finite number of rotations about lines through the origin is a rotation about a line through the origin. (Hint: Use Theorem 12.17.)

13 SIMILARITIES

If we examine the definitions of convexity, surface area, volume, and length we see that all these properties are invariant under motions. This means, for example, that if a curve has length L, then its image under a motion will also be a curve of length L. In this section we discuss certain transformations which do not preserve distance and describe their effect on sets of points.

Consider two planes π and π' and denote the points of π by A, B, C, $\ldots$ and the points of π' by A', B', C', $\ldots$. Let $\triangle ABC$ be any triangle on π and assume that $\triangle A'B'C'$ has the property that $|A'B'| = r|AB|$, $|B'C'| = r|BC|$, and $|C'A'| = r|CA|$ for some positive real number r. If P is any point of π, then the construction of Theorem 12.1 can be used to determine a unique point P' such that $|P'A'| = r|PA|$, $|P'B'| = r|PB|$, and $|P'C'| = r|PC|$. If P and Q are any two points of π, it follows that $|P'Q'| = r|PQ|$.

The transformation f just defined magnifies the distance between points by a factor r. The inverse transformation f^{-1} diminishes the distance between points by a factor $1/r$ (if r is less than 1, the roles of f and f^{-1} are interchanged). If M is any motion of π, then $M' = fMf^{-1}$ is a motion of π', and if N' is a motion of π', then $N = f^{-1}N'f$ is a motion of π. Multiplying on the right by f^{-1} and on the left by f, we obtain $N' = fNf^{-1}$. Also $(MN)' = f(MN)f^{-1} = (fMf^{-1})(fNf^{-1}) = M'N'$, therefore the group of motions of π is isomorphic to the group of motions of π'. In other words, the geometry of π' is exactly the same as the geometry of π when all distances are equally magnified. The conclusion we draw is that the properties of plane euclidean geometry do not depend upon the ruler we use for defining distance as long as we use the same ruler throughout.

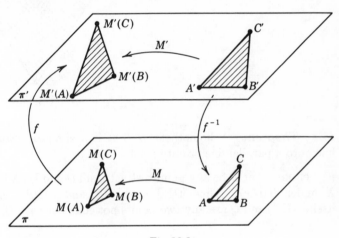

Fig. 13.1

13.1 Let r be any positive real number. A **similarity** is a transformation of the plane, or of space, onto itself such that $|f(P)f(Q)| = r|PQ|$ for every pair of points P and Q. r is called the **ratio** of the similarity.

The proof of the following theorem is an immediate consequence of the preceding discussion.

13.2 Theorem Let $\triangle ABC$ and $\triangle A'B'C'$ lie in the plane and suppose f is a similarity which maps $\triangle ABC$ onto $\triangle A'B'C'$. If g is a similarity which agrees with f on $\triangle ABC$, then $f = g$.

A similar result holds in 3-space.

The set of all similarities forms a group which contains the motions as a subgroup. The simplest similarity which is not a motion is a homothety.

13.3   Let O be a fixed point and let r be any nonzero real number. The **homothety** $H(O,r)$ is defined to be the transformation which maps each point P onto the point P' such that $\overset{\infty}{\overrightarrow{OP'}} = r\overrightarrow{OP}$. O is called the **center** of $H(O,r)$, and r is called the **ratio** of $H(O,r)$.

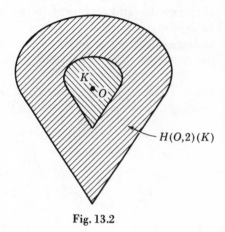

Fig. 13.2

13.4   **Theorem**   A homothety $H(O,r)$ is a similarity which maps each line onto a parallel line or onto itself.

PROOF   Let P be any point distinct from O and let X' be the image of X under $H(O,r)$. Then $|OP'| = |r| \, |OP|$, and $L(O,P)$ is mapped onto itself. If P and Q are any two points not collinear with O, then $\triangle OPQ$ is

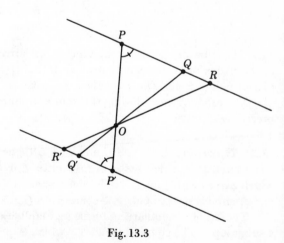

Fig. 13.3

similar to $\triangle OP'Q'$ and $|P'Q'| = |r|\,|PQ|$. Since $\angle QPO = \angle Q'P'O$, line $L(P,Q)$ is parallel to $L(P',Q')$. Since any line through O cuts $L(P,Q)$ and $L(P',Q')$ in points R and R' with $|OR'| = |r|\,|OR|$, it follows that $L(P,Q)$ is mapped onto $L(P',Q')$, and $H(O,r)$ is a similarity with ratio $|r|$.

We notice that a plane homothety preserves the sense of a triangle regardless of the sign of r. In space, however, the sense of a tetrahedron is preserved iff r is positive and is reversed iff r is negative. We call a similarity **direct** (**opposite**) iff it preserves (reverses) sense.

The converse of Theorem 13.4 is not quite true.

13.5   Theorem   Any similarity which sends each line onto a parallel line or itself is either a translation or a homothety.

PROOF   Let $\triangle ABC$ be any triangle in the plane and let $\triangle A'B'C'$ be its image under a plane similarity f with ratio r which sends each line onto a parallel line. If the triangles are congruent, then the translation T_P maps $\triangle ABC$ onto $\triangle A'B'C'$ where $\overrightarrow{OP} = \overrightarrow{AA'}$, and therefore $f = T_P$.

If the triangles are not congruent, then $L(A,A')$, $L(B,B')$, and $L(C,C')$ intersect in a point O, and the homothety $H(O,r)$ or $H(O,-r)$ maps $\triangle ABC$ onto $\triangle A'B'C'$. By Theorem 13.2, $f = H(O,r)$ or $H(O,-r)$.

Using tetrahedra instead of triangles, the proof in space follows the same pattern.

Since the product of a translation and a homothety is a similarity which sends parallel lines onto parallel lines, it must be equivalent to a single homothety.

13.6   Theorem   Every similarity which is not a motion has exactly one fixed point.

PROOF   Let f be a similarity with ratio $r \neq 1$ and let P be any point such that $|Pf(P)| \neq 0$. Let $f^2 = ff$ and in general let $f^n = ff^{n-1}$ for any positive integer n. We can assume $r < 1$, for if not we can replace f by f^{-1} in what follows. Consider the sequence S of distinct points P, $f(P)$, $f^2(P)$, $\ldots$, $f^n(P)$, $\ldots$ By construction $|f^n(P)f^{n+1}(P)| = r^n|Pf(P)|$. If $R = (1 + r + r^2 + \cdots)|Pf(P)| = |Pf(P)|/(1-r)$, then the sphere with center P and radius R contains all the points of S. It follows that S must have at least one point of accumulation O, i.e., every neighborhood of O contains infinitely many points of S. By construction all points of S from $f^n(P)$ onward must lie in the sphere with center $f^n(P)$ and radius $R_n = r^n|Pf(P)|/(1-r)$, and therefore $O \,\varepsilon\, \bar{N}[f^n(P),R_n]$.   But then $f^n(P) \,\varepsilon\, \bar{N}(O,R_n)$, and since $R_n > R_{n+1}$, it follows that all but a finite number of points of S lie inside $N(O,R_n)$ for each positive integer n.

Since f is continuous, for each $\epsilon > 0$ there is a $\delta > 0$ such that $f[N(O,\delta)] \subset N[f(O),\epsilon]$. Suppose $f(O) \neq O$ and choose $\epsilon < |Of(O)|/2$. Let m be chosen so that $R_m < \min (\delta,\epsilon)$. Then $f^i(O)$ all lie in $N(O,\delta)$, for $i > m$ and $f^j(O)$ all lie in $N[f(O),\epsilon]$ for all $j > m + 1$. Clearly this is impossible, and therefore $f(O) = O$.

There can be no other invariant point, for if Q is also invariant, then $r|OQ| = |f(O)f(Q)| = |OQ|$, which is impossible.

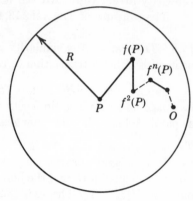

Fig. 13.4

13.7 Theorem Every plane similarity f with ratio $r \neq 1$ is either the product of a homothety and rotation about its fixed point O or the product of a homothety about O and a reflection about a line through O.

PROOF   Let $\triangle OAB$ be any triangle in the plane with the fixed point O as vertex and let $\triangle OA'B'$ be the image of $\triangle OAB$ under $H(O,r)$. $\triangle OA'B'$ is congruent to $\triangle Of(A)f(B)$. It follows that either the reflection about the bisector of $\angle AOf(A)$ or the rotation $R[O, \angle AOf(A)]$ must map $\triangle OA'B'$ onto $\triangle Of(A)f(B)$.

13.8 Theorem Every space similarity f with ratio $r \neq 1$ is the product of a homothety about its fixed point O and a rotation about a line through O.

PROOF   Let $OABC$ be any tetrahedron in space and let $OA'B'C'$ be its image under f. If the image of $OABC$ under $H(O,r)$ has the same sense as $OA'B'C'$, then by Theorem 12.17 $f = R_l H(O,r)$ for some line l through O. If the sense is reversed, then $f = R_{l'} H(O,-r)$ for some line l' through O.

Let f be any similarity with ratio r and consider an arbitrary curve Γ in the plane or in space. If Π is any polygonal curve inscribed to Γ, then $f(\Pi)$ is a polygonal curve inscribed to $f(\Gamma)$. Since each segment of $f(\Pi)$

has length r times the length of the corresponding segment of Γ, it follows that $L[f(\Pi)] = rL(\Pi)$ and also $L[f(\Gamma)] = rL(\Gamma)$. $L(X)$ stands for the length of X.   The Jordan measure of a plane set is defined in terms of inscribed and circumscribed polygonal regions (see Sec. 3).   Since the area of each triangle is multiplied by r^2 under f, it follows that the area of each polygonal region, and therefore of each plane measurable set, is multiplied by r^2.   Similar considerations give us a factor of r^3 for volumes.

Exercises

13.1   Prove that a similarity is a continuous transformation.

13.2   Prove that a similarity either sends each line onto a parallel line or onto itself, or sends no line onto a parallel line or onto itself.

13.3   Prove that the image of a convex set under a similarity is convex.

13.4   Given two spheres, describe all similarities which map one onto the other.

13.5   Show that no two points of the sequence S in the proof of Theorem 13.6 can coincide.

13.6   Let f be a similarity of the plane with ratio r.   Prove that the area $A[f(\triangle)] = r^2 A(\triangle)$ for any triangle $\triangle$.

13.7   Let f be a similarity of 3-space with ratio r.   Prove that the volume $V[f(T)] = r^3 V(T)$ for any tetrahedron T.

13.8   Show that any homothety H of the xy plane which leaves the origin fixed has equations of the form $x' = rx$, $y' = ry$, and conversely.

13.9   Use Exercises 12.12 and 12.13 to show that every plane similarity with ratio r which leaves the origin fixed has equations of the form $x' = a_{11}x + a_{12}y$, $y' = a_{21}x + a_{22}y$ where $\begin{vmatrix} a_{11}a_{12} \\ a_{21}a_{22} \end{vmatrix} = \pm r$ and $a_{11}^2 + a_{12}^2 = a_{21}^2 + a_{22}^2 = r^2$

13.10   Prove the converse of the proposition in Exercise 13.9.

13.11   Prove that the similarities of 3-space form a group.

13.12   State and prove theorems similar to those in Exercises 12.16 and 12.17 for similarities instead of motions.

13.13   Show that a similarity always maps a line segment onto a line segment.

14   VECTOR ADDITION OF SETS

Let K be a convex body and let P be an arbitrary fixed point.   Consider the set K' of all points Q' such that $Q' = P + Q$ and $Q \in K$. K' is the image of K under the translation T_P.   Now consider the set K'' of all points Q'' such that $Q'' = M + N$ and $M, N \in K$.   We shall see that K'' is the image of K under the homothety with center at the origin and ratio 2.

We can think of $T_P(K)$ as the vector sum of K and $\{P\}$, and we can think of $H(O,2)(K)$ as the scalar product of 2 and K. We generalize this to arbitrary sets.

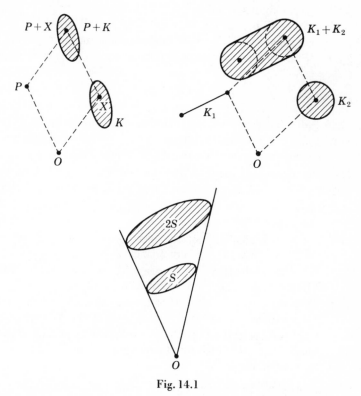

Fig. 14.1

14.1   The **vector sum** of sets S_1 and S_2 is denoted by $S_1 + S_2$ and defined to be the set of all points $P = P_1 + P_2$ where $P_1 \varepsilon S_1$ and $P_2 \varepsilon S_2$. If r is a real number and S is a set, then the **scalar product** rS is the set of all points $P = rQ$, where $Q \varepsilon S$.

We note that rS is the image of S under the homothety with center at the origin and ratio r. Some frequently used properties of the vector sum are collected in the following.

14.2   Theorem   a.   Let π_1 and π_2 be parallel planes and let l be the line perpendicular to π_1 through the origin. If $P_1 = l \cap \pi_1$ and $P_2 = l \cap \pi_2$, then $\pi_1 + \pi_2$ is the plane through $P_1 + P_2$ perpendicular to l.

b.   Let l_1 and l_2 be parallel lines and let $P_1 \varepsilon l_1$, $P_2 \varepsilon l_2$. Then $l_1 + l_2$ is the line through $P_1 + P_2$ parallel to l_1.

c. Let $S[A_1,B_1]$ and $S[A_2,B_2]$ be parallel line segments such that vectors $\overrightarrow{A_1B_1}$ and $\overrightarrow{A_2B_2}$ have the same sense, that is, $B_2 - A_2 = k(B_1 - A_1)$ for $k > 0$. Then $S[A_1,B_1] + S[A_2,B_2] = S[A_1 + A_2, \ B_1 + B_2]$, and the length of the sum is the sum of the lengths of the summands.

PROOF **a.** Let π be the plane through $P_1 + P_2$ perpendicular to l. $P_1 \neq P_2$, so we can assume that P_1 is not the origin. If $X_1 \varepsilon \pi_1$, then $P_1 \cdot (X_1 - P_1) = 0$. If $X_2 \varepsilon \pi_2$, then $P_2 \cdot (X_2 - P_2) = 0$. Therefore $P_1 \cdot [(X_1 + X_2) - (P_1 + P_2)] = P_1 \cdot (X_1 - P_1) + P_2 \cdot (X_2 - P_2) = 0$. Therefore $X_1 + X_2 \varepsilon \pi$, and $\pi_1 + \pi_2 \subset \pi$. On the other hand, suppose $X \varepsilon \pi$ and let $X_2 = X - P_1$. Since $P_1 + P_2$, P_2, X_2, and X form a rectangle (see Fig. 14.2), we have $X_2 \varepsilon \pi_2$. Since $X = X_2 + P_1$, we have $X \varepsilon \pi_1 + \pi_2$ and $\pi = \pi_1 + \pi_2$.

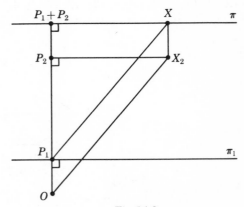

Fig. 14.2

b. Let the equation of l_1 be $X_1 = P_1 + rP$, the equation of l_2 be $X_2 = P_2 + sP$, and the equation of l be $X = (P_1 + P_2) + tP$. Then if $X_1 \varepsilon l_1$, $X_2 \varepsilon l_2$ we have $X_1 + X_2 = (P_1 + P_2) + (r + s)P$ and $X_1 + X_2 \varepsilon l$. On the other hand, if $X \varepsilon l$, then $X = (P_1 + P_2) + tP = (P_1 + P) + [P_2 + (t - 1)P]$ and $X \varepsilon l_1 + l_2$. Therefore $l_1 + l_2 = l$.

c. Suppose $A_2B_2B_1A_1A_2$ is a trapezoid and suppose $B_2 - A_2 = \alpha(B_1 - A_1)$, $0 \leq \alpha \leq 1$. Then if $X_1 \varepsilon S[A_1,B_1]$, $X_1 = A_1 + r(B_1 - A_1)$, $0 \leq r \leq 1$, and if $X_2 \varepsilon S[A_2,B_2]$, $X_2 = A_2 + s(B_2 - A_2)$, $0 \leq s \leq 1$. Therefore $X_1 + X_2 = (A_1 + A_2) + (r + s\alpha)(B_1 - A_1) = (A_1 + A_2) + [(r + s\alpha)/(1 + \alpha)](1 + \alpha)(B_1 - A_1)$. Since $r + s\alpha \leq 1 + \alpha$, it follows that $X_1 + X_2 \varepsilon S[A_1 + A_2, \ A_1 + A_2 + (1 + \alpha)(B_1 - A_1)]$. But $A_1 + A_2 + (1 + \alpha)(B_1 - A_1) = B_1 + B_2$ (see Fig. 14.4, where A_1, B_1, X and $A_1 + A_2$ are vertices of a parallelogram). Therefore $X_1 + X_2 \varepsilon S[A_1 + A_2, \ B_1 + B_2]$. Conversely if $X \varepsilon S[A_1 + A_2, \ B_1 + B_2]$, then $X = A_1 + A_2 +$

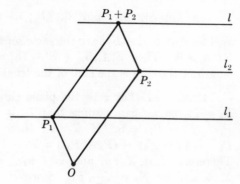

Fig. 14.3

$t(1 + \alpha)(B_1 - A_1)$, $0 \le t \le 1$.   Therefore $X = [A_1 + t(B_1 - A_1)] +$
$[A_2 + t(B_2 - A_2)]$ and $X \varepsilon S[A_1,B_1] + S[A_2,B_2]$.   Finally $|A_1 + A_2,$
$B_1 + B_2| = (1 + \alpha)|A_1B_1| = |A_1B_1| + |A_2B_2|$.

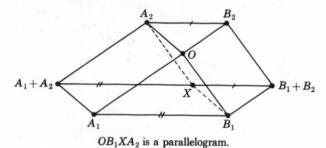

OB_1XA_2 is a parallelogram.

Fig. 14.4

It is obvious that the vector sum and scalar product depend upon the
origin.   Let $(S_1 + S_2)_0$ be the sum with O as origin and let $(rS)_0$ be the
scalar product with O as origin.   If O and O' are any two points, $P_1 \varepsilon S_1$
and $P_2 \varepsilon S_2$, then $\overrightarrow{OP_1} + \overrightarrow{OP_2} = 2\overrightarrow{OO'} + (\overrightarrow{O'P_1} + \overrightarrow{O'P_2})$. It follows that
$(S_1 + S_2)_0$ is the image of $(S_1 + S_2)_{0'}$, under a translation.   Also if
$S_3 = T_P(S_1)$, then $\overrightarrow{OT_P(P_1)} + \overrightarrow{OP_2} = \overrightarrow{OP} + (\overrightarrow{OP_1} + \overrightarrow{OP_2})$ and $(S_3 + S_2)_0$
is the image of $(S_1 + S_2)_0$ under a translation.   Finally, if $P \varepsilon S$, then
$\overrightarrow{rO'P} = \overrightarrow{rO'O} + \overrightarrow{rOP}$ and $(rS)_{0'}$ is the image of $(rS)_0$ under a translation.
This proves the following.

14.3   Theorem   If the origin is changed, or if either summand is translated, then the sum $S_1 + S_2$ is subjected to a translation.   If the origin
is changed, or equivalently if S is translated, then rS is subjected to a
translation.

Unless otherwise indicated we shall always consider $S_1 + S_2$ as any member of the equivalence class of all sets obtained by translating $(S_1 + S_2)_0$. Similarly we consider rS as any translate of $(rS)_0$. An appropriate choice of the origin will often simplify our constructions and proofs.

If we restrict ourselves to convex sets, it turns out that vector addition and scalar multiplication have many linearity properties which otherwise do not hold. First we need the following.

14.4   Theorem   If K_1 and K_2 are convex sets, then $K = K_1 + K_2$ is also convex.

PROOF   Let P and Q be any two points of $K_1 + K_2$. By the definition of vector set addition there are points P_1, $Q_1 \, \varepsilon \, K_1$ and P_2, $Q_2 \, \varepsilon \, K_2$ such that $P = P_1 + P_2$ and $Q = Q_1 + Q_2$. Now let $S_1 = S[P_1,Q_1]$ and $S_2 = S[P_2Q_2]$. Since K_1 and K_2 are convex, $S_1 \subset K_1$ and $S_2 \subset K_2$. Therefore $S_1 + S_2 \subset K_1 + K_2$. If S_1 is parallel to S_2, then $S_1 + S_2$ is a line segment containing $S[P,Q]$. If S_1 is not parallel to S_2, then $S_1 + S_2$ is a parallelogram and $S[P,Q]$ is one of its diagonals. In either case $S[P,Q] \subset S_1 + S_2 \subset K_1 + K_2$, so that $K_1 + K_2$ is convex.

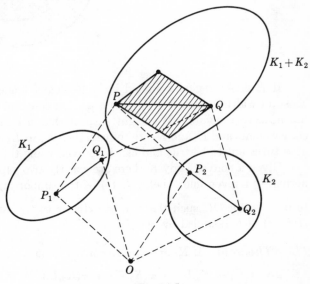

Fig. 14.5

14.5   Theorem   a.   If α and β are nonnegative real numbers not both zero and K is a convex set, then $(\alpha + \beta)K = \alpha K + \beta K$.

b. If K_1 and K_2 are convex sets and r is a nonnegative real number, then $r(K_1 + K_2) = rK_1 + rK_2$.

PROOF Let $X \varepsilon (\alpha + \beta)K$. Then $X = (\alpha + \beta)P = \alpha P + \beta P$ for some $P \varepsilon K$ and $X \varepsilon \alpha K + \beta K$. Conversely suppose $X \varepsilon \alpha K + \beta K$. Then $X = \alpha P + \beta P'$ where $P, P' \varepsilon K$. Therefore $X = (\alpha + \beta)$ $[\alpha P/(\alpha + \beta) + \beta P'/(\alpha+\beta)] = (\alpha+\beta)P''$, where $P'' \varepsilon S[P,P'] \subset K$. We leave the proof of part (**b**) to the reader.

We sometimes call $K + N(O,\epsilon)$ the spherical neighborhood of K with radius ϵ. This is equivalent to $\underset{P \varepsilon K}{\bigcup} N(P,\epsilon)$ and by Theorem 14.4 is always convex when K is convex.

14.6 The spherical neighborhood of set K with radius ϵ, $\epsilon > 0$, is defined to be $N(K,\epsilon) = \underset{P \varepsilon K}{\bigcup} N(P,\epsilon)$.

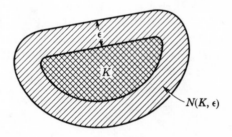

Fig. 14.6

If R is the region bounded by a Reuleaux triangle (see Sec. 10) of constant width ω, then $R + N(O,\epsilon)$ is a set of constant width $\omega + 2\epsilon$ which has no corner points. We might suspect that if either K_1 or K_2 has no corner points and K_1 and K_2 are convex, then $K_1 + K_2$ has no corner points. This turns out to be true and can be proved using the next theorem.

Given a convex body K there are exactly two supporting planes of K normal to a given line. Let $\pi(K,U)$ be the supporting plane of K normal to unit vector $\overrightarrow{OU}$ such that $\overrightarrow{OU}$ is exterior to the supporting half space $H(K,U)$ of K bounded by $\pi(K,U)$.

14.7 Theorem If K_1 and K_2 are convex bodies, then

  a. $\pi(K_1 + K_2,U) = \pi(K_1,U) + \pi(K_2,U)$
  b. $\pi(K_1 + K_2,U) \cap (K_1 + K_2) = \pi(K_1,U) \cap K_1 + \pi(K_2,U) \cap K_2$
  c. $H(K_1 + K_2,U) = H(K_1,U) + H(K_2,U)$

PROOF **a.** Let l be the line through the origin containing $\overrightarrow{OU}$ and let $P_1 = l \cap \pi(K_1,U)$, $P_2 = l \cap \pi(K_2,U)$. If $X_1 \varepsilon K_1 \cap \pi(K_1,U)$ and

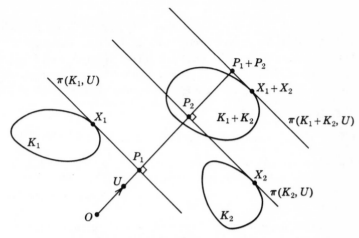

Fig. 14.7

$X_2 \in K_2 \cap \pi(K_2,U)$, it follows from Theorem 14.2 that $\pi(K_1,U) + \pi(K_2,U)$ is the plane through $X_1 + X_2$ parallel to $\pi(K_1,U)$. Also $H(K_1,U) = \{X | X \cdot U \leq P_1 \cdot U\}$ and $H(K_2,U) = \{X | X \cdot U \leq P_2 \cdot U\}$. Suppose $Q_1 \in K_1$ and $Q_2 \in K_2$. Then $(Q_1 + Q_2) \cdot U = Q_1 \cdot U + Q_2 \cdot U \leq P_1 \cdot U + P_2 \cdot U = (P_1 + P_2) \cdot U$. Therefore $\pi(K_1,U) + \pi(K_2,U)$ contains all of $K_1 + K_2$ on the side opposite to $\overrightarrow{OU}$, and $\pi(K_1,U) + \pi(K_2,U) = \pi(K_1 + K_2,U)$.

 b. It follows from part **(a)** that $\pi(K_1,U) \cap K_1 + \pi(K_2,U) \cap K_2 \subset \pi(K_1 + K_2,U) \cap (K_1 + K_2)$. Suppose $X_1 + X_2 \in \pi(K_1 + K_2,U) \cap (K_1 + K_2)$, where $X_1 \in K_1$ and $X_2 \in K_2$. We assert that $X_1 \cdot U = P_1 \cdot U$ and $X_2 \cdot U = P_2 \cdot U$. For suppose that $X_1 \cdot U < P_1 \cdot U$. Then $(X_1 + X_2) \cdot U = X_1 \cdot U + X_2 \cdot U < P_1 \cdot U + P_2 \cdot U = (P_1 + P_2) \cdot U$. But this contradicts the fact that $X_1 + X_2$ lies on $\pi(K_1 + K_2,U)$. Therefore $X_1 \in \pi(K_1,U)$, $X_2 \in \pi(K_2,U)$, and $\pi(K_1 + K_2,U) \cap (K_1 + K_2) = \pi(K_1,U) \cap K_1 + \pi(K_2,U) \cap K_2$.

 c. If $X \in H(K_1 + K_2,U)$, then $X \cdot U \leq (P_1 + P_2) \cdot U$, and if $X_2 = X - P_1$, it follows that $X_2 \in H(K_2,U)$. Since $P_1 \in H(K_1,U)$, we have $X \in H(K_1,U) + H(K_2,U)$. Conversely, if $X \in H(K_1,U) + H(K_2,U)$, then $X = X_1 + X_2$, where $X_1 \in H(K_1,U)$ and $X_2 \in H(K_2,U)$. But then $X \cdot U = X_1 \cdot U + X_2 \cdot U \leq P_1 \cdot U + P_2 \cdot U = (P_1 + P_2) \cdot U$. Therefore $X \in H(K_1 + K_2,U)$, and our proof is complete.

14.8   Theorem   If K_1 and K_2 are convex bodies and K_1 has no corner points, then $K_1 + K_2$ has no corner points.

 PROOF   Suppose P is a corner point of $K_1 + K_2$ and let $H(U)$ and

$H(U')$, with exterior unit normals $\overrightarrow{OU}$ and $\overrightarrow{OU'}$, be distinct supporting half spaces of $K_1 + K_2$ passing through P. It follows from Theorem 14.7 that there are points P_1 and P_2 of $H(K_1,U) \cap K_1$ and $H(K_2,U) \cap K_2$ respectively such that $P = P_1 + P_2$ and also points P_1' and P_2' of $H(K_1,U') \cap K_1$ and $H(K_2,U') \cap K_2$ respectively such that $P = P_1' + P_2'$. Since K_1 has no corner points, $P_1 \neq P_1'$. Therefore $\overrightarrow{OO} = \overrightarrow{OP} + \overrightarrow{PO} = \overrightarrow{OP_1} + \overrightarrow{OP_2} + \overrightarrow{P_1'O} + \overrightarrow{P_2'O} = \overrightarrow{P_1'P_1} + \overrightarrow{P_2'P_2}$. Since $\overrightarrow{P_1'P_1} \neq \overrightarrow{OO}$, it follows that $\overrightarrow{P_1'P_1}$ and $\overrightarrow{P_2'P_2}$ are in opposite directions. Let $\overrightarrow{P_1Q_1} = \overrightarrow{P_2Q_2} = \overrightarrow{OU}$. Then $\angle Q_1P_1P_2' > 90°$, and it follows that $\angle Q_2P_2P_2' < 90°$. This is impossible since $H(K_2,U)$ supports K_2. Therefore P is not a corner point of $K_1 + K_2$, and the proof is complete.

An immediate consequence of this theorem is that every spherical neighborhood of a convex set has no corner points.

If B is the boundary of a convex body K, it is easy to see that $N(K,\varepsilon) = K \cup N(B,\epsilon)$. The boundary of $N(K,\varepsilon)$ is the surface parallel to B and a distance ε from B which contains B in its interior. In general there is another surface a distance ϵ from B, but this one is inside B.

14.9   The spherical neighborhood of K with radius $-\epsilon$, $\epsilon > 0$, is defined to be $N(K,-\epsilon) = K - N(B,\epsilon)$, where B is the boundary of K (the minus sign stands for set subtraction, not vector subtraction).

14.10   Theorem   If K is a convex body and ϵ is positive, then $N(K,-\epsilon)$ is either the null set or a convex body.

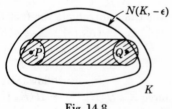

Fig. 14.8

PROOF   Suppose $N(K,-\epsilon)$ is not null and let $P,Q \in N(K,-\epsilon)$. Both $N(P,\epsilon)$ and $N(Q,\epsilon)$ lie entirely inside K, therefore the convex cover S of $N(P,\epsilon)$ and $N(Q,\epsilon)$ lies inside K. But $S = N[S(P,Q),\epsilon]$, and if $X \in S(P,Q)$, then $N(X,\epsilon) \subset S \subset K$. Therefore $X \in N(K,-\epsilon)$ and $N(K,-\epsilon)$ is convex.

We conclude this section with a comparison of the lengths of two plane convex bodies with the length of their sum.

14.11   Theorem   If Π_1 and Π_2 are plane polygonal regions, then $\Pi_1 + \Pi_2$ is a polygonal region and the length $L(\Pi_1 + \Pi_2) = L(\Pi_1) + L(\Pi_2)$.

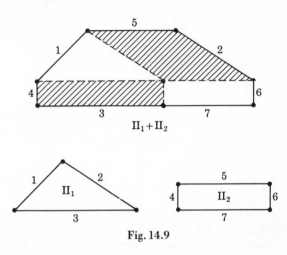

Fig. 14.9

PROOF   Let U be an arbitrary point on the unit circle and use the same notation as in Theorem 14.7.   For any fixed U we have $\pi(\Pi_1,U) \cap \Pi_1 + \pi(\Pi_2,U) \cap \Pi_2 = \pi(\Pi_1 + \Pi_2,U) \cap (\Pi_1 + \Pi_2)$.   Since each term on the left is a line segment or a single point, it follows from Theorem 14.2 that each term on the right is a line segment or a single point.   As we rotate U continuously in a clockwise sense around the unit circle, the boundary of $\Pi_1 + \Pi_2$ is formed by joining a succession of line segments.   Since the boundary of $\Pi_1 + \Pi_2$ is a simple closed curve, $\Pi_1 + \Pi_2$ is a polygonal region. Each edge of $\Pi_1 + \Pi_2$ is the sum of a point and of an edge of Π_1 or Π_2, or the sum of an edge of Π_1 and an edge of Π_2.   Since each edge of Π_1 and Π_2 is used exactly once in forming an edge of $\Pi_1 + \Pi_2$, it follows from Theorem 14.2 that $L(\Pi_1 + \Pi_2) = L(\Pi_1) + L(\Pi_2)$.

Next we see that the preceding theorem still holds if Π_1 is a polygonal region and Π_2 is a disk.

14.12   Theorem   If Π is a plane convex polygon with length L and area A, then $\Pi + N(P,r)$ is a plane convex body with length $L' = L + 2\pi r$ and area $A' = A + Lr + \pi r^2$.

PROOF   Let Π be a convex n-gon.   As shown in Fig. 14.10, $[\Pi + N(P,r)] - \Pi$ can be partitioned into rectangles and circular sectors. The n circular sectors have a total central angle of $360°$, so that the sum of their areas is πr^2.   The n rectangles have the same height r and their bases add up to L, so that the sum of their areas is Lr.   Therefore $A' = A + $

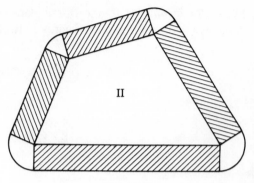

Fig. 14.10

$Lr + \pi r^2$. Similarly $L' = L + 2\pi r$, and the theorem is proved for convex polygons.

The preceding two theorems are still true if we replace the polygonal regions by arbitrary plane convex bodies. However, the proof is much easier using the results of Sec. 18, so we will not give a proof here. In fact Theorem 14.12 for plane convex bodies is a special case of Theorem 19.12 and Exercise 19.8.

Exercises

14.1 Give examples to show that in general $2S \neq S + S$.

14.2 If R is the region bounded by a Reuleaux triangle of width ω, prove that $R + N(O,\epsilon)$ is a set of constant width $\omega + 2\epsilon$ which has no corner points. Do not use Theorem 14.8.

14.3 Prove that the vector sum of two convex bodies is a convex body.

14.4 Give examples to show that the vector sum of the boundary of two convex bodies K_1 and K_2 is not the boundary of $K_1 + K_2$.

14.5 Let a class C of convex sets in n-space, $n = 1, 2,$ or 3, be given such that for every $n + 1$ members of C there exists a point whose distance from each of the $n + 1$ sets is less than or equal to a constant ϵ. Prove that there is a point whose distance from each member of C is less than or equal to ϵ.

14.6 Let T be a tetrahedron and let ϵ be positive. Partition $N(T,\epsilon)$ in a manner similar to the partition used in Theorem 14.12, and write formulas for the surface area and volume of $N(T,\epsilon)$.

14.7 Let H be a closed half space and let P be a point on its boundary. (**a**) If $X \in H$, show that $R[P,X] \subset H$. (**b**) If $X_1, X_2 \in H$, show that $X_1 + X_2 \in H$.

(**c**) If $\overrightarrow{PQ}$ is an exterior vector normal to the boundary of H and $\angle QPR$ is smaller than a right angle, show that $R \notin H$.

14.8 Prove part (**b**) of Theorem 14.5.

14.9 Describe all possible vector sums of the following sets in the plane:
  a. An equilateral triangle and its reflection about the origin
  b. A square and a line segment
  c. A parabola and a straight line
  d. A circle and a disk

14.10 Describe all possible vector sums of the following sets in 3-space:
  a. A regular tetrahedron and its reflection about the origin
  b. Two equilateral triangles

14.11 Use Exercise 14.10 to show that the surface area of the sum is not the sum of the surface areas of the summands.

14.12 Describe the following sets in the plane for $0 \leq r \leq 1$:
  a. $(1 - r)l_1 + rl_2$, where l_1 and l_2 are parallel lines.
  b. $(1 - r)S_1 + rS_2$, where S_1 and S_2 are parallel line segments.

14.13 Describe the following sets in 3-space for $0 \leq r \leq 1$:
  a. $(1 - r)\pi_1 + r\pi_2$, where π_1 and π_2 are parallel planes.
  b. $(1 - r)D_1 + rD_2$, where D_1 and D_2 are disks lying in parallel planes.

14.14 Using the same notation as in Theorem 14.7, prove that $\pi(\alpha K_1 + \beta K_2, U) = \alpha\pi(K_1, U) + \beta\pi(K_2, U)$ for positive real numbers α and β.

14.15 In a manner similar to that given in Exercise 14.14 extend parts (**b**) and (**c**) of Theorem 14.7.

14.16 Prove the commutative and associative laws for vector set addition.

14.17 What properties of an abstract vector space are not satisfied by vector set addition and scalar multiplication?

14.18 Show that the vector sum of a set of constant width and its reflection about the origin is a set of constant width. Hence show that the vector sum is a ball.

14.19 Prove that $(A \cup B) + C = (A + C) \cup (B + C)$ and $(A \cap B) + C \subset (B + C)$. Find conditions under which equality will hold in the second formula.

15 MOTIONS AND DECOMPOSITIONS

In this section we will investigate properties of polyhedral regions and their vector sums which are related to various groups of motions. Since we want to restrict ourselves to polyhedral regions, the following theorem is important.

15.1 Theorem   If Π_1 and Π_2 are convex polyhedral regions, then so is $\Pi_1 + \Pi_2$.

  PROOF   Let U be an arbitrary point on the unit circle and use the same notation as in Theorem 14.7. Let $\pi(\Pi_i, U) \cap \Pi_i = Q_i$, $i = 1, 2$, and let $\pi(\Pi_1 + \Pi_2, U) \cap (\Pi_1 + \Pi_2) = Q$. According to Theorem 14.7, $Q = Q_1 + Q_2$. Since a translation of the summands simply translates the vector sum, we may assume in what follows that Q_1 and Q_2 have been projected onto $\pi(\Pi_1 + \Pi_2, U)$. Let the faces of Π_1 be $F_1, \ldots, F_j$ and let the faces of Π_2 be $F_1', \ldots, F_k'$. If $Q_1 = F_i$, then Q_2 is either a face F_j', a single point P, or an edge S. According to Theorem 14.11, $F_i + F_j'$ is a polygonal region if they lie in the same plane. $F_i + P$ is a translation of F_i and is therefore a polygonal region. If a segment S lies in the plane of F_i, then $F_i + S$ is a plane convex body. Since the boundary of $F_i + S$ is a simple closed curve which is the union of a finite number of line segments, $F_i + S$ is a polygonal region. Similar remarks hold whenever $Q_2 = F_i'$. This implies that the boundary of $\Pi_1 + \Pi_2$ is the union of a finite number of plane polygonal regions. Since $\Pi_1 + \Pi_2$ is a convex body, it follows that $\Pi_1 + \Pi_2$ is a polyhedral region.

We now turn to a discussion of decomposition. In Definition 3.3 we were allowed to rearrange each piece of a decomposition by any kind of motion to form an equidecomposable set. We will investigate the possibility of restricting the group of motions.

15.2 Let G be a group of motions of 3-space. If polyhedral region Π is decomposed into polyhedral regions $\Pi_1, \ldots, \Pi_k$, polyhedral region Π' is decomposed into $\Pi_1', \ldots, \Pi_k'$, and $\Pi_i' = f_i(\Pi_i)$, $i = 1, \ldots, k$, where $f_i \varepsilon G$ for each i, then we say that Π and Π' are G-**equidecomposable.**

We make a similar definition for motions of the plane.

We saw in Sec. 3 that two polygonal regions have equal area iff they are equidecomposable. Two questions arise. Do polygonal regions have equal area iff they are G-equidecomposable, where G is a proper subgroup of the group of all plane motions? What subclass of polyhedral regions are G-equidecomposable for a given group of motions? First we consider the **group T of all translations.**

15.3 Theorem Any two parallelograms in the plane with equal area are T-equidecomposable.

PROOF Let $\Pi = ABED$ and $\Pi' = BCGF$ be the rectangle and parallelogram constructed in the proof of Theorem 3.5 (see Figs. 3.4 and 3.5). Every triangle in the triangular decomposition of Π used in the abovementioned proof is obtained by a translation from the corresponding triangle in the decomposition of Π'. It follows that two parallelograms with a side of one equal in length and parallel to a side of the other are T-equidecomposable.

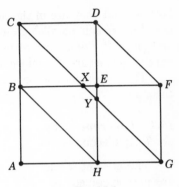

Fig. 15.1

Now let $ACDH$ and $ABFG$ be two rectangles of equal area positioned as shown in Fig. 15.1. We assert that $\triangle ACG$ and $\triangle EDF$ are similar and therefore $L(C,G)$ and $L(D,F)$ are parallel. To see this we notice that $|AB|\,|AG| = |AH|\,|AC|$. Therefore $\triangle ABH \sim \triangle ACG$. Also $|BX| = |HG| = |EF|$ and $|BC| = |ED|$. Therefore $\triangle BCX \cong \triangle EDF$. Since $\triangle BCX \sim \triangle ACG$, we have $\triangle EDF \sim \triangle ACG$, which proves the assertion. Since $\triangle CDY$ is a translate of $\triangle XFG$ and since $BCYH$ is T-equidecomposable with $BXGH$, it follows that $ACDH$ and $ABFG$ are T-equidecomposable.

To complete the proof let $ABCD$ and $PQMN$ be any two parallelograms in the xy plane with equal area. Translate $S[B,C]$ along $L(B,C)$ to $S[B',C']$ so that $S[A,B']$ is parallel to an axis, say the x axis. Then translate $S[D,C']$ along $L(D,C')$ to $S[D',C'']$ so that $S[B',C'']$ is parallel to the y axis. Apply similar transformations to $PQMN$ and then translate them

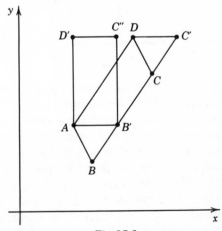

Fig. 15.2

both so that they are in the position shown in Fig. 15.1. Since each step transforms each parallelogram into a T-equidecomposable parallelogram, and since the final two rectangles are T-equidecomposable, our original parallelograms are T-equidecomposable.

The corresponding theorem in 3-space is a consequence of the preceding theorem.

15.4 Theorem   Any two parallelepipeds in 3-space with equal volume are T-equidecomposable.

PROOF   Let π and π' be parallel planes and suppose that Π_1 and Π_2 are parallelepipeds of equal volume each of which has a pair of parallel faces lying in π and π' respectively.   Let F_1 be the face of Π_1 in π and let F_2 be the face of Π_2 in π.   Since Π_1 and Π_2 have the same volume, the area of F_1 equals the area of F_2.   According to Theorem 15.3 F_1 and F_2 are each

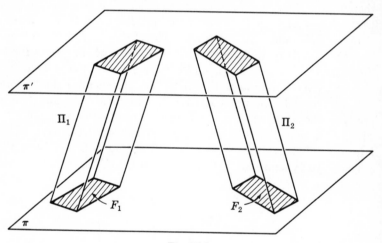

Fig. 15.3

T-equidecomposable with any square in π having the same area.   Through any point P in π draw a line l_1 parallel to the generator of Π_1 with F_1 as base and a line l_2 parallel to the generator of Π_2 with F_2 as base.   Let m be the intersection with π of a plane σ through l_1 and l_2, and construct a square S in π with a pair of sides parallel to m and with area equal to the area of F_1. Now let Π_1' be the parallelepiped with base S, having the same volume as Π_1 and having a generator parallel to l_1.   Similarly let Π_2' be the parallelepiped with base S, having the same volume as Π_2 and having a generator parallel to l_2.   It follows from Theorem 15.3 that Π_i and Π_i' are T-equidecomposable, $i = 1, 2$.   Let F_1' and F_2' be the faces of Π_1' and Π_2' respectively

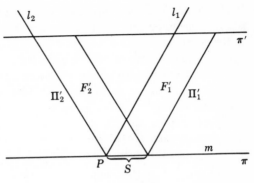

Fig. 15.4

which lie in σ. By construction F_1' and F_2' have equal areas. Since the generators of Π_1' and Π_2' are parallel when F_1' and F_2' are taken as bases, it follows that Π_1' and Π_2' are T-equidecomposable. Therefore Π_1 and Π_2 are T-equidecomposable.

Let $\Pi(P,Q,R)$ be the parallelepiped spanned by the vectors $\overrightarrow{OP}$, $\overrightarrow{OQ}$, and $\overrightarrow{OR}$, where O is the origin of the xyz coordinate system. Let $\pi(X,Y,Z)$ stand for the plane through points X, Y, and Z. Through P draw plane π parallel to $\pi(O,R,Q)$, and let P' be the intersection of π with one of the coordinate axes, say the x axis. Then $\Pi(P',Q,R)$ is T-equidecomposable with $\Pi(P,Q,R)$. Now draw plane π' through Q parallel to $\pi(O,P',R)$ and let Q' be the intersection of π' with a coordinate axis, say the y axis. $\Pi(P',Q',R)$ is T-equidecomposable with $T(P',Q,R)$. Finally, let R' be the projection of R onto the z axis parallel to the xy plane. It follows that

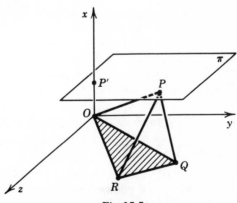

Fig. 15.5

$\Pi(P,Q,R)$ is T-equidecomposable with $\Pi(P',Q',R')$ and any parallelepiped is T-equidecomposable with a rectangular parallelepiped with edges parallel to the coordinate axes.

To complete the proof we shall show that any rectangular parallelepiped with edges parallel to the coordinate axes is T-equidecomposable with a cube of the same volume with edges parallel to the coordinate axes. Since any two cubes of the same volume with corresponding faces parallel are T-equidecomposable, it follows that any two parallelepipeds of the same volume are T-equidecomposable. Let F be a face of a rectangular parallelepiped Π lying in plane π and let its opposite face F' lie in π'. Let R be a rectangle in π with sides of length $x = \sqrt[3]{V(\Pi)}$ and $y = A(F)/x$, and parallel to the sides of F. If Π' is the rectangular parallelepiped with R as base and its opposite face in π', then Π and Π' are T-equidecomposable. Let G and G' be opposite faces of Π' adjacent to R which contain the sides of R of length y. Suppose G lies in plane σ and G' lies in plane σ'. Construct a square H in σ equal in area to G with sides parallel to the sides of G,

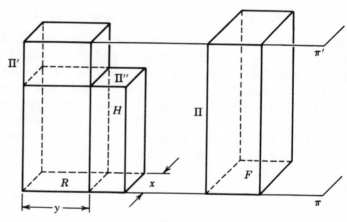

Fig. 15.6

and let Π'' be the cube with H as base and its opposite face in σ'. Π' is T-equidecomposable with Π''. Therefore Π is T-equidecomposable with Π'', and we have finished.

In order to show that not all polyhedra of equal volume are T-equidecomposable we shall use the notion of the directed surface area of a polyhedral region.

15.5 Let Π be a polyhedral region with faces $F_1, \ldots, F_k$, and let $\overrightarrow{OU_i}$ be the unit vector normal to F_i exterior to Π. We define the **directed**

surface area of Π in the direction $\overrightarrow{OU}$ to be $\mathbf{D}(\Pi,U) = \sum A(F_i)U_i \cdot U$, where the summation ranges over all faces of Π whose normals are parallel to $\overrightarrow{OU}$. If Π is a plane polygonal region with sides $S_1, \ldots, S_k$, then $\mathbf{D}(\Pi,U) = \sum L(S_i)U_i \cdot U$ is called the **directed length of** Π in the direction $\overrightarrow{OU}$, where the summation ranges over all sides of Π with normals parallel to $\overrightarrow{OU}$. If all faces (edges) in the direction $\overrightarrow{OU}$ degenerate to segments or points (degenerate to points), then we set $\mathbf{D}(\Pi,U) = 0$.

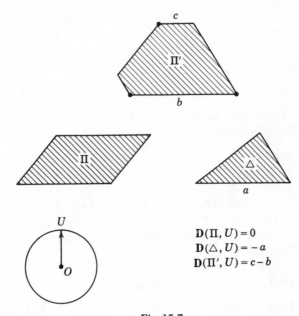

$$\mathbf{D}(\Pi, U) = 0$$
$$\mathbf{D}(\triangle, U) = -a$$
$$\mathbf{D}(\Pi', U) = c - b$$

Fig. 15.7

15.6   Theorem   If polyhedral regions Π and Π' are T-equidecomposable and $\overrightarrow{OU}$ is an arbitrary unit vector, then $\mathbf{D}(\Pi,U) = \mathbf{D}(\Pi',U)$.

PROOF   Let $\Pi_1, \ldots, \Pi_k$ be a polyhedral decomposition of the polygonal region Π. We assert that $\mathbf{D}(\Pi,U) = \sum_{i=1}^{k} \mathbf{D}(\Pi_i,U)$. Suppose Π_i has a face F_i and Π_j has a face F_j which both lie in the same plane. We may assume that F_i and F_j either coincide or else intersect, if at all, only on their boundaries. For if F_i and F_j overlap, they intersect in a finite number of polygonal regions $G_1, \ldots, G_n$. If we consider all the vertices of the G_i as vertices of both Π_i and Π_j, then we can consider each G_i as a

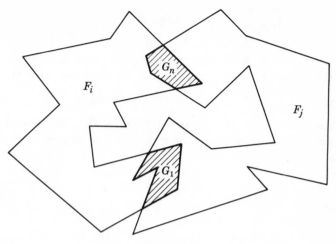

Fig. 15.8

face of both Π_i and Π_j, and the sum of the directed areas is unchanged. Now consider all the faces of $\Pi_1, \ldots, \Pi_k$ whose normal vectors are parallel to $\overrightarrow{OU}$. If face F is such a face, then either F is common to two polygonal regions Π_i and Π_j or F lies on a face of Π. Suppose the former occurs. Then the contribution to the sum of the directed areas due to F is zero, since the unit vector normal to F exterior to Π_i is equal and opposite to the unit vector normal to F exterior to Π_j. The remaining faces make up the boundary of Π, and their directed areas add up to precisely $\mathbf{D}(\Pi,U)$. This proves the assertion.

To complete the proof let $\Pi_1', \ldots, \Pi_k'$ be a decomposition of Π' such that Π_i' is a translate of Π_i, $i = 1, \ldots, k$. Since $\mathbf{D}(\Pi_i,U) = \mathbf{D}(\Pi_i',U)$ for each i, we have $\mathbf{D}(\Pi,U) = \sum_{i=1}^{k} \mathbf{D}(\Pi_i,U) = \sum_{i=1}^{k} \mathbf{D}(\Pi_i',U) = \mathbf{D}(\Pi',U)$. This completes the proof.

The proof of the corresponding theorem in the plane is very similar to the above and is left to the reader.

15.7   Theorem   (a)   If Δ is a triangle in the plane and Π is any parallelogram in the plane with equal area, then Δ and Π are not T-equidecomposable.   (b)   If T is a tetrahedron and Π is any parallelepiped with equal volume, then T and Π are not T-equidecomposable.

PROOF   Let $\triangle ABC$ be the triangle Δ and let Π be the parallelogram $PQRS$ of equal area where $\overrightarrow{PQ} = \overrightarrow{AB}$. If $\overrightarrow{OU}$ is the exterior normal to side AB, then $\mathbf{D}(\Delta,U) = |AB|$ and $\mathbf{D}(\Pi,U) = 0$. Therefore Π and Δ

are not T-equidecomposable. Suppose Δ is T-equidecomposable with parallelogram Π' of equal area. Since Π' is T-equidecomposable with Π, we then have Δ T-equidecomposable with Π, which is impossible. This completes the proof of part (a). The proof of part (b) is very similar and is omitted.

Even though the group T of plane translations is too small to allow all polygonal regions of equal area to be T-equidecomposable, it turns out that there is a group C, not the whole group of plane motions, which will allow equal area polygonal regions to be C-equidecomposable. Let C be the **group of plane motions generated by all the translations and central reflections** (rotations through 180°) of the plane. C is a proper subgroup of the motions of the plane. For each central reflection and each translation sends a line onto itself or onto a parallel line. Therefore, the rotations (other than half turns) do not belong to C.

15.8 Theorem   Let Π and Π' be polygonal regions in the plane. Π and Π' are equidecomposable iff Π and Π' are C-equidecomposable.

PROOF   The proof of Theorem 3.4 shows that any triangle is C-equidecomposable with some rectangle. Since T is a subgroup of C, it follows from Theorem 15.3 that any two parallelograms of equal area are C-equidecomposable. Therefore any triangle and parallelogram of equal area are C-equidecomposable. The proof of Theorem 3.6 can now be followed to show that Π and Π' are C-equidecomposable whenever Π and Π' are equidecomposable. The converse is left to the reader.

Let L be the **group of motions of 3-space generated by all the line reflections and all the translations.** Since each member of L is the product of an even number of plane reflections, it follows that L is a proper subgroup of the group of all motions of 3-space. The following is a three-dimensional analog to the preceding theorem.

15.9 Theorem   Let Π and Π' be prisms in 3-space. Π and Π' are equidecomposable iff Π and Π' are L-equidecomposable.

PROOF   It follows from Exercise 4.7 that any two prisms are equidecomposable iff they have the same volume. Let Π be a right prism with parallel bases F in plane π and F' in plane π'. In the plane π construct a rectangle P of area equal to the area of F and let Π' be the rectangular parallelepiped with parallel bases P in π and P' in π'. Since F and P are C-equidecomposable, it follows that Π and Π' are L-equidecomposable. If Π is not a right prism, choose a coordinate system so that the generator of Π is parallel to the z axis, Π lies in the first octant, and F and F' are parallel bases with F closest to the xy plane. Let P be a point of F closest to the xy plane and let Q be a point of F farthest from the xy plane. Let P' and Q' be the corresponding points of F'. Let π be a plane parallel to the xy plane which contains a point X of $S[P,P']$. If π can be chosen so that it also contains a point of $S[Q,Q']$, then π determines a decomposition of Π which shows that Π is T-equidecomposable with a right prism. If π does not intersect $S[Q,Q']$, let π_1 be the plane through X_1 such that $\overrightarrow{OX_1} = \overrightarrow{OX} + \overrightarrow{PP'}$, and in general let π_n be the plane through X_n such that $\overrightarrow{OX_n} = \overrightarrow{OX} + n\overrightarrow{PP'}$. Eventually we must reach a plane π_k which intersects $S[Q,Q']$. The case $k = 1$ is illustrated in Fig. 15.9. The planes π,

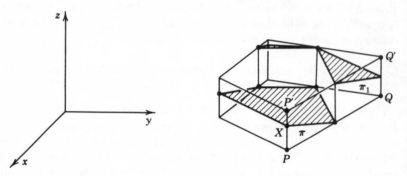

Fig. 15.9

$\pi_1, \ldots, \pi_k$ determine a decomposition of Π which shows that Π is T-equidecomposable with a right prism. Therefore any prism is L-equidecomposable with a rectangular parallelepiped of equal volume. Since any two rectangular parallelepipeds of equal volume are T-equidecomposable it follows that any two prisms of equal volume are L-equidecomposable. Therefore if Π and Π' are equidecomposable, then Π and Π' are L-equidecomposable. It is easy to see that the converse is also true.

If we restrict the class of sets under discussion to plane convex polygonal regions with center, then we get the following.

15.10   Theorem   Let Π and Π' be two plane convex polygonal regions each having a center. Π and Π' are equidecomposable iff Π and Π' are T-equidecomposable.

PROOF   We assert that any convex polygonal region Π with a center C is T-equidecomposable with a parallelogram. Since any two parallelograms of equal area are T-equidecomposable, it will then follow that whenever Π and Π' are convex polygonal regions with a center having equal area, then Π and Π' are T-equidecomposable. To see this we will use induction on the number of sides, $2n$, of Π.   If $n = 2$, then Π is a parallelogram and the assertion is true.   Suppose the assertion is true for all convex polygons with center having less than $2k$ sides and suppose Π has $2k$ sides. Let $S[A,B]$ be any side of Π and let $S[A',B']$ be the reflection of $S[A,B]$

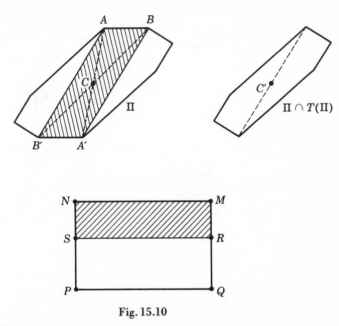

Fig. 15.10

about the center C.   If T is the translation which sends A onto B, then $\Pi \cap T(\Pi)$ is a convex polygonal region with center having $2(k - 1)$ sides. By the induction hypothesis $\Pi \cap T(\Pi)$ is T-equidecomposable with a parallelogram $PQRS$.   Let $SRMN$ be a parallelogram such that $S \varepsilon S[P,N]$, $R \varepsilon S[Q,M]$, and the area of $ABA'B'$ equals the area of $SRMN$.   Since $ABA'B'$ is T-equidecomposable with $SRMN$, it follows that Π is T-equidecomposable with parallelogram $PQMN$.

The converse follows from the fact that if Π and Π' are T-equidecomposable, then Π and Π' are equidecomposable.

We conclude this section with some relationships between decompositions and vector set addition.   First we need an important theorem whose proof is due to Hadwiger.[1]

15.11   Theorem   Let Π and Π' be convex polyhedral regions and suppose the origin O is an interior point of Π.   Let $\overrightarrow{OU_1}, \ldots, \overrightarrow{OU_n}$ be all

[1] See H. Hadwiger, "Altes und Neues über konvexe Körper," p. 14, Birkhäuser Verlag, Basel, 1955.

the unit exterior normal vectors to the faces of both Π and Π', and let Π_i be the convex cover of $\pi(\Pi, U_i) \cap \Pi$ and O [$\pi(\Pi, U)$ is the supporting plane of Π in the direction $\overrightarrow{OU}$]. Then Π', $\Pi_1 + \pi(\Pi', U_1) \cap \Pi'$, . . . , $\Pi_n + \pi(\Pi', U_n) \cap \Pi'$ is a decomposition of $\Pi + \Pi'$.

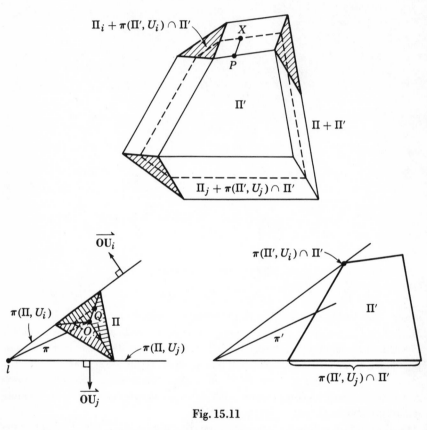

Fig. 15.11

PROOF Let $K_i = \Pi_i + \pi(\Pi', U_i) \cap \Pi'$, $i = 1, \ldots, n$. Since $O \varepsilon \Pi$, we have $\Pi' \subset \Pi + \Pi'$. Also K_i belongs to $\Pi + \Pi'$ for each i. Therefore $\Pi' \cup K_1 \cup \cdots \cup K_n \subset \Pi + \Pi'$. Suppose $X \varepsilon \Pi + \Pi'$ and suppose $X \notin \Pi'$. Then there is a real number λ, $0 \leq \lambda \leq 1$, such that X lies on the boundary of $\Pi' + \lambda\Pi$. It follows that $X = P + Q$ where $P \varepsilon \pi(\Pi', U_i) \cap \Pi'$ and Q lies on the boundary of $\lambda\Pi_i$ for some fixed i (see Fig. 15.11). But then $Q \varepsilon \Pi_i$ and $X \varepsilon \Pi' \cup K_1 \cup \cdots \cup K_n$. Therefore $\Pi + \Pi' = \Pi' \cup K_1 \cup \cdots \cup K_n$. It remains to show that any pair of sets from the class $\{\Pi', K_1, \ldots, K_n\}$ intersect (if at all) only on their boundaries. Let $\overrightarrow{OU_i}$ and $\overrightarrow{OU_j}$ be any two of the unit normals, $\overrightarrow{OU_i} \neq -\overrightarrow{OU_j}$, and let $l = \pi(\Pi, U_i) \cap \pi(\Pi, U_j)$.   If π is the plane spanned by O and l, and if π' is the plane through $\pi(\Pi', U_i) \cap \pi(\Pi', U_j)$ parallel to π, then K_i lies on one half space bounded by π' and K_j lies on the other.

Therefore K_i and K_j can only intersect on their boundaries.   If $\overrightarrow{OU_i} = -\overrightarrow{OU_j}$, then any plane π' perpendicular to $\overrightarrow{OU_i}$ passing through an interior point of Π' will separate K_i from K_j.   Since the plane $\pi' = \pi(\Pi'(U_i))$ separates K_i from Π' except for boundary points, the proof is complete.

The proof of the corresponding theorem in the plane can be carried over almost word for word.   We use this in the following.

15.12   Theorem   If Π and Π' are convex polygonal regions having no interior point of one in common with the other, then $\Pi + \Pi'$ is T-equidecomposable with the union of Π, Π', and a finite number of parallelograms.

PROOF   Use the same notation as in Theorem 15.11 and let $\overrightarrow{OU_i}$ be any unit exterior normal to one of the edges of Π or Π'.   If $l(\Pi', U_i) \cap \Pi'$ is a point and $l(\Pi, U_i) \cap \Pi$ is a line segment, then K_i is a translate of Π_i. If $l(\Pi', U_i) \cap \Pi'$ is a segment and $l(\Pi, U_i) \cap \Pi$ is a point, then K_i is a parallelogram.   If both $l(\Pi, U_i) \cap \Pi$ and $l(\Pi', U_i) \cap \Pi'$ are line segments, then K_i can be decomposed into a translate of Π_i and a parallelogram.   It follows that $\Pi + \Pi'$ is T-equidecomposable with Π, Π', and a finite number of parallelograms.

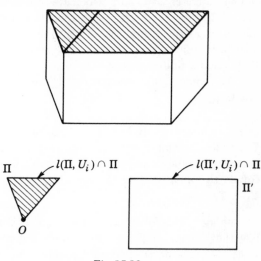

Fig. 15.12

We now use the preceding result to prove the corresponding theorem in 3-space.

15.13   Theorem   If Π and Π' are convex polyhedral regions having no interior point of one in common with the other, then $\Pi + \Pi'$ is T-equidecomposable with the union of Π, Π', and a finite number of prisms.

PROOF   Use the same notation as in Theorem 15.11 and let $\overrightarrow{OU_i}$ be any unit exterior normal to one of the faces of Π or Π'. Suppose $\pi(\Pi, U_i) \cap \Pi$ is a face. If $\pi(\Pi', U_i) \cap \Pi'$ is a point, then K_i is a translate of Π_i. If $\pi(\Pi', U_i) \cap \Pi'$ is a line segment of length s, then K_i can be decomposed into a prism with lateral edge length s and a translate of Π_i. Now suppose $\pi(\Pi', U_i) \cap \Pi'$ is a face. If $\pi(\Pi, U_i) \cap \Pi$ is a point P, then K_i is a prism with lateral edge length $|OP|$. If $\pi(\Pi, U_i) \cap \Pi$ is a line segment, then K_i can be decomposed into a triangular prism and a translate of Π_i. Finally, suppose both $F' = \pi(\Pi', U_i) \cap \Pi'$ and $F = \pi(\Pi, U_i) \cap \Pi$ are faces. Then $F + F'$ and F' are parallel faces of K_i. According to Theorem 15.12, if we pick a point X interior to the face F and form the triangles spanned by X with each edge of F, then $F + F'$ can be decomposed into translates of these triangles, a translate of F', and a finite number of parallelograms. It follows that K_i can be decomposed into a prism with base F', a finite number of triangular prisms determined by the edges of F' and the corresponding parallelograms of the decomposition of $F + F'$ and a number of tetrahedra which are translates of a tetrahedral decomposition of Π_i. Since Π', K_1, . . . , K_n is a decomposition of $\Pi + \Pi'$, and each K_i is T-equidecomposable with the union of Π_j and a finite number of prisms, it follows that $\Pi + \Pi'$ is T-equidecomposable with the union of Π, Π', and a finite number of prisms.

An immediate consequence of the two preceding theorems is the following.

15.14   Theorem   If Π_1, Π_2, Σ_1, Σ_2 are convex polygonal regions each T-equidecomposable with a parallelogram, then $\Pi_1 + \Pi_2$ and $\Sigma_1 + \Sigma_2$ are each T-equidecomposable with a parallelogram. If the area of $\Pi_1 + \Pi_2$ equals the area of $\Sigma_1 + \Sigma_2$, then $\Pi_1 + \Pi_2$ is T-equidecomposable with $\Sigma_1 + \Sigma_2$.

PROOF   This follows from Theorems 15.3 and 15.12, together with the fact that the union of any finite number of nonoverlapping parallelograms P_i is T-equidecomposable with a single parallelogram whose area is the sum of the areas of the P_i.

15.15 **Theorem** If II_1, II_2, Σ_1, Σ_2 are convex polyhedral regions each L-equidecomposable with a prism, then $II_1 + II_2$ and $\Sigma_1 + \Sigma_2$ are each L-equidecomposable with a prism. If the volume of $II_1 + II_2$ equals the volume of $\Sigma_1 + \Sigma_2$, then $II_1 + II_2$ is L-equidecomposable with $\Sigma_1 + \Sigma_2$.

PROOF This follows from Theorems 15.9 and 15.13, together with the fact that the union of any finite number of nonoverlapping prisms P_i is L-equidecomposable with a single prism whose volume is the sum of the volumes of the P_i.

Exercises

15.1 Let II_1 and II_2 be plane convex polygonal regions. If II_1 has i sides and II_2 had k sides, what can be said about the number of sides of $II_1 + II_2$?

15.2 Generalize Exercise 15.1 to 3-space.

15.3 Use the proof of Theorem 15.3 suggested by Fig. 15.1 to show that any two parallelograms of equal area with each side of one parallel to a side of the other are T-equidecomposable.

15.4 Prove the two-dimensional counterpart to Theorem 15.6.

15.5 Prove part (b) of Theorem 15.7.

15.6 Let T be a tetrahedron and let T' be the reflection of T about the origin. Show that T and T' are not T-equidecomposable. Do the same for a triangle.

15.7 Generalize Exercise 15.6.

15.8 Show that the group C generated by all translations and all central reflections of 3-space is a proper subgroup of the group of all motions of 3-space.

15.9 Let S be a square with sides parallel to the coordinate axes and let S' be any square with the same area. Construct decompositions of S and S' which show that S and S' are C-equidecomposable.

15.10 Let S and S' be the squares in Exercise 15.9. Construct decompositions of S and S' which show that S and S' are T-equidecomposable.

15.11 If II is a plane convex polygonal region, show that II has a center iff
$$\mathbf{D}(II,U) = 0 \text{ for all unit vectors } \overrightarrow{OU}.$$

15.12 Show that a plane convex polygonal region II is T-equidecomposable with a square iff II has a center.

15.13 Let S be a square and let H be a regular hexagon with the same area as S. Construct decompositions of S and H which show that S and H are T-equidecomposable.

15.14 Prove the two-dimensional counterpart to Theorem 15.11.

15.15 Construct the decomposition described in Theorem 15.12 of the vector sum of an equilateral triangle and a square.

15.16   Construct the decomposition described in Theorem 15.13 of the vector sum of a regular tetrahedron and a cube.

15.17   Let Π_1, Π_2, Σ_1, Σ_2 be plane convex polygonal regions and suppose the area $A(\Pi_1) = A(\Sigma_1)$ and $A(\Pi_2) = A(\Sigma_2)$.   Give examples which show that **(a)** $A(\Pi_1 + \Pi_2)$ may equal $A(\Sigma_1 + \Sigma_2)$ and **(b)** $A(\Pi_1 + \Pi_2)$ may not equal $A(\Sigma_1 + \Sigma_2)$.

15.18   Generalize Exercise 15.17 to 3-space.

15.19   If S is a square and R is a rhombus with a side parallel to a side of S, find a decomposition of $S + R$ which can be rearranged to form a rectangle.

15.20   If C is a cube and T is a triangular prism with its base parallel to a face of C, find a decomposition of $C + T$ which can be rearranged to form a prism.

16   DUALITY

In Sec. 9 we found it useful to set up a correspondence between points and lines in a plane and between points and half spaces in 3-space.   We conclude this chapter with a discussion of a similar transformation which maps a set onto its polar dual, sometimes called its polar reciprocal.

16.1   Let K be any subset of space (the plane).   The **polar dual of** K is the set $K^* = \{Y \,|\, X \cdot Y \le 1 \text{ for all } X \,\varepsilon\, K\}$.

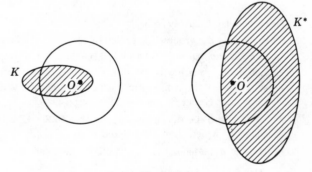

Fig. 16.1

It is easily seen that this definition depends upon the origin O.   If K is the origin, then K^* is the whole space.   If K is any other single point, then K^* is the closed half space bounded by the plane π perpendicular to $L(O,K)$ which contains O and has the property that if $P = \pi \cap L(O,K)$, then $|OP||OK| = 1$.   The following theorem now follows immediately.

16.2   *Theorem*   The polar dual K^* of set K is the intersection of all half spaces dual to points of K.

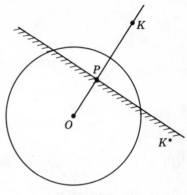

Fig. 16.2

Since a half space is convex, it follows that regardless of K the polar dual K^* is always a convex set which contains the origin.

We can form the polar dual K^{**} of K^*, and the principal reason for the name "polar dual" is the following theorem.

16.3   Theorem   If K is a closed set, then K^{**} is the convex cover of $K \cup \{O\}$.   In particular if K is a closed convex set containing the origin O, then $K^{**} = K$.

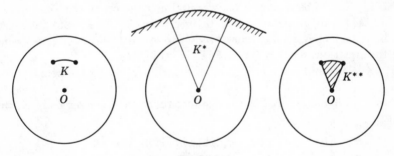

Fig. 16.3

PROOF   Let M be the convex cover of $K \cup \{O\}$.   We assert that $K^* = M^*$.   Let $X \varepsilon M^*$.   Then $X \cdot Y \leq 1$ for all $Y \varepsilon M$, and therefore $X \cdot Y \leq 1$ for all $Y \varepsilon K$.   By definition of K^* it follows that $X \varepsilon K^*$ and $M^* \subset K^*$.   Now suppose that $X \notin M^*$.   Then there is a point $Y_1 \varepsilon M$ such that $X \cdot Y_1 > 1$.   Let π bound the supporting half space H of $K \cup \{O\}$ in the direction $\overrightarrow{OX}$, and let $P_1 \varepsilon \pi \cap (K \cup \{O\})$. $P_1 \neq O$, since then we would have $X \cdot Y_1 \leq O$, contrary to assumption.   Therefore $P_1 \varepsilon K$.   But H is also a supporting half space of M.   By comparing the projections of

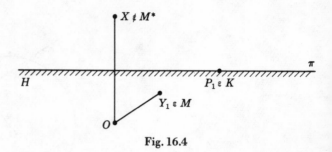

Fig. 16.4

$\overrightarrow{OP_1}$ and $\overrightarrow{OY_1}$ onto $\overrightarrow{OX}$, we see that $X \cdot P_1 \geq X \cdot Y_1 > 1$. Therefore $X \not\in K^*$ and $K^* = M^*$.

It remains to show that $K^{**} = K$ for a closed convex set K containing the origin. For any $X \in K$ we have $X \cdot Y \leq 1$ for $Y \in K^*$, and it follows that $X \in K^{**}$. Therefore $K \subset K^{**}$. Assume $P \not\in K$, then there is a plane π which separates P from K. Let the equation of π be $X \cdot Y = 1$. Since K contains O, if $X_1 \in K$ then $X_1 \cdot Y < 1$, and therefore $Y \in K^*$. But $P \cdot Y > 1$, therefore $P \not\in K^{**}$ and $K^{**} \subset K$.

If we restrict ourselves to convex bodies which contain the origin in their interior, then there is a close relationship between the polar dual and certain functions which we now define.

16.4 Let K be a convex body containing the origin O in its interior and let X be an arbitrary point distinct from O. If $R[O,X]$ intersects the boundary of K in X_B, then the **distance function** F of K is defined by the equations $F(O) = 0$ and $F(X) = |OX|/|OX_B|$.

We collect some properties of F in the following theorem.

16.5   Theorem   If F is the distance function of convex body K, then

  a. $K = \{X | F(X) \leq 1\}$,
  b. $F(X) \geq 0$, where equality holds iff $X = O$,
  c. $F(\lambda X) = \lambda F(X)$ for any real number $\lambda \geq 0$,
  d. $F(X + Y) \leq F(X) + F(Y)$.

PROOF We shall prove only part (**d**). Since $F[X/F(X)] = F[Y/F(Y)] = 1$, both $X/F(X)$ and $Y/F(Y)$ belong to K. Since K is convex for $0 \leq r \leq 1$, we have $F[(1 - r)X/F(X) + rY/F(Y)] \leq 1$. If $r = F(Y)/[F(X) + F(Y)]$, then we get $F\{(X + Y)/[F(X) + F(Y)]\} = F(X + Y)/[F(X) + F(Y)] \leq 1$, which proves the theorem.

16.6   Theorem   If F is a finite real-valued function with the following properties:

a. $F(X) \geq 0$, where equality holds iff $X = O$,

b. $F(\lambda X) = \lambda F(X)$ for any real number $\lambda \geq 0$,

c. $F(X + Y) \leq F(X) + F(Y)$.

then $K = \{X | F(X) \leq 1\}$ is a convex body with distance function F.

PROOF Suppose $P, Q \in K$ and $0 \leq r \leq 1$. Then $F[(1 - r)P + rQ] \leq F[(1 - r)P] + F(rQ) = (1 - r)F(P) + rF(Q) \leq (1 - r) + r = 1$. Therefore K is convex. The boundary of K is the set $\Sigma = \{X | F(X) = 1\}$, so that K is closed. Since O is an interior point of K, there is a sphere S with center O lying in K. Since every ray $R[O,X]$ intersects Σ in exactly one point $X/F(X)$, we can follow the proof of Theorem 11.9 to conclude that Σ is a simple closed surface. It follows that K is bounded. To complete the proof let X be any point not the origin and let $R[O,X]$ intersect the boundary of K in X_B. Then $F(X) = F(|OX|X_B/|OX_B|) = |OX|F(X_B)/|OX_B| = |OX|/|OX_B|$, and F is the distance function of K.

16.7 Let K be a convex body and let P be an arbitrary point distinct from the origin O. Let π be the supporting plane of K with exterior normal $\overrightarrow{OP}$. If $H(O) = 0$ and if the equation of π is $X \cdot P = H(P)$, then the function H is called the **support function** of K.

We note that if $\overrightarrow{OP}$ is a unit vector, then $H(P)$ is the signed distance from the origin to the supporting plane of K in the direction $\overrightarrow{OP}$.

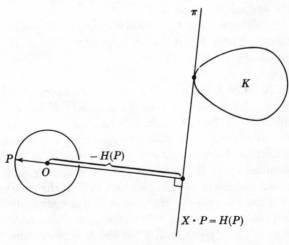

Fig. 16.5

16.8   Theorem   If H is the support function of convex body K, then

   a. $K = \{X | X \cdot P \leq H(P) \text{ for all points } P\}$,
   b. $H(\lambda P) = \lambda H(P)$ for any real number $\lambda \geq 0$,
   c. $H(P + Q) \leq H(P) + H(Q)$.

PROOF   We leave the proof of parts (**a**) and (**b**) to the reader. Let P and Q be any two points distinct from O. For each point $X \in K$ we have $X \cdot P \leq H(P)$ and $X \cdot Q \leq H(Q)$. Therefore $X \cdot (P + Q) \leq H(P) + H(Q)$ for each $X \in K$. It follows from the definition of H that there is at least one point $X_1 \in K$ such that $X_1 \cdot (P + Q) = H(P + Q)$. Therefore $H(P + Q) \leq H(P) + H(Q)$, and we have finished.

16.9   Theorem   If F and H are the distance function and support function respectively of a convex body K containing the origin in its interior, then F is the support function of K^* and H is the distance function of K^*.

PROOF   Since no supporting hyperplane of K passes through the origin, it follows that $H(P) \geq 0$, where equality holds iff $P = O$. According to Theorem 16.6, H is the distance function of the convex body $K' = \{P | H(P) \leq 1\}$. We assert that $K' = K^*$. Suppose $P \in K'$, then $X \cdot P \leq H(P) \leq 1$ for all $X \in K$, and $P \in K^* = \{Y | X \cdot Y \leq 1 \text{ for all } X \in K\}$. If $P \in K^*$, then $P \cdot X \leq 1$ for all $X \in K$. But there is at least one point $X_1 \in K$ such that $P \cdot X_1 = H(P)$. Therefore $H(P) \leq 1$, $P \in K'$ and $K' = K^*$.

To complete the proof we need only notice that $K^{**} = K$ and apply the preceding part to K^*. This shows that the distance function of K is the support function of K^*.

We now turn to a brief discussion of convex cones and their polar duals. These sets play an important role in the theory of linear programming (see Sec. 27).

16.10   Let K be a convex set. The union of all rays beginning at the origin O and passing through points of K is called a **convex cone** with **directrix** K (see Definition 28.12).

It is easily seen that a convex cone is a convex set. If K is a three-dimensional set which contains the origin in its interior, then the cone spanned by K is the whole space. Similarly, if K is two- or one-dimensional and contains O in its interior, then the cone spanned by K is a plane or a line through O. Suppose K is a convex body in the plane which does not contain the origin. Then the cone C spanned by K is a convex angular region. The polar dual C^* is also a convex cone. C can be constructed as follows. Let R_1 and R_2 be the bounding rays of C and let l_1 and l_2 be the lines through O perpendicular to R_1 and R_2 respectively. If H_1 and H_2 are the closed half planes bounded by l_1 and l_2 which do not contain R_1 and R_2 respectively, then $C^* = H_1 \cap H_2$. This can be generalized to 3-space.

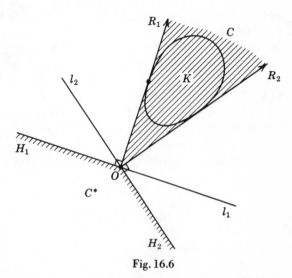

Fig. 16.6

16.11 **Theorem** Let C be a convex cone. If C' is the union of all rays $R[O,P)$ such that $\overrightarrow{OP}$ is a unit normal vector exterior to a supporting half space of C through O, then $C' = C^*$.

PROOF Suppose $X \varepsilon C'$. Then $X = \lambda P$, $\lambda > 0$, where $|OP| = 1$ and $Y \cdot P \leq 0$ is the inequality of a half space supporting C at O. Therefore $Y \cdot X \leq 0 < 1$ for all $Y \varepsilon C$ and $X \varepsilon C^*$. Suppose $X \varepsilon C^*$, then $X \cdot Y \leq 1$ for all $Y \varepsilon C$. We assert that $X \cdot Y \leq 0$ for all $Y \varepsilon C$. For suppose $X \cdot Y_1 = r, 0 < r \leq 1$, and $Y_1 \varepsilon C$. Then $\alpha Y_1, \alpha > 0$, also belongs to C, and $X \cdot \alpha Y_1 = r\alpha$. If we choose α large enough, then $X \cdot \alpha Y_1 > 1$, contrary to the choice of X. Therefore $X \cdot Y \leq 0$ for all $Y \varepsilon C$. It follows that $X \varepsilon C'$, and our proof is complete.

We will have occasion to use the following theorem in Sec. 27.

16.12 **Theorem** Suppose C is a convex cone with the property that every point $P \varepsilon C$, $P \neq O$, has at least one negative coordinate. Then there is at least one supporting half space of C with inequality $X \cdot P \leq 0$ such that every coordinate of P is positive.

PROOF This is equivalent to showing that C^* contains at least one point P with all coordinates positive. Let K be the set of points with all coordinates nonpositive.   Since K is convex, so is $C + K$.   Also $C + K$ contains no point with all coordinates positive.   For if $P \in C$ and $Q \in K$, then $P + Q$ has at least one coordinate which is nonpositive.   Since every neighborhood of O contains at least one point with all coordinates positive, O is a boundary point of $C + K$.   Let π be a supporting plane of $C + K$ at O.   Since $C \subset C + K$ and $K \subset C + K$, it follows that π is also a supporting plane of C and of K.   If $X \cdot P \leq 0$ is the inequality of the supporting half space of K bounded by π, then $X \cdot P \leq 0$ for all $X \in C$.   Therefore $P \in C^*$, and P has all coordinates nonnegative.   Suppose, for example, that the z coordinate of P is zero and the x coordinate is positive.   If all points of C^* lie in the half space H with inequality $z \leq 0$, then $H^* \subset C^{**} = C$ (see Exercise 16.4).   But H^* is the positive z axis, which contradicts the fact that every point of C contains at least one negative coordinate.   If $P' \in C^*$ and the z coordinate of P' is positive, then we can find a small positive number α such that $\alpha P' + P$ has both the x and z coordinates positive.

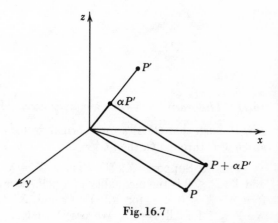

Fig. 16.7

But $(\alpha P' + P) \cdot X = \alpha P' \cdot X + P \cdot X \leq 0$ for all $X \in C$.   Therefore $\alpha P' + P \in C^*$.   If we replace P by $\alpha P' + P$ and repeat the preceding argument, we arrive at a point in C^* with all coordinates positive, and our proof is complete.

The reader may have wondered whether the polar dual has anything to do with the pole and polar line of analytic geometry.   This is indeed the case.   We conclude this section with a few properties of pole and polar. For simplicity we restrict ourselves to the plane, although similar results also hold in 3-space.

16.13   If point P is not the origin and p is the boundary line of the polar dual P^*, then we call p the **polar line** of P with respect to the unit circle and call P the **pole** of line p.

The polar line p to point P can be easily constructed by geometric means as follows.   If P lies outside the unit circle C, let the tangents to C through P touch C in points X and Y.   The line $L(X,Y)$ is the polar of P. If P lies inside C, then we draw line l through P perpendicular to $L(O,P)$. Let $\{X,Y\} = l \cap C$ and let t_1, t_2 be the tangent lines to C through X and Y. The line through $t_1 \cap t_2$ perpendicular to $L(O,P)$ is the polar of P.   If P lies on C, then the tangent to C at P is the polar of P.

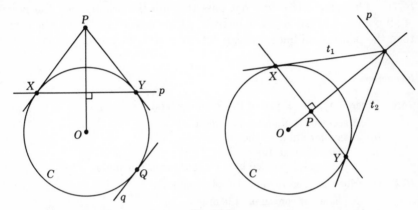

Fig. 16.8

16.14   Theorem   If point $P \neq O$ lies on line q and q does not pass through the origin, then the pole Q of q lies on the polar p of P.

PROOF   Let $Q' = L(O,Q) \cap q$,   let $P' = L(O,P) \cap p$,   and let $Q'' = L(O,Q) \cap p$.   We shall show that $Q = Q''$ and therefore Q lies on p. By construction $\triangle OP'Q''$ is similar to $\triangle OQ'P$.   Therefore $|OP'|/|OQ'| = |OQ''|/|OP|$.   It follows that $|OQ''| = 1/|OQ'|$.   But $|OQ| = 1/|OQ'|$. Therefore $Q = Q''$.

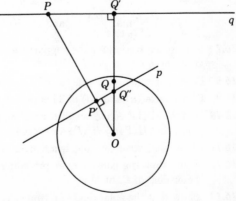

Fig. 16.9

The following two theorems are immediate consequences of the preceding result. We omit the proofs.

16.15   Theorem   If O, P, and Q are distinct noncollinear points and if $r = L(P,Q)$, then the pole R of r is the intersection of the polars p and q of P and Q respectively.

16.16   Theorem   If l does not pass through the origin, then the polars of all points of l form a pencil of lines.   Conversely, if P is not the origin, then the poles of all lines through P form a straight line of points.

Exercises

16.1   Describe the polar dual of the following sets:
  a.   A segment containing the origin
  b.   A ray beginning at the origin
  c.   A plane through the origin
  d.   A half space bounded by a plane through the origin

16.2   Describe the polar dual of the following sets:
  a.   A plane not containing the origin
  b.   A line not containing the origin
  c.   A line segment not containing the origin

16.3   Describe the polar dual of a sphere and a cube with center at the origin.

16.4   Prove (**a**) $K^{***} = K^*$; (**b**) if $M \subset N$, then $M^* \supset N^*$.

16.5   Use the law of cosines to find expressions in terms of P and r for the distance function and support function of a sphere with center P and radius r.

16.6   If K is a cube with edge length s in $x_1x_2x_3$-space with edges parallel to the coordinate axes, show that the distance and support functions of K are given by

$$F(X) = \max_{i=1,2,3} \frac{|x_i|}{s} \quad \text{and} \quad H(X) = \sum_{i=1}^{3} s|x_i|$$

16.7   Find an expression for the support function of a line segment with midpoint at the origin.

16.8   Prove parts (**a**), (**b**), and (**c**) of Theorem 16.5.

16.9   Prove parts (**a**) and (**b**) of Theorem 16.6.

16.10   Let K, K' be convex bodies with support functions H, H'. If $K \subset K'$, show that $H(P) \leq H'(P)$ for every point P.

16.11   Show that a convex cone is a convex set.

16.12   Show that the construction preceding Theorem 16.11 actually gives the polar dual of C.

16.13   Show that the polar dual of a convex cone is a convex cone.

16.14 Prove that if K is a convex body, then the cone spanned by K is the convex cover of the union of all rays which begin at O and pass through an extreme point of K.

16.15 Prove the constructions preceding Theorem 16.14.

16.16 Prove Theorems 16.15 and 16.16.

16.17 Two lines are called conjugate if each contains the pole of the other. Show that if two conjugate lines intersect outside the unit circle, then one cuts the circle and the other does not.

16.18 A triangle is called self-polar iff each vertex is the pole of the line through the remaining two vertices. Show how to construct a self-polar triangle.

16.19 Prove that a self-polar triangle is obtuse.

16.20 Extend Definition 16.13 to 3-space and prove theorems similar to Theorems 16.15 and 16.16 for points and planes.

INTRODUCTION

4

EXTREMUM PROBLEMS

Extremum problems have interested mathematicians for centuries. An important branch of applied mathematics called the "calculus of variations" was developed to solve certain extremum problems which involve the solution of integral equations. Since the advent of the electronic computing machine, "linear programming" was developed to solve extremum problems which occur in economics and the theory of games. Many of these problems cannot be solved by the methods of the calculus of variations but can often be solved using the theory of convex bodies.

In this chapter we discuss in detail one of the oldest extremum problems, the isoperimetric problem. We first solve the plane isoperimetric problem, paying close attention to the existence of a solution. The problem of Dido is also solved. The question of the existence of a solution to the iso-perimetric problem illustrates the need for the Blaschke selection theorem, which is then proved in Sec. 18.

In order to even formulate the isoperimetric problem in 3-space we need a definition of surface area. This is done in Sec. 19 by introducing the notion of mixed volumes and linear arrays. The relation between sur-face area and mixed volumes is shown, and incidentally the existence of the surface area of a convex body is also shown.

We next introduce the important technique of Steiner symmetrization. The effect of symmetrization on volume, surface area, diameter, etc., is discussed, and a few applications are given. Convex functions are then defined, and the Brunn-Minkowski theorem and Minkowski's inequality are proved. This gives a complete solution to the isoperimetric problem in 3-space.

The final section is devoted to the solution of geometric inequalities us-ing the techniques developed throughout the chapter. Particular atten-tion is given to problems related to the Brunn-Minkowski theorem.

17   THE ISOPERIMETRIC PROBLEM

The theory of convex bodies turns out to be particularly suited to geometric solutions of many extremum problems. Some extremum problems, how-ever, have eluded solution for many years. For an example, consider the following problem. What is the set of greatest area which can be covered by every plane convex body of minimum width 1? It is known that such a set exists, but it is not known what the set looks like.

One of the most famous of all extremum problems is the isoperimetric problem. Of all plane simple closed curves with the same length, which one (or ones) encloses the greatest area? It is easy to see that any solution Γ to the isoperimetric problem must bound a convex body K. For, if not, let X be a point on the boundary of the convex cover of K which does not belong to K. It follows from Theorem 9.7 that $X \varepsilon S[P,Q]$ where $P, Q \varepsilon K$ and $L(P,Q)$ is a supporting line of K. Let Γ_1 and Γ_2 be the arcs of Γ deter-mined by P and Q (see Fig. 17.1), and let Γ_1' be the reflection of Γ_1 about $L(P,Q)$. The curve $\Gamma_1' \cup \Gamma_2$ has the same length as Γ but bounds a larger area.

17.1 Theorem Given any plane convex body K which is not a closed disk, there is another convex set K' with the same length which bounds a greater area.

PROOF   To prove this we will make use of the fact that of all triangles with two given sides the triangle in which the given sides are at right angles has the greatest area. To see this let $S[A,B]$ and $S[A,C]$ be the given sides, and consider the circle with center A and radius $|AC|$. As the point C traces the circle, the altitude of triangle ABC dropped from C reaches a maximum when $L(C,A)$ is perpendicular to $L(A,B)$.

We now assert that if a chord of a convex body K bisects the boundary of K, and if K is divided into unequal areas by this chord, then there is a set K' with the same length as K but with greater area. For let K be divided into K_1 and K_2 by chord $S[P,Q]$, and suppose the area of K_1 is greater than the area of K_2. Reflect K_1 about $L(P,Q)$ to obtain K_1'. Then $K_1' \cup K_1$ is the desired set.

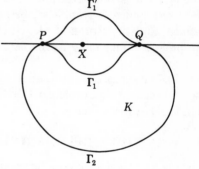

Fig. 17.1

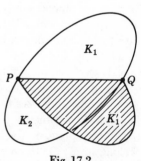

Fig. 17.2

Suppose that both the length and the area of K are bisected by $S[P,Q]$. If K is not a closed disk, there must be at least one boundary point R of K such that $\angle PRQ$ is not a right angle. Let A be the set bounded by $S[P,R]$ and Γ, and let B be the set bounded by $S[R,Q]$ and Γ. Rotate B about point R until $\angle PRQ$ is a right angle and reflect $M = A \cup B \cup \triangle PRQ$ about $L(P,Q)$ to obtain M'. The resulting set $M \cup M'$ has the same perimeter as K but has greater area.

The preceding proof was first presented by the Swiss mathematician Steiner. At first it was felt that it also solved the isoperimetric problem,

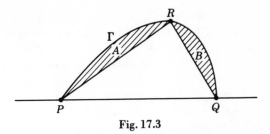

Fig. 17.3

but later the need to show the existence of a solution was recognized. For example, it is easy to see that of all triangles ABC with the same side $S[A,B]$ and with $L(C,A)$ perpendicular to $L(A,B)$, the ones which are not isosceles cannot have minimum area. However, this does not imply that the isosceles right triangle with side $S[A,B]$ has minimum area, since there is no such triangle with minimum area.

The existence of a solution to the isoperimetric problem in both 2- and 3-space will be proved by the use of symmetrization in Sec. 21. However, we will now give a solution for the plane case only with the aid of the following theorem.

17.2 Theorem Let Π be a simple closed polygon with length L and area A. Let Π' be the polygon circumscribed to the unit circle which has exactly the same unit exterior vectors normal to its faces as does Π. If A' is the area of Π' and r is the inradius of Π, then $Lr - A - A'r^2 \geq 0$.

PROOF Let Π_ϵ be the spherical neighborhood of Π with radius $-\epsilon$, $\epsilon > 0$ (see Definition 14.9). Π_r must be a line segment or a single point. For if Π_r were two-dimensional, then it would contain a neighborhood $N(P,\delta)$ and the circle with center P and radius $r + \delta$ would be contained in Π contrary to the choice of r. As we increase ϵ from 0 to r, the number of sides of Π_ϵ decreases until we reach a line segment or point (see Fig. 17.4a).

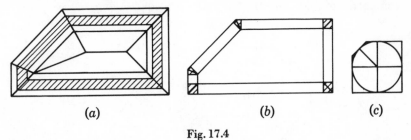

(a)   (b)   (c)

Fig. 17.4

Let Π_δ and Π_ϵ, $\delta < \epsilon$, be two neighborhoods of Π which have the same number of sides. If we use subscripts to indicate the quantities associated with these neighborhoods, and if $x = \epsilon - \delta$, then we have $r_\delta = r_\epsilon + x$ and $A'_\delta = A'_\epsilon$. If we decompose Π_δ and Π_ϵ as shown in Fig. 17.4b, then it follows that $A_\delta = A_\epsilon + L_\epsilon x + A'_\epsilon x^2$. Finally, if we compute the area of A'_ϵ according to Theorem 3.8, it also follows that $L_\delta = L_\epsilon + 2A'_\epsilon x$. Therefore $L_\epsilon r_\epsilon - A_\epsilon - A'_\epsilon r_\epsilon^2 = L_\delta r_\delta - A_\delta - A'_\delta r_\delta^2$ for any two neighborhoods with the same number of sides. As ϵ passes through a value for which the number of sides of Π_ϵ is decreased, A'_ϵ is always increased. Therefore $L_\epsilon r_\epsilon - A_\epsilon - A'_\epsilon r_\epsilon^2$ is monotone decreasing as ϵ goes from 0 to r. For $\epsilon = r$ we have $L_\epsilon r_\epsilon - A_\epsilon - A'_\epsilon r_\epsilon^2 = 0$. Therefore $Lr - A - A'r^2 \geq 0$, and our proof is complete.

We can rearrange the above formula to get $L^2 - 4A'A \geq (L - 2A'r)^2$. It follows that $L^2 - 4\pi A > L^2 - 4A'A \geq 0$ for any polygon. If Γ is any simple closed curve in the plane with length L and area A, we assert that $L^2 - 4\pi A \geq 0$. If Γ is a circle, then equality holds. Suppose Γ is not a circle, then it is possible to find an n-gon of length λ and area α arbitrarily close to L and A respectively. If $L^2 - 4\pi A < 0$, then it would follow that $\lambda^2 - 4\pi\alpha < 0$, contradicting the preceding theorem. Therefore $L^2 - 4\pi A \geq 0$. The equality cannot hold, since by Theorem 17.1 there is a curve Γ_1 with $L_1 = L$ and $A_1 > A$, and then $L^2 - 4\pi A > L_1^2 - 4\pi A_1 \geq 0$. This proves the existence of a solution to the isoperimetric problem.

17.3 Theorem Of all plane simple closed curves with the same length the circle, and only the circle, bounds the maximum area.

We conclude this section with a few consequences of Theorem 17.3.

17.4 Theorem Let $\Pi = P_0P_1 \cdots P_nP_0$ and $\Pi' = Q_0Q_1 \cdots Q_nQ_0$ be two polygonal regions. If Π is inscribed to a circle K and $|Q_iQ_{i+1}| = |P_iP_{i+1}|$ for $i = 0, \ldots, n$ then the area of Π is greater than the area of Π'.

PROOF We can assume that Π' is convex. Let C_i be the circular sector cut from K by $S[P_i,P_{i+1}]$ and let C'_i be directly congruent to C_i and positioned so that $S[Q_i,Q_{i+1}] = C'_i \cap \Pi'$. The set $K' = \bigcup_{i=0}^{n} C'_i \cup \Pi'$

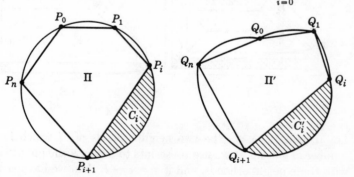

Fig. 17.5

has the same perimeter as K and therefore has smaller area. But the congruent circular sectors have equal areas, and it follows that the area of Π' is less than the area of Π.

17.5   Theorem   Of all n-gons with the same length the regular n-gon, and only the regular n-gon, has maximum area.

PROOF   Let Π be an n-gon of area A and let Π' be a regular n-gon of the same length L.

Suppose $\Pi = P_1 P_2 \cdots P_n P_1$ is not regular and suppose $S[P_1,P_2]$ is a side of smallest length. Let $S[P_k,P_{k+1}]$ be a side of largest length. If $S[P_{k-1},P_{k+1}]$ is not contained inside Π, replace P_k by its reflection about $L(P_{k-1},P_{k+1})$. If $k \neq 2$, replace P_k by its reflection about the perpendicular bisector of $S[P_{k-1},P_{k+1}]$ so that $S[P_{k-1},P_k]$ is now a largest side. Repeat the preceding two steps if necessary (first repeat it on $\triangle P_{k-2}P_{k-1}P_k$) until Π has area equal to or larger than A, a smallest side $S[A,B]$ is adjacent to a largest side $S[B,C]$, and $S[A,C]$ is contained inside Π.

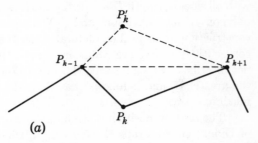

(a)

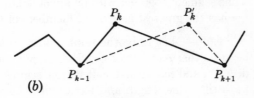

(b)

Fig. 17.6

Consider the set of all points P in the plane such that $|AP| + |PC| = |AB| + |BC|$. This is an ellipse E with foci A and B. Let B' lie on the same side of $L(A,C)$ as B so that $\triangle ABC$ is congruent to $\triangle AB'C$. As P traverses E through the smaller arc from B to B', because $|AP|$ is a continuous function of P, it must reach a position B'' for which $|AB''| = L/n$. The altitude of $\triangle AB''C$ dropped from B'' is greater than the altitude of $\triangle ABC$ dropped from B, therefore the area of $\triangle AB''C$ is greater than the

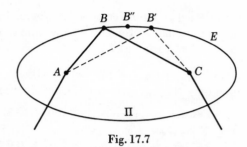

Fig. 17.7

area of $\triangle ABC$. If A, B, and C are collinear, we let B'' be the point on $S[A,C]$ such that $|AB''| = L/n$. If we replace B by B'', Π now has area equal to or greater than A, and $|AB| = L/n$.

If all sides are not of length L/n there must be at least one side smaller and one side larger than L/n. Repeat the whole process again on the smallest side so that Π has area equal to or greater than A and two sides have length equal to L/n. By repetition Π eventually becomes a polygon with all sides of length L/n. It follows from Theorem 17.4 that the regular polygon Π' has maximum area. We notice that in the last step of our construction to make Π equilateral either the area of Π is increased or three consecutive vertices are collinear. In the latter case Π is equilateral but not inscribed to a circle. By Theorem 17.4 the area of Π' is greater than the area of Π, and it follows that Π' is the only polygon of length L and maximum area.

The next proposition is often referred to as the solution to the problem of Dido. Given a rope of fixed length, what is the largest portion of land that can be enclosed by the rope and the straight edge of a seashore?

17.6   Theorem   If C is the class of all simple closed curves consisting of a line segment together with an arc of length l, then the semicircle of radius l/π has the greatest area of all members of C.

PROOF   Let K be the semicircular region with radius l/π, and let M be any other member of C. Reflect K about its diameter to get a closed disk K', and reflect M about its line segment to get a set M'. K' and M' have the same length and have twice the area of K and M respectively. Since area $M' < $ area K', it follows that area $M < $ area K.

Exercises

17.1   Let $\Pi = P_1P_2 \cdots P_nP_1$ be an n-gon and let $\overrightarrow{OU_i}$ be the unit exterior normal to edge $S[P_i,P_{i+1}]$. Using the notation of Theorem 17.2 show that $A' = \sum_{i=1}^{n} \tan(\alpha_i/2)$, where $\alpha_i = \angle U_iOU_{i+1}$.

17.2   Use Theorem 17.2 to prove that among all convex polygons of the same length which have the same unit normal exterior vectors to their edges the one circumscribed to a circle has the maximum area.

17.3   Let C be the class of all simple closed curves consisting of a line segment of length l and an arc of length l'. What members of C have the largest area?

17.4   Without using Theorem 17.5 prove that of all triangles with equal length the equilateral triangle has maximum area.

17.5   Show that among all triangles inscribed to a given circle the equilateral triangle has maximum area.

17.6   Use Exercise 17.5 to show that among all n-gons inscribed to a given circle the regular n-gon has the greatest area.

17.7   Show that among all triangles with the same base inscribed to a given circle the isosceles triangle has the greatest length. (Hint: Let $\triangle ABC$ and $\triangle ABC'$ be two such triangles and suppose $|AC| = |BC|$. Extend $S[B,C]$ to X so that $|BX| = |AC| + |BC|$, and extend $S[B,C']$ to X' so that $|BX'| = |BC'| + |C'A|$. Show that A, B, X, and X' lie on the same circle and that $S[B,X]$ is a diameter of this circle. Hence show that $|BX| > |BX'|$.)

17.8   Use Exercise 17.7 to show that among all triangles inscribed to a circle the equilateral triangle has the greatest length.

17.9   Use the method of proof suggested in Exercise 17.7 to show that if $\triangle ABC$ and $\triangle ABC'$ are inscribed to the same circle so that $\angle ACB = \angle AC'B$, then the length of $\triangle ABC$ is greater than the length of $\triangle ABC'$ if the distance from C to $L(A,B)$ is greater than the distance from C' to $L(A,B)$.

17.10   Use Exercise 17.9 to show that among all n-gons inscribed to a given circle the regular n-gon has the greatest length. (Hint: Follow the method of proof in Theorem 17.5.)

17.11   Let C be the class of all curves of a given length in the positive quadrant joining a point of the positive x axis to a point of the positive y axis. Which curves of C cut off a region of greatest area from the positive quadrant?

17.12   Generalize Exercise 17.11.

18   BLASCHKE'S SELECTION THEOREM

If we knew beforehand that a solution to the isoperimetric problem exists, then Theorem 17.1 would completely solve the problem. The solution of this and many other extremum problems would be greatly simplified if we had a simple procedure for showing the existence of a solution. The Blaschke selection theorem is a very powerful tool for setting up such a procedure. In order to present this theorem we will need to generalize the notion of the limit of a sequence of real numbers. The reader will recall the following theorem from the calculus.

18.1   Theorem   Every bounded infinite sequence of real numbers S contains a subsequence which converges to a limit.

PROOF   In order to simplify our discussion we assume that all the numbers of our sequence lie between 0 and 1. Consider the intervals $[0,.1]$, $[.1,.2]$, . . . , $[.9,1.0]$. At least one of these intervals must contain an infinite number of terms of S. Let $[.a_1,.(a_1 + 1)]$ be such an interval. Now divide $[.a_1,.(a_1 + 1)]$ into ten equal parts and let $[.a_1a_2,.a_1(a_2 + 1)]$ be an interval which contains infinitely many terms of S. Continue this procedure indefinitely to obtain the real number $r = .a_1a_2 \cdots a_n \cdots$. Now let S_{N_1} be a member of S such that $|S_{N_1} - r| \leq 1/2$. Let S_{N_2} be a member of $\{S_{N_1+1},\ S_{N_1+2},\ S_{N_1+3},\ \ldots\}$ such that $|S_{N_2} - r| \leq 1/2^2$. Repeat this procedure so that $S_{N_{(k+1)}}$ is a member of $\{S_{N_k+1},\ S_{N_k+2},\ S_{N_k+3},\ \ldots\}$ and $|S_{N_{(k+1)}} - r| \leq 1/2^{k+1}$. The sequence $\{S_{N_i}\}$ is a subsequence of S which converges to r.

We define the limit of a sequence of points in space so that the limit of a sequence of points on a line agrees with the limit of the corresponding sequence of real numbers.

18.2   Let $S = \{P_1,P_2,\ \ldots\ ,P_n,\ \ldots\}$ be an infinite sequence of points in space. If there is a point P such that given $\epsilon > 0$ there is a positive integer $N(\epsilon)$ such that $|PP_n| \leq \epsilon$ whenever $n \geq N(\epsilon)$, then we say that the **sequence S converges to the limit point** P.

18.3   Theorem   Every bounded infinite sequence of points S contains a subsequence which converges to a limit point.

PROOF   For convenience we assume that all the points of $S = \{P_1,P_2,\ \ldots\}$ lie in the cube spanned by three unit segments with one end at the origin and the other ends lying on the positive x, y, and z axes. Let P_i have coordinates (x_i,y_i,z_i). The sequence $\{x_i\}$ satisfies the hypotheses of Theorem 18.1. Therefore there is a subsequence $\{P_{i_j}\}$ and a real number x such that $x_{i_j} \rightharpoonup x$. In the same manner we can find a subsequence $\{P_{i_k}\}$ of the sequence $\{P_{i_j}\}$ and a real number y such that $y_{i_k} \rightharpoonup y$. By Exercise 18.1 we also have $x_{i_k} \rightharpoonup x$. Repeating this process on the z coordinates we obtain a subsequence $\{P_{i_l}\}$ of S such that $x_{i_l} \rightharpoonup x$, $y_{i_l} \rightharpoonup y$, and $z_{i_l} \rightharpoonup z$. But then if P has coordinates (x,y,z), given $\epsilon > 0$, we have $|PP_{i_l}| \leq |x - x_{i_l}| + |y - y_{i_l}| + |z - z_{i_l}| \leq \epsilon/3 + \epsilon/3 + \epsilon/3$, provided l is large enough. This completes our proof.

Convex bodies in some ways behave very much like points, and what we would like to do now is to define the limit set of a sequence of convex bodies. This can be done only if we have some measure of the "distance" between two sets.   We have already used the distance between two sets K_1 and K_2 as the inf $|P_1P_2|$, where $P_1 \varepsilon K_1$ and $P_2 \varepsilon K_2$.   This definition is unsatisfactory in many ways.   For example, a line segment tangent to a sphere has zero distance from the sphere.   Intuitively, however, we would like a definition of "distance" to imply that two sets close to each other will have each boundary point of one set close to a boundary point of the other.   The following definition is admirably suited for this purpose.

18.4   Let K_1 and K_2 be any two closed bounded sets in space. The **distance between K_1 and K_2** is defined to be $D(K_1,K_2) = \inf\{\epsilon \geq 0 | K_1 \subset N(K_2,\epsilon)$ and $K_2 \subset N(K_1,\epsilon)\}$.

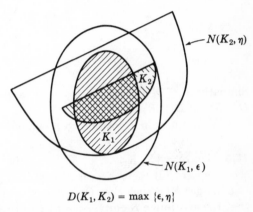

$$D(K_1, K_2) = \max\{\epsilon, \eta\}$$

Fig. 18.1

In anticipation of a later discussion of metric spaces (see Sec. 28), we prove the following properties of D.

18.5   Theorem   Let K be the class of all closed bounded sets in space. If A, B, and C are any three members of K, then

    a. $D(A,B) \geq 0$, where equality holds iff $A = B$,
    b. $D(A,B) = D(B,A)$,
    c. $D(A,B) \leq D(A,C) + D(C,B)$.

PROOF   Since A and B are bounded, there is a sphere of radius R which contains both A and B. $A \subset N(B,2R)$ and $B \subset N(A,2R)$, therefore $D(A,B)$ is well defined and $0 \leq D(A,B) \leq 2R$.   If $A = B$, then of course $D(A,B) = 0$.   Suppose that $D(A,B) = 0$.   Then since A and B are closed, $A \subset \bigcap_\epsilon N(B,\epsilon) = B$ and $B \subset A$, so that $A = B$.   This proves part (***a***).   Part (***b***) follows directly from the definition of D, so that it remains to prove part (c). Let $D(A,C) = \epsilon$ and $D(C,B) = \eta$, then $A \subset N(C,\epsilon)$, $C \subset N(A,\epsilon)$, $C \subset N(B,\eta)$, and $B \subset N(C,\eta)$. Since $C \subset N(B,\eta)$, we also have $N(C,\epsilon) \subset N(B,\epsilon + \eta)$. Therefore $A \subset N(C,\epsilon) \subset N(B,\epsilon + \eta)$.

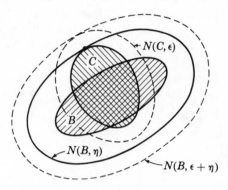

Fig. 18.2

Similarly $B \subset N(C,\eta) \subset N(A,\eta + \epsilon)$, and therefore $D(A,B) \leq \epsilon + \eta = D(A,C) + D(C,B)$.

We are now in a position to prove our main theorem.

18.6   Let $S = \{K_1,K_2, \ldots ,K_n, \ldots\}$ be a sequence of closed bounded sets in space. If there is a set K such that given $\epsilon > 0$ we can find a positive integer $N(\epsilon)$ such that $D(K,K_n) \leq \epsilon$ whenever $n \geq N(\epsilon)$, then we say that the **sequence S converges to the limit set K**.

18.7   Blaschke's selection theorem   Let $S = \{K_i\}$ be an infinite sequence of convex bodies which all lie in some fixed sphere. Then there is a subsequence of S which converges to a convex body K.

PROOF   Let C be a cube circumscribed to the fixed sphere and let x be the length of its edge. Let C_1 be the collection of eight congruent cubes, each with edge length $x/2$, obtained from C by passing planes through the center of C parallel to each face of C. Repeat the process for each cube of C_1 to partition C into 8^2 congruent cubes with edge length $x/2^2$. Continuing this procedure we arrive at a partition C_i of C consisting of 8^i congruent cubes each with edge length $x/2^i$. For each partition C_i we can form $2^{(8^i)} - 1$ different combinations of cubes.

For any fixed i there is exactly one maximum union of cubes for each member K of S such that each cube contains at least one point of K. Since the number of combinations of cubes is finite for fixed i and since the number of members of S is infinite, it follows that at least one combination of cubes of C_i is repeated infinitely often in this correspondence. Let $\{K_{1\nu}\}$ be a subsequence of S such that $K_{1\nu}$ all correspond to the same combination of cubes in C_1. Let $\{K_{2\nu}\}$ be a subsequence of $\{K_{1\nu}\}$ such that $K_{2\nu}$ all correspond to the same combination of cubes in C_2. In general let $\{K_{i\nu}\}$ be a subsequence of $\{K_{(i-1)\nu}\}$ such that $K_{i\nu}$ all correspond to the same combination of cubes in C_i.

Now for any fixed i we have $D(K_{i\nu},K_{i\mu}) \leq x\sqrt{3}/2^i$, since $K_{i\nu}$ and $K_{i\mu}$ correspond to the same combination of cubes in C_i. For $j \geq i$, $\{K_{j\nu}\}$ is a subsequence of $\{K_{i\nu}\}$, therefore $D(K_{j\nu},K_{i\mu}) \leq x\sqrt{3}/2^i$ for all $j \geq i$. Consider now the diagonal sequence $K_n = K_{nn}$. From what we have just shown it follows that $D(K_m,K_n) \leq x\sqrt{3}/2^n$ for all $m \geq n$. This means that given $\epsilon > 0$ there is an $N(\epsilon)$ such that $D(K_m,K_n) \leq \epsilon$ provided $m, n \geq N(\epsilon)$.

Consider an arbitrary sequence of points $\{P_i\}$ such that $P_i \, \epsilon \, K_i$ for $i = 1, 2, 3, \ldots$. According to Theorem 18.2 there is a subsequence $\{P_{i_j}\}$ which converges to some point P. We assert that the set K of all such points is a convex body and $\lim_{n \to \infty} K_n = K$. First we show that K is closed. Suppose P is a boundary point of K and let N be an arbitrary neighborhood of P. Since N contains a point Q of K, it follows that there is a neighborhood of Q contained in N and N contains points of infinitely many of the sets K_i. As in the proof of Theorem 18.1 we can construct a subsequence from these points which converges to P and $P \, \epsilon \, K$. Therefore K is closed. Next we show that K is convex. Suppose $\{P_{i_j}\}$ and $\{Q_{i_j}\}$ are two sequences such that $P_{i_j}, Q_{i_j} \, \epsilon \, K_{i_j}$ and $\lim_{i_j \to \infty} P_{i_j} = P$, $\lim_{i_j \to \infty} Q_{i_j} = Q$. Suppose there is a point R on $S[P,Q]$ which does not belong to K, and let $N(R,\delta)$ be a neighborhood of R which does not intersect K. Choose ϵ so small that every segment joining a point of $N(P,\epsilon)$ to a point of $N(Q,\epsilon)$ intersects $N(R,\delta/2)$. Then $S[P_{i_j},Q_{i_j}]$ intersects $N(R,\delta/2)$ for i_j large enough. But then $N(R,\delta)$ contains at least one point of K, giving a contradiction. Therefore $S[P,Q] \subset K$ and K is convex. It remains to show that $\lim_{n \to \infty} K_n = K$. To see this let $\epsilon > 0$ be given. We assert that there is an N such that $K_n \subset N(K,\epsilon)$ for all $n \geq N$. Suppose the converse; then infinitely many of the sets K_i each contain a point P_i such that $P_i \, \epsilon \, N(K,\epsilon)$. But then there is a subsequence $\{P_{i_j}\}$ which converges to a point outside of K. This is impossible. Therefore $K_n \subset N(K,\epsilon)$ for all n greater than some fixed N. On the other hand $K_m \subset N(K_n,\epsilon/2)$ for all $m \geq n$. If $P \, \epsilon \, K$, we then have $P \subset \bar{N}(K_n,\epsilon/2) \subset N(K_n,\epsilon)$. Therefore $K \subset N(K_n,\epsilon)$ for all n and $\lim_{n \to \infty} K_n = K$.

We now apply Blaschke's selection theorem to the following existence theorems.

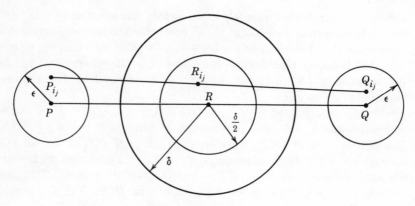

Fig. 18.3

18.8   Theorem   Of all spheres contained in a given three-dimensional convex body K there is at least one with maximum radius.

PROOF   Since K is a convex body, it is contained in some sphere S of radius R. Since K is three-dimensional, it contains at least one sphere. Let $\{r_\alpha\}$ be the set of all radii of spheres contained in K. Then sup r_α exists, and $r = \sup r_\alpha \leq R$. Now let B_i be a sequence of balls contained in K such that their radii r_i converge to r and their centers C_i converge to C. By Exercise 18.4 the ball B with radius r and center C is the limit of $\{B_i\}$.

We assert that $B \subset K$. Assume the contrary; then there is a point X on the boundary of B such that $X \notin K$ and $S(C,X)$ intersects the boundary of K in a point Y. Otherwise B would lie inside K. Let $\epsilon = |XY|/2$. Since $B_n \to B$, we can find a positive integer N such that $D(B_n,B) \leq \epsilon$ for

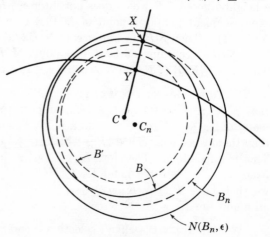

Fig. 18.4

all $n \geq N$.   Therefore $B \subset N(B_n,\epsilon)$.   If B' is the ball with center C and radius $r - \epsilon$, it follows that $B' \subset B_n$.   But then B_n intersects ray $R[C,X)$ in a point outside of K, contradicting the choice of B_n.

In the next section we shall prove that Theorem 14.12 holds not only for polygonal regions but for any plane convex body.   We use this to show the following.

18.9   Theorem   If K_1 and K_2 are plane convex bodies such that $D(K_1,K_2)$ $\leq \epsilon$, and if L_i, A_i are the length and area of K_i, than $|L_2 - L_1| \leq 2\pi\epsilon$ and $|A_2 - A_1| \leq \epsilon \max (L_1,L_2) + \pi\epsilon^2$.   Consequently if $\{K_i\}$ is a sequence of plane convex bodies such that $K_i \rightharpoonup K$, then $L_i \rightharpoonup L$ and $A_i \rightharpoonup A$, where L and A are the length and area of K.

PROOF   Since $D(K_1,K_2) \leq \epsilon$, we have that $K_1 \subset N(K_2,\epsilon)$.   From Theorem 14.12 for arbitrary convex bodies it follows that $L_1 \leq L_2 + 2\pi\epsilon$ and $A_1 \leq A_2 + L_2\epsilon + \pi\epsilon^2$.   Similarly $K_2 \subset N(K_1,\epsilon)$, $L_2 \leq L_1 + 2\pi\epsilon$, and $A_2 \leq A_1 + L_1\epsilon + \pi\epsilon^2$.   Therefore $|L_1 - L_2| \leq 2\pi\epsilon$ and $|A_1 - A_2| \leq \epsilon \max (L_1,L_2) + \pi\epsilon^2$.

18.10   Theorem   Among all plane convex bodies with the same length l there exists at least one with maximum area.

PROOF   Let S be a circle with radius l and center O.   Let C be the class of all convex bodies with length l.   If $K \varepsilon C$ and $S(A,B)$ is a diameter of K, then translate K to K' so that A is mapped onto O.   Let C' be the class of all such sets K'.   Then every member of C' is contained in S and every member of C has a congruent image in C'.   If $K'_\alpha \varepsilon C'$, let A_α be its area and let $A = \sup A_\alpha$. A exists, since A_α are all bounded above by the area of S.   Pick a sequence $\{A_i\}$ such that $A_i \rightharpoonup A$, then use the selection theorem to pick a subsequence $\{A_j\}$ such that $K'_j \rightharpoonup K$ and $A_j \rightharpoonup A$.   By Theorem 18.9 $A(K'_j) \rightharpoonup A(K)$ and $L(K'_j) \rightharpoonup L(K)$.   Therefore $A(K) = A$ and $L(K) = l$, and we have finished.

Exercises

18.1   Prove that every subsequence of a convergent sequence S of points in space converges to the limit point of S.

18.2   Prove that $D(K_1,K_2) = D[N(K_1,\epsilon), N(K_2,\epsilon)]$.

18.3   Give an example of three closed bounded sets A, B, and C with $A \subset B \subset C$ having the property that $A \neq B \neq C$ and $D(A,B) = D(B,C) = D(A,C)$.

18.4   If $\{r_i\}$ is a sequence of positive real numbers and $\{P_i\}$ is a sequence of points such that $r_i \rightharpoonup r$ and $P_i \rightharpoonup P$, prove that $B_i \rightharpoonup B$, where B_i is the ball with center P_i and radius r_i and B is the ball with center P and radius r.

18.5 Prove that among all spheres enclosing a given convex body there is a smallest.

18.6 Prove Helly's theorem for an infinite sequence of convex bodies $K_1, K_2, \ldots,$ $K_n, \ldots$ all lying in a fixed sphere. (Hint: For any $n \geq 4$, Helly's theorem for a finite number of sets can be used to pick a point $P_n \in \bigcap\limits_{i=1}^{n} K_i$. Let P be an accumulation point of $\{P_n\}$ and show that $P \in \bigcap\limits_{i=1}^{\infty} K_i$.)

18.7 Prove Helly's theorem for an infinite sequence of closed convex sets at least one of which is bounded.

18.8 If an infinite number of convex bodies K_α all lie in a given sphere, show that given $\epsilon > 0$ there is a finite number of these sets $K_{\alpha 1}, \ldots, K_{\alpha k}$ such that any set K_α is a distance less than ϵ from at least one of the sets $K_{\alpha i}$, $i = 1$, $\ldots, k$.

18.9 Give examples to show that the limit of a convergent sequence of three-dimensional convex bodies may be three-dimensional, two-dimensional, or a single point.

18.10 Show that for any plane convex body K, given $\epsilon > 0$, there are polygonal regions Π_1 and Π_2 such that $\Pi_1 \subset K \subset \Pi_2$ and $D(\Pi_1, \Pi_2) < \epsilon$. Hence show that K is the limit of a sequence of polygonal regions.

18.11 Generalize Exercise 18.10 to 3-space.

18.12 Show that whenever convex bodies $K_n \rightharpoonup K$ and $L_n \rightharpoonup L$, then $(K_n + L_n) \rightharpoonup (K + L)$.

18.13 Let K_1 and K_2 be convex bodies. If $\epsilon_1 = \inf\{\epsilon \geq 0 | K_2 \subset N(K_1, \epsilon)\}$ and $\epsilon_2 = \inf\{\epsilon \geq 0 | K_1 \subset N(K_2, \epsilon)\}$, show that $\Delta(K_1, K_2) = \epsilon_1 + \epsilon_2$ possesses all three properties stated in Theorem 18.5.

18.14 Referring to Exercise 18.13, show that $\lim\limits_{n \to \infty} D(K_n, K) = 0$ iff $\lim\limits_{n \to \infty} \Delta(K_n, K) = 0$.

18.15 Let K_1 and K_2 be convex bodies. For any point X and closed bounded set K let $\delta(X, K) = \inf\{|XY| \,|\, Y \in K\}$. Show that $\rho(K_1, K_2) = \sup |\delta(X, K_1) - \delta(X, K_2)|$ possesses all three properties stated in Theorem 18.5.

18.16 Referring to Exercise 18.15, show that $\rho(K_1, K_2) = D(K_1, K_2)$.

19 SURFACE AREA AND MIXED VOLUMES

Let us now turn our attention to the isoperimetric problem in space. Of all closed surfaces with the same surface area which one (or ones) encloses the greatest volume? Immediately we are faced with the problem of giving a general definition of surface area. This we now proceed to discuss. Throughout this section we let $V(K)$, $A(K)$, and $L(K)$ stand for the Jordan two- or three-dimensional measure, surface area, and length of a set K, and we let B_r stand for the ball with radius r.

Consider the following formula taken from Theorem 14.12.

19.1 $V(K + B_r) = V(K) + L(K)r + \pi r^2$

If we solve this equation for $L(K)$ and take the limit as $r \to +0$, we get
$L(K) = \lim_{r \to +0} [V(K + B_r) - V(K)]/r$.

We notice that $L(K)$ is determined entirely by areas of plane sets. We can generalize this expression to define surface area in terms of volume.

19.2   If K is a three-dimensional convex body, then we define its **surface area** as $A(K) = \lim_{r \to +0} [V(K + B_r) - V(K)]/r$.

It is noteworthy that this definition agrees with the usual high school definition of surface area described in Sec. 4. We already know that the length of a plane convex body always exists (see Theorem 7.12). We would like to show now that the surface area of a convex body in space always exists. In order to do this we shall find it convenient to introduce the idea of mixed volumes and linear arrays.

If we turn again to Eq. 19.1 and let r vary from 0 to 1, there is a nice geometric way of displaying the bodies $K + B_r$. Given a fixed coordinate

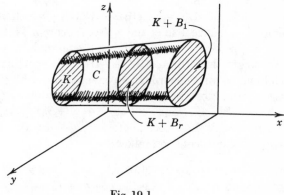

Fig. 19.1

system in 3-space, let K lie in the plane $x = 0$ and let $K + B_1$ be translated to the plane $x = 1$. Let C be the convex cover of K and $K + B_1$ and let π_r be the plane $x = r$. Then $C \cap \pi_r = (1 - r)K + r(K + B_1) = K + B_r$. Instead of taking cross sections of a three-dimensional convex body to get plane convex bodies we reverse the process and build up an array of plane convex bodies to form a three-dimensional convex body. We generalize this as follows.

19.3 Let A and B be any two convex bodies and let r be any number between 0 and 1. We call the collection of sets $C_r = rA + (1 - r)B$ a **linear array,** where rK is the homothetic image of K with ratio r and center at the origin.

As above if A and B lie in parallel planes a unit distance apart, then C_r is the intersection of the convex cover of A and B with the plane $1 - r$ units from A and r units from B.

We now proceed to a discussion of mixed volumes. In terms of linear arrays Eq. 19.1 expresses the volume of a member C_r of a linear array as a polynomial in r. In the following we see that this holds not only for the linear array of a convex set K and the set $K + B_1$ but for any linear array. The coefficients of this polynomial, called mixed volumes, each have geometric meanings which we shall investigate.

19.4   Theorem   Let $\Pi_{r_1} = r_1\Pi_1 + r_2\Pi_2$, where $r_1 = 1 - r_2$, $0 \leq r_1 \leq 1$, and Π_1, Π_2 are convex polyhedral regions lying in n-space, $n = 1, 2, 3$. Then $V(\Pi_{r_1})$ is a homogeneous polynomial of degree n in the variables r_1 and r_2.

PROOF Suppose $n = 1$. Then Π_1 and Π_2 are segments $S[P_1,Q_1]$ and $S[P_2,Q_2]$ lying on a line l. Translate $S[P_1,Q_1]$ and $S[P_2,Q_2]$ along l so that $P_1 = P_2 = O$ and Q_2 lies on the ray $R[O,Q_1]$. $\Pi_{r_1} = r_1\Pi_1 + r_2\Pi_2$ is a segment, and $V(\Pi_{r_1}) = r_1V(\Pi_1) + r_2V(\Pi_2)$, which is a homogeneous polynomial of degree 1 in r_1 and r_2 (see Theorem 14.2 and Exercise 14.12).

Suppose $n = 2$ and let K^l be the normal projection of K onto a line l. We assert that $\Pi_{r_1}^l = r_1\Pi_1^l + r_2\Pi_2^l$. To see this let $P_1 \varepsilon \Pi_1$ and $P_2 \varepsilon \Pi_2$, and choose an xy coordinate system so that the equation of l is $y = 0$, P_1 has coordinates (x_1,y_1), and P_2 has coordinates (x_2,y_2). The point $P = r_1P_1 + r_2P_2 \varepsilon \Pi_{r_1}$ and $r_1(x_1,y_1) + r_2(x_2,y_2) = (r_1x_1 + r_2x_2, r_1y_1 + r_2y_2)$. Therefore P^l has coordinates $(r_1x_1 + r_2x_2, 0)$. Therefore $P^l = r_1P_1^l + r_2P_2^l$, and our assertion follows.

Now let $\overrightarrow{OU_i}$ be the unit exterior normal to the edge F^i, $i = 1, \ldots, k$, of Π_{r_1} and let F_1^i, F_2^i be the edges of Π_1 and Π_2 respectively which have $\overrightarrow{OU_i}$ for unit exterior normal. These may degenerate to a single point. Also let $H(U)$, $H_1(U)$, and $H_2(U)$ be the support function of Π_{r_1}, Π_1, and Π_2 respectively. If we write the formula for area given in Theorem 3.8 using the preceding notation we get

19.5 $V(\Pi_{r_1}) = \dfrac{1}{2} \sum\limits_{i=1}^{k} H(U_i)|F^i|$

where $|S|$ stands for the length of edge S. If we project $F_1{}^i$ and $F_2{}^i$ onto the line containing F^i, it follows from Theorem 14.7 and the first part of the proof that $|F^i| = r_1|F_1{}^i| + r_2|F_2{}^i|$. In addition it is a consequence of the definition of support function, Theorem 14.2 and Theorem 14.7, that $H(U_i) = r_1H_1(U_i) + r_2H_2(U_i)$. Therefore

19.6 $V(\Pi_{r_1}) = \dfrac{1}{2} \sum\limits_{i=1}^{k} [r_1H_1(U_i) + r_2H_2(U_i)](r_1|F_1{}^i| + r_2|F_2{}^i|)$

which is a homogeneous polynomial of degree 2 in the variables r_1 and r_2.

Consider now the case $n = 3$. Exactly as for $n = 2$ it can be shown that $\Pi_{r_1}{}^\sigma = r_1\Pi_1{}^\sigma + r_2\Pi_2{}^\sigma$ for projections onto a plane σ. Let F^i, $F_1{}^i$, $F_2{}^i$ be the faces of Π_{r_1}, Π_1, Π_2 which have unit exterior normals U_i, and let $H(U)$, $H_1(U)$, $H_2(U)$ be the support functions of Π_{r_1}, Π_1, and Π_2 respectively. If we write the formula for volume given in Theorem 4.5 using the preceding notation, we get

19.7 $V(\Pi_{r_1}) = \dfrac{1}{3} \sum\limits_{i=1}^{k} H(U_i)|F^i|$

where $|S|$ is the two-dimensional Jordan measure of set S. Since $F^i = r_1F_1{}^i + r_2F_2{}^i$, it follows that $|F^i|$ is a homogeneous polynomial of degree 2 in r_1 and r_2, and since $H(U_i) = r_1H(U_i) + r_2H_2(U_i)$, it follows that $V(\Pi_n)$ is a homogeneous polynomial of degree 3 in the variables r_1 and r_2. This completes the proof.

We are now in a position to define mixed volumes for polyhedral regions.

19.8 Let Π_1 and Π_2 be polyhedral regions in n-space.

a. If $n = 2$, we have $V(r_1\Pi_1 + r_2\Pi_2) = ar_1{}^2 + br_1r_2 + cr_2{}^2$. Put $V(\Pi_1,\Pi_1) = a$, $V(\Pi_1,\Pi_2) = V(\Pi_2,\Pi_1) = b/2$, and $V(\Pi_2,\Pi_2) = c$. We call $V(\Pi_i,\Pi_j)$ the **mixed volumes** of the linear array $r_1\Pi_1 + r_2\Pi_2$.

b. If $n = 3$, we have $V(r_1\Pi_1 + r_2\Pi_2) = ar_1{}^3 + br_1{}^2r_2 + cr_1r_2{}^2 + dr_2{}^3$. Put $V(\Pi_1,\Pi_1,\Pi_1) = a$, $V(\Pi_1,\Pi_1,\Pi_2) = V(\Pi_1,\Pi_2,\Pi_1) = V(\Pi_2,\Pi_1,\Pi_1) = b/3$, $V(\Pi_1,\Pi_2,\Pi_2) = V(\Pi_2,\Pi_1,\Pi_2) = V(\Pi_2,\Pi_2,\Pi_1) = c/3$, and finally $V(\Pi_2,\Pi_2,\Pi_2) = d$. We call $V(\Pi_i,\Pi_j,\Pi_l)$ the **mixed volumes** of the linear array $r_1\Pi_1 + r_2\Pi_2$.

It is conceivable that $V(\Pi_n)$ could be expressed as either of two distinct homogeneous polynomials so that

$$V(\Pi_n) = (a - b + c - d)r_1{}^3 + (b - 2c + 3d)r_1{}^2 + (c - 3d)r_1 + d$$
$$= (a' - b' + c' - d')r_1{}^3 + (b' - 2c' + 3d')r_1{}^2 + (c' - 3d')r_1 + d'$$

But then from the identity theorem for polynomials we have $d = d'$, $c = c'$, $b = b'$, and $a = a'$. It follows that mixed volumes are uniquely defined for polyhedral regions. In addition, if either Π_1 or Π_2 is translated, Π_{r_i} is subjected to a translation and $V(\Pi_{r_i})$ remains unchanged. As above, it follows from the identity theorem for polynomials that the homogeneous polynomial expression for $V(\Pi_{r_i})$ remains unchanged. Therefore the mixed volumes of Π_{r_i} are also unchanged. The following two theorems give us upper and lower bounds for the mixed volumes of a linear array.

19.9   Theorem $V(\Pi_{i_1},\Pi_{i_2},\Pi_{i_3})$ and $V(\Pi_{i_1},\Pi_{i_2})$ are all nonnegative.

PROOF   Translate Π_1 and Π_2 so that they both contain the origin, and consider Eq. 19.6. $|F_j{}^i|$ are positive or zero. The support functions are all nonnegative since Π_1 and Π_2 contain the origin. Therefore all the coefficients of the rs are nonnegative, and by definition the mixed volumes are nonnegative for $n = 2$. For $n = 3$ consider Eq. 19.7. We have just shown that $|F^i|$ is a homogeneous polynomial in r_1 and r_2 with nonnegative coefficients. Since the support functions are nonnegative, it follows that the mixed volumes are nonnegative.

19.10   Theorem   Let K be a convex body such that $\Pi_1 \subset K$ and $\Pi_2 \subset K$. Then $V(\Pi_{i_1},\Pi_{i_2},\Pi_{i_3}) \leq 8V(K)$ and $V(\Pi_{i_1},\Pi_{i_2}) \leq 4V(K)$.

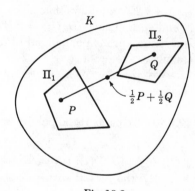

Fig. 19.2

PROOF   Since Π_1 and Π_2 are both contained in K, it follows that $\frac{1}{2}\Pi_1 + \frac{1}{2}\Pi_2 \subset K$. Now if $n = 2$, we have $\frac{1}{2} \times \frac{1}{2}V(\Pi_{i_1},\Pi_{i_2}) \leq V(\frac{1}{2}\Pi_1 + \frac{1}{2}\Pi_2) \leq V(K)$, since the left term is one member of the expansion of the middle expression.

Similarly for $n = 3$ we have $\frac{1}{2} \times \frac{1}{2} \times \frac{1}{2} V(\Pi_{i_1},\Pi_{i_2},\Pi_{i_3}) \leq V(\frac{1}{2}\Pi_1 + \frac{1}{2}\Pi_2) \leq V(K)$.

19.11   Theorem   If $\{K_n\}$ is a sequence of convex bodies and $\lim_{n \to \infty} K_n = K$, then $\lim_{n \to \infty} V(K_n) = V(K)$.

PROOF   Suppose K has an interior point (which we choose to be the origin) and let r be the radius of a sphere with center at the origin which lies in K. We assert that $[1 - (\epsilon/r)]K \subset K_n \subset [1 + (\epsilon/r)]K$ whenever $D(K_n,K) \leq \epsilon < r$. To see this, let B_s be the ball with center at the origin and radius s. Then $B_r \subset K$ implies $\epsilon B_r/r = B_\epsilon \subset \epsilon K/r$, and we have $K_n \subset K + B_\epsilon \subset K + \epsilon K/r = [1 + (\epsilon/r)]K$. Similarly $K \subset K_n + B_\epsilon \subset [1 + (\epsilon/r)]K_n$. Therefore $[1 - (\epsilon/r)]K \subset K/[1 + (\epsilon/r)] \subset K_n$, provided $\epsilon < r$. It follows that $[1 - (\epsilon/r)]^3 V(K) \leq V(K_n) \leq [1 + (\epsilon/r)]^3 V(K)$ for n large enough. Therefore $\lim_{n \to \infty} V(K_n) = V(K)$.

Suppose that K has no interior points. Then K must lie entirely in a plane and K lies in some disk C with radius R. If K contains the origin, then for large n we have $K_n \subset K + B_\epsilon \subset C + B_\epsilon$ and $0 \leq V(K_n) \leq 2\epsilon\pi(R + 2\epsilon)^2$. Therefore $\lim_{n \to \infty} V(K_n) = 0 = V(K)$, and our proof is complete.

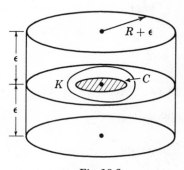

Fig. 19.3

19.12   Theorem   Let $K_{r_1} = r_1 K_1 + r_2 K_2$ be a linear array where K_1 and K_2 are arbitrary convex bodies in n-space, $n = 1, 2,$ or 3. Then $V(K_{r_1})$ is a homogeneous polynomial of degree n in r_1 and r_2 with nonnegative coefficients. $V(K_i,K_j,K_l)$ or $V(K_i,K_j)$ are defined as in Definition 19.8 and are called the **mixed volumes** of the linear array $r_1 K_1 + r_2 K_2$.

PROOF   We shall prove the theorem for $n = 2$. The proof for $n = 3$ follows the same pattern. Let $\{\Pi_1{}^\nu\}$ be a sequence of polygonal regions that converges to K_1, and let $\{\Pi_2{}^\nu\}$ be a sequence of polygonal regions that converges to K_2 (see Exercise 18.10). We can assume that all $\Pi_i{}^\nu$ are contained in a convex body M. Then $V(r_1 \Pi_1{}^\nu + r_2 \Pi_2{}^\nu) = \sum_{i,j=1}^{2} V(\Pi_{i_1}{}^\nu, \Pi_{i_2}{}^\nu) r_{i_1} r_{i_2}$. By Theorems 19.9 and 19.10 we have $0 \leq V(\Pi_{i_1}{}^\nu, \Pi_{i_2}{}^\nu) \leq 4V(M)$. For a fixed pair i_1 and i_2 pick a subsequence of $V(\Pi_{i_1}{}^\nu, \Pi_{i_2}{}^\nu)$ which converges. For a second pair j_1 and j_2 pick a subsequence of the first one such that $V(\Pi_{j_1}{}^\mu, \Pi_{j_2}{}^\mu)$ converges. Continue this process until we arrive at a subsequence such that $V(\Pi_{i_1}{}^\mu, \Pi_{i_2}{}^\mu) \to V(K_{i_1}, K_{i_2})$ for all combinations of i_1 and i_2. We notice that $V(K_{i_1}, K_{i_2}) \geq 0$, since $V(\Pi_{i_1}{}^\mu, \Pi_{i_2}{}^\mu) \geq 0$. Since a polynomial is a continuous function of its coefficients, we also have $V(r_1\Pi_1{}^\mu + r_2\Pi_2{}^\mu) \to \sum\limits_{ij=1}^{2} V(K_{i_1}, K_{i_2}) r_{i_1} r_{i_2}$. But it follows from Exercise 18.12 and Theorem 19.11 that $V(r_1\Pi_1{}^\mu + r_2\Pi_2{}^\mu) \to V(r_1 K_1 + r_2 K_2)$. Therefore $V(r_1 K_1 + r_2 K_2) = \sum\limits_{ij=1}^{2} V(K_{i_1}, K_{i_2}) r_{i_1} r_{i_2}$, and we have finished.

We now consider the geometric interpretation of mixed volumes.

19.13 Theorem In 3-space $V(K,K,K)$ is the three-dimensional Jordan measure of K, and in 2-space $V(K,K)$ is the two-dimensional Jordan measure of K.

PROOF For $n = 3$ let $r_1 = 1$, $r_2 = 0$, and $K_1 = K$ in the expression $V(r_1 K_1 + r_2 K_2) = \sum\limits_{ij=1}^{2} V(K_{i_1}, K_{i_2}, K_{i_3}) r_{i_1} r_{i_2} r_{i_3}$. A similar proof holds for $n = 2$.

19.14 Theorem In 3-space $3V(K,K,L) = \lim\limits_{\epsilon \to +0} [V(K + \epsilon L) - V(K)]/\epsilon$, and in 2-space $2V(K,L) = \lim\limits_{\epsilon \to +0} [V(K + \epsilon L) - V(K)]/\epsilon$.

PROOF Suppose $n = 3$; then $r_1{}^3 V[K + (r_2/r_1)L] = V(r_1 K + r_2 L) = V(K) r_1{}^3 + 3V(K,K,L) r_1{}^2 r_2 + 3V(K,L,L) r_1 r_2{}^2 + V(L) r_2{}^3$. Divide through by $r_1{}^3$ and let $\epsilon = r_2/r_1$. Then $V(K + \epsilon L) - V(K) = 3V(K,K,L)\epsilon + 3V(K,L,L)\epsilon^2 + V(L)\epsilon^3$. Divide both sides by ϵ, take the limit as $\epsilon \to +0$, and we get the desired result. The proof for $n = 2$ is similar.

19.15 Theorem Let K be a convex body with support function $H(U)$ and let Π be a convex polyhedral region with faces F_i and corresponding unit exterior normals $\overrightarrow{OU_i}$, $i = 1, \ldots, k$. Then $3V(K,\Pi,\Pi) = \sum\limits_{i=1}^{k} H(U_i)|F_i|$, where $|S|$ is the two-dimensional Jordan measure of set S.

PROOF. Assume K contains the origin. From Theorem 19.14 we have $3V(K,\Pi,\Pi) = 3V(\Pi,\Pi,K) = \lim\limits_{\epsilon \to +0} [V(\Pi + \epsilon K) - V(\Pi)]/\epsilon$. Now let X_i be a point of K which lies on the supporting plane of K with exterior

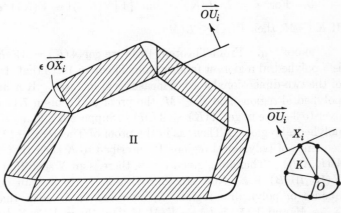

Fig. 19.4

normal $\overrightarrow{OU_i}$. Using $S[0,\epsilon X_i]$ as generator we can construct a prism on the face F_i of Π (see Fig. 19.4). It follows that $\Pi + \epsilon K$ can be decomposed into Π, a set of prisms with F_i as bases, a set of triangular prisms with the edges S_i of Π as lateral edges, and a set of corner pieces with the vertices P_i of Π as corners (see Theorems 15.12 and 15.13). If we translate each corner piece so that P_i is mapped onto the origin O, then the union of their images is congruent to ϵK and lies inside the sphere with center O and radius ϵ times the diameter d of K. Also if the base of each triangular prism is similarly translated, its image lies inside the same sphere. It follows that

$$V(\Pi + \epsilon K) = V(\Pi) + \left[\sum_{i=1}^{k} H(U_i)|F_i| \right]\epsilon + \sum_{i=1}^{n} \alpha_i|S_i|\epsilon^2 + \theta\frac{4}{3}\pi d^3\epsilon^3, \quad \text{where}$$

θ and the α_i are constants. Dividing by ϵ and passing to the limit we get the desired result.

The theorem just proved justifies the name "mixed volumes" for polyhedral regions. For we are "mixing" the support function of K with the faces of Π in the usual formula for the volume of a polyhedral region.

Even without the many other useful properties of mixed volumes the preceding work on mixed volumes is made worthwhile because of the following theorem.

19.16 Theorem Let B be the closed n-dimensional ball with unit radius and let K and M be any two n-dimensional convex bodies.

a. For $n = 3$, $A(K) = \lim_{\epsilon \to 0+} \{V[N(K,\epsilon)] - V(K)\}/\epsilon = 3V(K,K,B)$. If $K \subset M$, then $A(K) \leq A(M)$.

b. For $n = 2$, $L(K) = \lim_{\epsilon \to 0+} \{V[N(K,\epsilon)] - V(K)\}/\epsilon = 2V(K,B)$. If $K \subset M$, then $L(K) \le L(M)$.

PROOF   **a.** From Theorem 19.14 we get $A(K) = 3V(K,K,B)$. If K is a polyhedral region, it follows from Theorem 19.15 that $A(K)$ is the sum of the two-dimensional Jordan measures of its faces. If K and M are both polyhedral regions and $K \subset M$, the proof of Theorem 7.11 can be carried over to 3-space to get $A(K) \le A(M)$. Suppose K and M, $K \subset M$, are not polyhedral regions. Then, as in the proof of Theorem 19.12, we can find a sequence of polyhedral regions Π_i inscribed to K such that $V(\Pi_i, \Pi_i, B) \to V(K,K,B)$. Therefore, given $\epsilon > 0$, there is an N such that $V(K,K,B) \le V(\Pi_N, \Pi_N, B) + \epsilon$. Now starting with $\Sigma_0 = \Pi_N$ we can construct a sequence of polyhedral regions Σ_i inscribed to M such that $\Sigma_i \subset \Sigma_{i+1}$, $\Sigma_i \to M$ and $V(\Sigma_i, \Sigma_i, B) \to V(M,M,B)$. Since $V(\Sigma_i, \Sigma_i, B)$ is a monotone nondecreasing sequence, we have $V(\Pi_N, \Pi_N, B) \le V(M,M,B)$ and $V(K,K,B) \le V(M,M,B) + \epsilon$. Since $\epsilon > 0$ is arbitrary, we have $V(K,K,B) \le V(M,M,B)$.

b. Theorem 7.12 tells us that $L(K) \le L(M)$ whenever $K \subset M$. It remains to show that $L(K) = 2V(K,B)$. If K is a polygonal region, the desired result follows from the two-dimensional analog to Theorem 19.15. Let Π_i be polygonal regions inscribed to convex body K such that $\Pi_i \to K$ and $L(\Pi_i) = 2V(\Pi_i, B) \to L(K)$. As in the proof of Theorem 19.12 we can find a subsequence $V(\Pi_{i_j}, B)$ converging to $V(K,B)$. But $V(\Pi_{i_j}, B)$ also converges to $L(K)/2$. Therefore $2V(K,B) = L(K)$, and we have finished.

We note that we have already shown that mixed volumes exist for any linear array, therefore this theorem asserts the existence of surface area for any convex body.

We conclude this section by showing the existence of a solution to the isoperimetric problem in 3-space.

19.17   Theorem   Suppose $\{K_1{}^i\}$ and $\{K_2{}^i\}$ are sequences of convex bodies such that $K_1{}^i \to K_1$ and $K_2{}^i \to K_2$. Then $V(K_{j_1}{}^i, K_{j_2}{}^i, K_{j_3}{}^i) \to V(K_{j_1}, K_{j_2}, K_{j_3})$, where $j_k = 1$ or 2.

PROOF   From Exercise 18.12 we have $r_1 K_1{}^i + r_2 K_2{}^i \to r_1 K_1 + r_2 K_2$. Therefore $V(r_1 K_1{}^i + r_2 K_2{}^i) \to V(r_1 K_1 + r_2 K_2)$ and

$$\sum_{j_k=1}^{2} V(K_{j_1}{}^i, K_{j_2}{}^i, K_{j_3}{}^i) r_{j_1} r_{j_2} r_{j_3} \to \sum_{j_k=1}^{2} V(K_{j_1}, K_{j_2}, K_{j_3}) r_{j_1} r_{j_2} r_{j_3}$$

Considered as polynomials in r_1 this can be written as

$$(a_i r_1{}^3 + b_i r_1{}^2 + c_i r_1 + d_i) \to (a r_1{}^3 + b r_1{}^2 + c r_1 + d)$$

for each r_1, $0 \leq r_1 \leq 1$. But then when $r_1 = 0$, we have $d_i \rightharpoonup d$. Therefore $(a_i r_1^3 + b_i r_1^2 + c_i r_1) \rightharpoonup (a r_1^3 + b r_1^2 + c r_1)$, and $(a_i r_1^2 + b_i r_1 + c_i) \rightharpoonup (a r_1^2 + b r_1 + c)$ for each r, $0 < r \leq 1$. It follows that $c_i \rightharpoonup c$. In like manner we get $b_i \rightharpoonup b$ and $a_i \rightharpoonup a$. Now

$$V(K_2{}^i, K_2{}^i, K_2{}^i) = d_i \rightharpoonup V(K_2, K_2, K_2) = d$$

Further, $c_i = V(K_1{}^i, K_2{}^i, K_2{}^i) - 3V(K_2{}^i, K_2{}^i, K_2{}^i) \rightharpoonup c = V(K_1, K_2, K_2) - 3V(K_2, K_2, K_2)$. Therefore $V(K_1{}^i, K_2{}^i, K_2{}^i) \rightharpoonup V(K_1, K_2, K_2)$. Similarly we get $V(K_{j_1}{}^i, K_{j_2}{}^i, K_{j_3}{}^i) \rightharpoonup V(K_{j_1}, K_{j_2}, K_{j_3})$ for all $j_k = 1$ or 2.

19.18 Theorem   Among all convex bodies with the same surface area there exists at least one with maximum volume.

PROOF.   If we use Theorem 19.17 to show that $A(K_i) \rightharpoonup A(K)$ when $K_i \rightharpoonup K$, the proof follows the same pattern as the proof of Theorem 18.10.

Exercises

19.1   Let K_r be a convex body lying in the plane $x = r$, $0 \leq r \leq 1$. If $(1 - r)K_0 + rK_1 \subset K_r$, we call K_r a **concave array**.   (a) Show that every linear array is a concave array.   (b) Show that the intersections of a three-dimensional convex body with the planes $x = r$, $0 \leq r \leq 1$, form a concave array.

19.2   If $H_1(U)$, $H_2(U)$, and $H(U)$ are the support functions of convex bodies K_1, K_2 and $r_1 K_1 + r_2 K_2$ respectively, show that $H(U) = r_1 H_1(U) + r_2 H_2(U)$.

19.3   Let K^σ be the projection of convex body K onto plane σ. Show that $(r_1 K_1 + r_2 K_2)^\sigma = r_1 K_1{}^\sigma + r_2 K_2{}^\sigma$.

19.4   Using the terminology of Exercises 19.1 and 19.3 show that $(r_1 K_1 + r_2 K_2)^\sigma \supset r_1 K_1{}^\sigma + r_2 K_2{}^\sigma$ if $K_{r_1} = r_1 K_1 + r_2 K_2$ is a concave array. Prove a similar proposition for projections onto a line.

19.5   Prove Theorem 19.12 for $n = 3$.

19.6   Show that the definition of mixed volumes given in Theorem 19.12 is independent of the sequences used.   (Hint: See the discussion following Definition 19.8.)

19.7   Show that the mixed volumes of the linear array $r_1 K_1 + r_2 K_2$ are not changed if either K_1 or K_2 is subjected to a translation.

19.8   Show that in 3-space $V(K + M, N, N) = V(K, N, N) + V(M, N, N)$, and prove a similar result in the plane.   (Hint: First let N be a polyhedral region, and then use a limiting process.)

19.9   Prove Theorems 14.11 and 14.12 for arbitrary plane convex bodies.

19.10   Prove **Barbier's theorem**: Every plane convex body of constant width ω has the same length $\pi \omega$.   (Hint: Let K have constant width ω and let K' be the reflection of K about the origin. Show that $K + K'$ is a disk and use Exercise 19.8.)

19.11   Show that $V(K,N,N) \leq V(M,N,N)$ if $K \subset M$. (Hint: First let N be a polyhedral region.)

19.12   Prove the two-dimensional analog to Theorem 19.15.

19.13   Let K_1 and K_2 be two triangles in the plane with support functions H_1 and H_2. Let $F_1{}^i$ be the faces of K_1 with exterior unit normals $\overrightarrow{OU}_i$ and let $F_2{}^i$ be the faces of K_2 with exterior unit normal $\overrightarrow{OV}_i$. According to Exercise 19.12 we have $\sum H_2(U_i)|F_1{}^i| = \sum H_1(V_i)|F_2{}^i|$. Show this directly by comparing appropriate polygonal decompositions.

19.14   Do Exercise 19.13 for arbitrary polygonal regions K_1 and K_2.

19.15   Generalize Theorem 7.11 to 3-space.

19.16   Show that if convex body K is properly contained in the three-dimensional convex body L, then $A(K) < A(L)$.

19.17   Complete the proof of Theorem 19.18.

19.18   In Theorem 19.15 let K be an arbitrary convex body and let Π be a rectangle of unit area. Show that $3V(K,\Pi,\Pi)$ is the width of K in the direction perpendicular to the plane of Π.

19.19   State and prove the two-dimensional analog to Exercise 19.18.

20   SYMMETRIZATION

Because of Theorem 19.18 we now know that a solution to the isoperimetric problem in space exists. In order to solve this problem the techniques which worked in the plane are not very fruitful. Instead the technique of symmetrization, first exploited by Steiner, proves to be extremely useful.

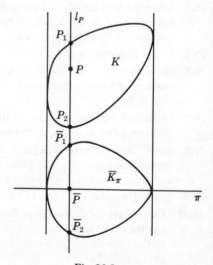

Fig. 20.1

20.1   Let K be a convex body and let π be any plane. Through each point P of K construct a line l_P perpendicular to π. Let $l_P \cap \pi = \bar{P}$ and let $l_P \cap K = S[P_1, P_2]$. Translate $S[P_1, P_2]$ along l_P to $S[\bar{P}_1, \bar{P}_2]$ so that $\bar{P}$ is the midpoint of $S[\bar{P}_1, \bar{P}_2]$. The union of all sets $S[\bar{P}_1, \bar{P}_2]$ is called the **Steiner symmetral $\bar{K}_\pi$ of K about plane π.** The process of obtaining $\bar{K}_\pi$ from K is called **symmetrization.**

If only one fixed plane π is under consideration, we will often write $\bar{K}$ for $\bar{K}_\pi$. Throughout this section we will use l_P to stand for the line through P perpendicular to the plane of symmetrization. It follows directly from the definition that $\bar{K} \subset \bar{M}$ whenever $K \subset M$. Also if the center of homothety lies on π, then $\overline{rK} = r\bar{K}$.

20.2   Theorem   If K is a convex body, then $\bar{K}$ is also a convex body.

PROOF   It is easily seen that $\bar{K}$ is closed and bounded. Let P and Q be any two points of $\bar{K}$ and let $S_X = l_X \cap K$ for any point X. Then $P \varepsilon \bar{S}_P$

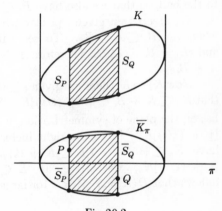

Fig. 20.2

and $Q \varepsilon \bar{S}_Q$. It is easily verified that the convex cover of $\bar{S}_P$ and $\bar{S}_Q$ is a trapezoid equal to the symmetral of the convex cover of S_P and S_Q. It follows that $(1 - r)P + rQ \varepsilon (1 - r)\bar{S}_P + r\bar{S}_Q \subset \bar{S}_{[(1-r)P+rQ]}$. Therefore $(1 - r)P + rQ \varepsilon \bar{K}$, and $\bar{K}$ is convex.

The preceding proof suggests the following.

20.3   Theorem   If K and M are convex bodies, then $\bar{K} + \bar{M} \subset \overline{K + M}$ whenever the plane of symmetrization π contains the origin.

PROOF   Let $P \varepsilon \bar{K}$ and $Q \varepsilon \bar{M}$, then $R = P + Q \varepsilon l_P \cap \bar{K} + l_Q \cap \bar{M}$. Since the origin lies on π, $l_P \cap \bar{K} + l_Q \cap \bar{M}$ is symmetric with respect to π, and $|l_P \cap \bar{K} + l_Q \cap \bar{M}| = |l_P \cap \bar{K}| + |l_Q \cap \bar{M}|$, where the bars indicate lengths of segments (see Theorem 14.2). In exactly the same way we see that $l_P \cap K$ and $l_Q \cap M$ are segments such that

$$|l_P \cap K + l_Q \cap M| = |l_P \cap K| + |l_Q \cap M|$$

It follows that

$$l_P \cap \bar{K} + l_Q \cap \bar{M} = \overline{l_P \cap K + l_Q \cap M} \subset \overline{l_R \cap (K + M)}$$

But then $R \, \varepsilon \, \overline{K + M}$, which completes the proof.

The following properties are extremely important for the solution of extremum problems.

20.4   Theorem   If $K_i \rightharpoonup K$, then $\bar{K}_i \rightharpoonup \bar{K}$.

PROOF   Suppose K contains the origin in its interior, and let B_r and B_R be two balls with center at the origin such that B_r is properly contained in K and K is properly contained in B_R. Since $K_i \rightharpoonup K$, it follows that $B_r \subset K_n \subset B_R$ for n large enough. The symmetral of a ball is congruent to the ball, so that we also have $B_r \subset \bar{K} \subset B_R$ and $B_r \subset \bar{K}_n \subset B_R$.

We assert that given ϵ positive, $A + B_\epsilon \subset [1 + (\epsilon/r)]A \subset A + B_{\epsilon R/r}$ whenever $B_r \subset A \subset B_R$. To see this, notice that $B_r \subset A$, $B_1 \subset A/r$, and $\epsilon B_1 = B_\epsilon \subset \epsilon A/r$. Therefore $A + B_\epsilon \subset A + \epsilon A/r \subset A + (\epsilon/r)B_R \subset A + B_{\epsilon R/r}$.

Now $K_i \rightharpoonup K$, therefore given $\epsilon \geq 0$, $K_n \subset K + B_\epsilon$ for large n. It follows that $K_n \subset K + B_\epsilon \subset [1 + (\epsilon/r)]K$. Since we can assume that the origin lies on the plane of symmetrization, it follows that $\bar{K}_n \subset \overline{[1 + (\epsilon/r)]K} = [1 + (\epsilon/r)]\bar{K}$. From the right inclusion of the above assertion we then have $\bar{K}_n \subset [1 + (\epsilon/r)]\bar{K} \subset \bar{K} + B_{\epsilon R/r}$. Similarly using $K \subset K_n + B_\epsilon \subset [1 + (\epsilon/r)]K_n$, we arrive at $\bar{K} \subset [1 + (\epsilon/r)]\bar{K}_n \subset \bar{K}_n + B_{\epsilon R/r}$. It follows that $D(\bar{K}, \bar{K}_n) \leq \epsilon R/r$ for large n, and our proof is complete.

20.5   Theorem   If $\bar{K}$ is the symmetral of the convex body K, then

    a. $V(\bar{K}) = V(K)$
    b. $A(\bar{K}) \leq A(K)$
    c. $D(\bar{K}) \leq D(K)$

where V, A, and D stand for volume, surface area, and diameter respectively.

PROOF   *a.*   In view of Theorems 19.11 and 20.4 it suffices to prove the first part for a polyhedron Π. Project each edge of Π orthogonally onto the plane of symmetrization and partition the resulting polygons into triangular regions T_i. Π is partitioned into sections of triangular prisms W_i having cross section T_i. If x_i, y_i, z_i are the lengths of the three parallel edges of W_i and if $|T_i|$ is the area of T_i, then from elementary geometry we have $V(W_i) = |T_i|(x_i + y_i + z_i)/3$. Since T_i, x_i, y_i, and z_i are not

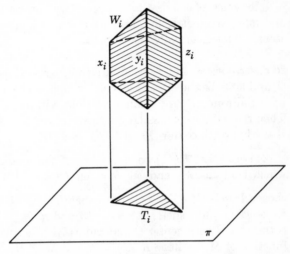

Fig. 20.3

changed under symmetrization, it follows that $V(W_i) = V(\bar{W}_i)$, and therefore $V(\bar{\Pi}) = V(\Pi)$.

b. As shown in the proof of Theorem 19.14, we have

$$V(K + B_\epsilon) = V(K) + 3A(K)\epsilon + 3V(K,B_1,B_1)\epsilon^2 + V(B_1)\epsilon^3$$

and

$$V(\bar{K} + B_\epsilon) = V(\bar{K}) + 3A(\bar{K})\epsilon + 3V(\bar{K},B_1,B_1)\epsilon^2 + V(B_1)\epsilon^3$$

By Theorem 20.3, $\overline{K + B_\epsilon} \supset \bar{K} + B_\epsilon$, therefore $V(K + B_\epsilon) = V\overline{(K + B_\epsilon)} \geq V(\bar{K} + B_\epsilon)$. It follows by subtraction that $A(K) + V(K,B_1,B_1)\epsilon \geq A(\bar{K}) + V(\bar{K},B_1,B_1)\epsilon$. Since ϵ is arbitrary, we get $A(K) \geq A(\bar{K})$.

c. Let $\bar{P}$ and $\bar{Q}$ be end points of a diameter of $\bar{K}$ and let $\bar{P}'$, $\bar{Q}'$ be their reflections with respect to the plane of symmetrization. Let trapezoid $\bar{P}\bar{P}'\bar{Q}\bar{Q}'$ be the symmetral of trapezoid $PP'QQ'$ contained in K. At least one diagonal of trapezoid $PP'QQ'$ has length greater than or equal to the length of the diagonals of $\bar{P}\bar{P}'\bar{Q}\bar{Q}'$. Therefore $D(K) \geq D(\bar{K})$. The result still holds when the trapezoids degenerate into triangles or line segments.

The reader should note the relationship between symmetrization and Cavalieri's principle (see Postulate 22 in Appendix 1). Cavalieri's principle in the plane can be used to show that $V(K) = V(\bar{K})$. Conversely Theorem 20.5 can be used to show that Cavalieri's principle holds for plane convex bodies. However, care must be exercised in applying Cavalieri's principle to more general sets. There are bounded sets in 3-space for which the principle does not hold.[1]

It seems plausible that an arbitrary convex body can be made more and more symmetric by applying a sequence of appropriate symmetrizations. This is actually the case.

20.6 Theorem Let K be an arbitrary convex body containing the origin O, and let C be the class of all convex bodies which can be obtained from K by a finite number of symmetrizations with respect to planes through O. Then there is a sequence $\{K_i\}$ of members of C such that $K_i \rightharpoonup B$, where B is the ball with center O and $V(B) = V(K)$.

PROOF   Let $R(M)$ be the radius of the smallest sphere with center O which contains M, and let $R = \inf_{M\epsilon C} R(M)$. Let $R(M_n)$ be a sequence chosen from $\{R(M)|M \epsilon C\}$ such that $R(M_n) \rightharpoonup R$, and then pick a subsequence of $\{M_n\}$ such that $M_i \rightharpoonup M$ and $R(M_i) \rightharpoonup R$. We assert that M is the ball B with center O and radius R. Because $R(M)$ is a continuous function of M, we have $R(M) = R$ and $M \subset B$.

It remains to show that $B \subset M$. Suppose the contrary, and let P be a point on the boundary S of B such that $N(P,\delta) \cap M = \emptyset$. Let $S_1 = N(P,\delta) \cap S$, and cover S with a finite number of pieces $S_1, \ldots, S_k$ congruent to S_1. Let π_i be the plane through O such that the reflection in π_i maps S_i onto S_1. It is easily seen that $S_1 \cap \bar{M}_{\pi_2} = \emptyset$ and $S_2 \cap \bar{M}_{\pi_2} = \emptyset$. Now symmetrize with respect to π_3 so that $S_1 \cap (\bar{M}_{\pi_2})_{\pi_3} = S_2 \cap (\bar{M}_{\pi_2})_{\pi_3} = S_3 \cap (\bar{M}_{\pi_2})_{\pi_3} = \emptyset$. Continuing this procedure we get a set

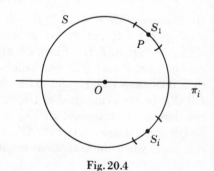

Fig. 20.4

[1] See R. P. Agnew, "Analytic Geometry and Calculus, with Vectors," p. 283, McGraw-Hill Book Company, New York, 1963.

M' which is obtained from M by a finite number of symmetrizations, and $M' \cap S = \emptyset$. If ϵ is taken small enough then there is an n such that $D(M_n, M) \leq \epsilon$ and the set M_n' obtained from M_n by the same finite number of symmetrizations has the property that $M_n' \cap S = \emptyset$. But M_n' belongs to C and $R(M_n') < R$, which is impossible. This contradiction proves the theorem.

If K is any convex body which is not a ball, then its surface area is never increased under symmetrization. It follows from Theorem 20.6 that the ball with the same volume cannot have surface area greater than $A(K)$. This implies that the sphere is a solution to the isoperimetric problem for convex bodies in space. This does not imply, however, that the sphere is the only solution. This fact will be proved in the next section.

We conclude this section with a few applications of symmetrization.

20.7 Theorem Among all triangles with a given area A the equilateral triangle, and only the equilateral triangle, has the smallest length, diameter, and circumradius.

PROOF We let $l(a)$ stand for a line perpendicular to the side with length a and consider the following sequence of triangles. Let Δ be an arbitrary triangular region with sides of length a, b, and c. Assume $a \geq b \geq c$, and symmetrize Δ about $l(a)$, getting a triangular region Δ_1 with sides of length a_1, b_1, and c_1. Now symmetrize Δ_1 with respect to $l(b_1)$, getting Δ_2, a_2, b_2, and c_2. Then symmetrize Δ_2 with respect to $l(a_2)$, getting Δ_3, a_3, b_3, and c_3. In general symmetrize with respect to $l(a_i)$, then $l(b_{i+1})$ and then $l(a_{i+2})$.

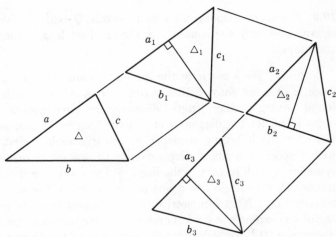

Fig. 20.5

We assert that there is a subsequence of $\{\Delta_i\}$ which converges to an equilateral triangular region. We assume that all triangular regions have been translated inside a given disk so that the selection theorem may be applied. We also use the fact that any subsequence of $\{\Delta_i\}$ which converges must converge to a triangular region (see Exercise 20.8). If at any stage Δ_n becomes an equilateral triangle, then Δ_{n+1} is congruent to Δ_n, and we have finished. Suppose that no member of $\{\Delta_i\}$ is equilateral and consider an arbitrary member Δ_n of the sequence. Let M_n be the length of the largest side of Δ_n and let m_n be the length of the smallest side. If we symmetrize with respect to $l(M_n)$, then $M_n = M_{n+1}$ and $m_n < m_{n+1}$. If we symmetrize with respect to $l(m_n)$, then $M_n > M_{n+1}$ and $m_n = m_{n+1}$. In either case $M_n - m_n > M_{n+1} - m_{n+1}$. $\{M_n - m_n\}$ is therefore a monotone decreasing sequence. Suppose $\lim (M_n - m_n) = \eta > 0$, and let Δ_η be a triangular region such that $\Delta_j \rightarrow \Delta_\eta$ and $M_\eta - m_\eta = \eta$ for some subsequence of $\{\Delta_i\}$. Let $\overline{\Delta}_\eta$ be a symmetral obtained by applying two successive symmetrizations of the above sequence to Δ_η. The resulting difference for $\overline{\Delta}_\eta$ is $M - m < \eta$. For n large enough Δ_n is arbitrarily close to Δ_η, and it follows from Theorem 20.4 that Δ_{n+2} is arbitrarily close to $\overline{\Delta}_\eta$. But then $M_{n+2} - m_{n+2} < \eta$, which is impossible. Therefore $M_n - m_n \rightarrow 0$, and there is a subsequence of $\{\Delta_i\}$ which converges to an equilateral triangular region.

Since the length, diameter, and circumradius are actually decreased at least once in the above sequence of symmetrizations, it follows that for any triangle not equilateral the equilateral triangle with the same area has smaller length, diameter, and circumradius.

20.8 Theorem Among all quadrilaterals Q with a given area A the square, and only the square, has the smallest length, diameter, and circumradius.

PROOF   We leave it to the reader to show that, in each of the three cases, if Q is not convex, then a convex quadrilateral with area A can be found having smaller length, diameter, or circumradius. Assume Q is convex and let the diagonals of Q have lengths M and m with $M > m$. Consider the following sequence of quadrilaterals. First symmetrize Q with respect to a line l perpendicular to one of its diagonals l'. Then symmetrize with respect to the line l'. The result is a rhombus Q_1. Symmetrize Q_1 with respect to a line perpendicular to one of its sides to get a rectangle Q_2. Next symmetrize Q_2 with respect to a line perpendicular to one of its diagonals to get a rhombus Q_3. We continue this process, getting a sequence $\{Q_i\}$ in which Q_i is a rhombus for i odd and a rectangle for i even. If at any stage Q_i becomes a square, then Q_{i+1} is congruent to Q_i. Suppose

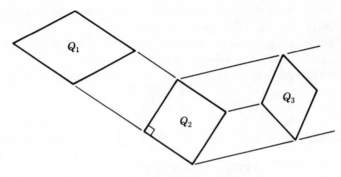

Fig. 20.6

that no member of $\{Q_i\}$ is a square.   Then starting with any rhombus Q_N we have $M_N > M_{N+2} > m_{N+2} > m_N$.   Therefore $M_N - m_N > M_{N+2} - m_{N+2} > \cdots$.   The remainder of the proof is similar to the preceding proof, and we leave it to the reader as an exercise.

Exercises

20.1 Show that the symmetral of a polyhedral region Π is a polyhedral region $\bar{\Pi}$, and prove that the number of vertices of $\bar{\Pi}$ is always greater than or equal to the number of vertices of Π.

20.2 Let $(1 - r)A + rB$ be a linear array. Show that $\overline{(1-r)\bar{A} + r\bar{B}} \subset \overline{(1-r)A + rB}$. If in addition A can be obtained from B by a homothety, show that $\overline{(1-r)A + rB}$ is the linear array of $\bar{A}$ and $\bar{B}$.

20.3 Prove that the radius of the circumsphere of a convex body cannot be increased by symmetrization.   What can be said about the insphere?

20.4 If K_r is a concave array (see Exercise 19.1) show that $\bar{K}_r$ is also a concave array.

20.5 Let $R(M)$ be defined as in the proof of Theorem 20.6. Show that $R(M_i) \rightharpoonup R(M)$ whenever $M_i \rightharpoonup M$.

20.6 Let $R(K)$ be the circumradius of K. Show that $R(K_i) \rightharpoonup R(K)$ whenever $\{K_i\}$ is a sequence of convex bodies such that $K_i \rightharpoonup K$.

20.7 According to Theorem 20.5 the maximum width of a convex body is not increased under symmetrization.   Give examples to show that the minimum width may be either increased or decreased under symmetrization.

20.8 If $\{\Delta_i\}$ is a sequence of triangular regions each with the same area, show that Δ is a triangular region whenever $\Delta_i \rightharpoonup \Delta$.

20.9 Show that the sphere is a solution to the isodiametric problem.   Of all closed surfaces bounding sets with the same diameter which one (or ones) bounds the greatest volume?

20.10   State and prove the three-dimensional analog to Theorem 20.7.

20.11   Complete the proof of Theorem 20.8.

20.12   Explain why the technique used in Theorems 20.7 and 20.8 cannot be used to obtain a similar theorem for pentagons.

20.13   Prove the following properties of symmetrization:
   a. $M \subset N$ implies $\bar{M} \subset \bar{N}$.
   b. $M \subset \bar{M}$ implies $M = \bar{M}$.
   c. $\overline{rK} = r\bar{K}$ if the plane of symmetry contains the origin.

20.14   Show that $V(K,K,M) \geq V(\bar{K},\bar{K},\bar{M})$. (Hint: Use Theorem 19.14.)

21   CONVEX FUNCTIONS

Before we take up further applications of the preceding sections, it will be useful to consider the idea of a convex function.   Let K be a three-dimensional convex body in 3-space and choose an arbitrary xyz coordinate system.   Let D be the orthogonal projection of K onto the plane $z = 0$. Each line parallel to the z axis passing through D intersects the boundary of K in two points (which may coincide).   Let $\overrightarrow{OP} = (x,y,0)$, $\overrightarrow{OP_1} = (x,y,z_1)$, and $\overrightarrow{OP_2} = (x,y,z_2)$ be position vectors of the point $P \varepsilon D$ and the corresponding boundary points $P_1, P_2 \varepsilon K$.   Furthermore always pick P_1 and P_2 so that $z_1 \leq z_2$.   Then we define two functions f_1 and f_2 with domain D such that $f_1(P) = z_1$ and $f_2(P) = z_2$.   We call f_1 a convex function and f_2 a concave function.   Throughout this section we will find it convenient to identify $\overrightarrow{OP}$ with P.

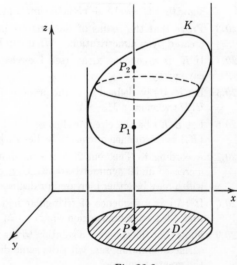

Fig. 21.1

21.1 Let $f(P)$ be a real-valued function of one or two variables over a convex domain D. If $f[(1 - r)P + rQ] \leq (1 - r)f(P) + rf(Q)$ for $0 \leq r \leq 1$, then we call f a **convex function** over D. If $f[(1-r)P + rQ] \geq (1 - r)f(P) + rf(Q)$, then we call f a **concave function**.

21.2 Theorem $f(x,y)$ is convex iff $K = \{(x,y,z)|z \geq f(x,y)\}$ is a convex set.

PROOF Suppose f is convex, $P_1 = (x_1,y_1,z_1)$, $= P_2 = (x_2,y_2,z_2)$, and $P_1, P_2 \in K$.   Then $(1 - r)z_1 + rz_2 \geq (1 - r)f(x_1,y_1) + rf(x_2,y_2) \geq f[(1 - r)(x_1,y_1) + r(x_2,y_2)]$.   Therefore $[(1 - r)x_1 + rx_2, (1 - r)y_1 + ry_2, (1 - r)z_1 + rz_2] \in K$, and by definition K is convex.

On the other hand suppose that K is convex. If $[x_1,y_1,f(x_1,y_1)] \in K$ and $[x_2,y_2,f(x_2,y_2)] \in K$, then $[(1 - r)x_1 + rx_2, (1 - r)y_1 + ry_2, (1 - r)f(x_1,y_1) + rf(x_2,y_2)] \in K$ and $(1 - r)f(x_1,y_1) + rf(x_2,y_2) \geq f[(1 - r)x_1 + rx_2, (1 - r)y_1 + ry_2]$.   Therefore f is convex.

We now present a few basic properties of convex functions of one variable.

21.3 Theorem f is convex on the interval $[a,b]$ iff given any three points $P_1 = (x_1,f(x_1))$, $P_2 = (x_2,f(x_2))$, and $P_3 = (x_3,f(x_3))$ such that $a \leq x_1 \leq x_2 \leq x_3 \leq b$, one of the following holds (and therefore all hold):

a. $m(P_1,P_2) \leq m(P_1,P_3)$
b. $m(P_1,P_3) \leq m(P_2,P_3)$
c. $m(P_1,P_2) \leq m(P_2,P_3)$

$m(P_i,P_j)$ is the slope of $L(P_i,P_j)$.

PROOF A proof of part (*a*) only will be given. Assume f is convex on $[a,b]$ and let V be the intersection of the vertical line l through P_2 and the line $L(P_1,P_3)$. Let $|\overrightarrow{AB}|$ be the directed length of vector $\overrightarrow{AB}$. Since f is convex, $|\overrightarrow{P_2V}| \geq 0$. Let the horizontal line through P_1 intersect l at H. Then $m(P_1,P_3) = \overrightarrow{|HV|}/\overrightarrow{|P_1H|} = (\overrightarrow{|HP_2|} + \overrightarrow{|P_2V|})/\overrightarrow{|P_1H|} = m(P_1,P_2) + \overrightarrow{|P_2V|}/\overrightarrow{|P_1H|}$. Therefore $m(P_1,P_3) \geq m(P_1,P_2)$. Retracing our steps we see that the converse also holds.

21.4 Theorem If f is convex on interval $[a,b]$, then f is continuous on $[a,b]$.

PROOF To see this let x be any number in $[a,b]$ and let $F(y) = [f(x) - f(y)]/(x - y)$. If $x_1 \leq x_2 \leq x_3$, then by Theorem 21.3 we have

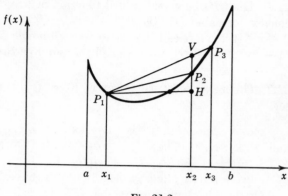

Fig. 21.2

$F(x_1) \leq F(x_2) \leq F(x_3)$. This implies that $F(y)$ is monotone increasing and bounded as y approaches x from below. Therefore the left derivative $\lim_{y \uparrow x} F(y) = f_l'(x)$ exists. Similarly the right derivative $\lim_{y \downarrow x} F(y) = f_r'(x)$ exists, and it follows that f is continuous at x.

In Sec. 19 the existence of mixed volumes, and therefore the existence of surface area, was shown under the implicit assumption that volumes of convex bodies always exist. This can be shown using Exercise 18.11 and the definition of Jordan measure. Another way to show this is as follows.

21.5 Theorem The volume of a three-dimensional convex body and the area of a two-dimensional convex body always exist.

PROOF We leave the proof for two-dimensional convex bodies to the reader. Let K be a three-dimensional convex body, and choose an xyz coordinate system so that K lies in the first octant. Let $D, f_1(x,y)$ and $f_2(x,y)$ be defined as in the first paragraph of this section. By Theorem 21.4 f_1 is a continuous function of each of its variables, and therefore the Riemann integral $\int\int_D f_1$ exists. By suitable modifications of Theorems 21.3 and 21.4 it also follows that f_2 is a continuous function of each of its variables, and therefore $V(K) = \int\int_D f_1 - \int\int_D f_2$ exists.

We now turn our attention to a very important convex function whose convexity was first shown by Brunn. First we need the following.

21.6 Theorem Let K_0 and K_1 be three-dimensional convex bodies, and let $K_r = (1 - r)K_0 + rK_1$ be a linear array. Then $\bar{K}_r = (1 - r)\bar{K}_0 + r\bar{K}_1$ iff K_0 is homothetic to K_1.

PROOF   If K_0 is homothetic to K_1, then Exercise 20.2 gives us $\bar{K}_r = (1 - r)\bar{K}_0 + r\bar{K}_1$. On the other hand suppose $\bar{K}_r = (1 - r)\bar{K}_0 + r\bar{K}_1$, and let l_P be the line through a point P perpendicular to the plane of symmetrization π. Also let $\sigma(X)$ stand for a supporting plane at X.

If P_0 is any interior point of $\bar{K}_0$, then $l_{P_0} \cap \bar{K}_0 = S[\bar{X}_0, \bar{Y}_0]$ where $\bar{X}_0 \ne \bar{Y}_0$. Let $\sigma(\bar{X}_1)$ be the supporting plane of $\bar{K}_1$ which has the same exterior normal as a fixed supporting plane $\sigma(\bar{X}_0)$. If $l_{\bar{X}_1} \cap \bar{K}_1 = S[\bar{X}_1, \bar{Y}_1]$,

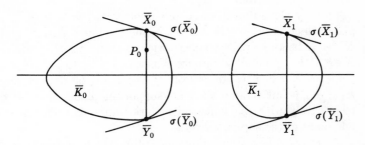

Fig. 21.3

by symmetry it follows that the reflections of $\sigma(\bar{X}_0)$ and $\sigma(\bar{X}_1)$ about π are parallel supporting planes $\sigma(\bar{Y}_0)$ and $\sigma(\bar{Y}_1)$. If $\bar{X}_r = (1 - r)\bar{X}_0 + r\bar{X}_1$ and $\bar{Y}_r = (1 - r)\bar{Y}_0 + r\bar{Y}_1$, then $\bar{X}_r$, $\bar{Y}_r$ are boundary points of $\bar{K}_r$, and $\sigma(\bar{X}_r) = (1 - r)\sigma(\bar{X}_0) + r\sigma(\bar{X}_1)$ is a supporting plane of $\bar{K}_r$ at $\bar{X}_r$ (see Theorem 14.7).

Let $l_{\bar{X}_r} \cap K_r = S[X_r, Y_r]$ for $0 \le r \le 1$. Since $S[X_0, Y_0] \subset K_0$ and $S[X_1, Y_1] \subset K_1$, we have $(1 - r)S[X_0, Y_0] + rS[X_1, Y_1] \subset K_r \cap L(\bar{X}_r, \bar{Y}_r)$. But $|K_r \cap L(\bar{X}_r, \bar{Y}_r)| = |\bar{X}_r \bar{Y}_r| = |(1 - r)S[X_0, Y_0] + rS[X_1, Y_1]|$. It follows that $(1 - r)S[X_0, Y_0] + rS[X_1, Y_1] = S[X_r, Y_r]$, $X_r = (1 - r)X_0 + rX_1$, and $Y_r = (1 - r)Y_0 + rY_1$. Moreover, both X_r and Y_r are boundary points

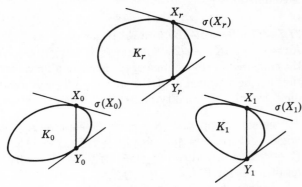

Fig. 21.4

of K_r. If $\sigma(X_r)$ and $\sigma(Y_r)$ are supporting planes of K_r, then the planes through X_0, X_1 parallel to $\sigma(X_r)$ and the planes through Y_0, Y_1 parallel to $\sigma(Y_r)$ are also supporting planes. We conclude that given any boundary point $X_0 \, \varepsilon \, K_0$ and a supporting plane $\sigma(X_0)$, and given that X_1 is any boundary point of K_1 on supporting plane $\sigma(X_1)$ with the same exterior normal, then whenever $S[X_0, Y_0]$ and $S[X_1, Y_1]$ are two parallel chords of K_0 and K_1 respectively, there exist supporting planes $\sigma(Y_0)$, $\sigma(Y_1)$ with the same exterior normal.

Every three-dimensional convex body K has at least one supporting plane which intersects K in a single point. For if I is an interior point of K, let S be the smallest sphere with center I which contains K and let $X \, \varepsilon \, S \cap K$. The plane through X perpendicular to $L(I,X)$ is a supporting plane of K which contains exactly one point of K. Moreover, if $K = K_1 + K_2$, it follows that there are supporting planes σ_1 and σ_2 of K_1 and K_2 respectively with the same unit exterior normals each containing exactly one point of the supported set.

Let $\sigma(P_r)$ be a supporting plane of K_r which contains exactly one point P_r of K_r. If $\sigma(P_r) = (1 - r)\sigma(P_0) + r\sigma(P_1)$, then $\sigma(P_i)$ is a supporting plane of K_i at exactly one point P_i, $i = 0$ and 1, and $\sigma(P_0)$ and $\sigma(P_1)$ have the same exterior normal. Let $S[P_0, Q_0]$ and $S[P_1, Q_1]$ be parallel chords of K_0 and K_1. Let R_0 be an arbitrary boundary point of K_0, and construct chord $S[P_1, R_1]$ parallel to $S[P_0, R_0]$ and chord $S[Q_1, R_1']$ parallel to $S[Q_0, R_0]$. We assert that $R_1 = R_1'$. For if not, the line through R_0 parallel to $L(R_1', P_1)$ would intersect $\sigma(P_0)$ in a point X which belongs to K_0. But $P_0 \neq X$, so that $S[P_0, X] \subset \sigma(P_0)$, contrary to the choice of $\sigma(P_0)$. It follows that $\triangle P_0 Q_0 R_0$ is similar to $\triangle P_1 Q_1 R_1$. If $\triangle P_0 Q_0 R_0$ is congruent to $\triangle P_1 Q_1 R_1$, then K_1 is a translation of K_0. Otherwise let H be the homothety which maps $\triangle P_0 Q_0 R_0$ onto $\triangle P_1 Q_1 R_1$. H also maps K_0 onto K_1, and our proof is complete.

21.7 The Brunn-Minkowski theorem

If $f(r) = [V(K_r)]^{1/3}$, where $K_r = (1 - r)K_0 + rK_1$, then $f(r) \geq (1 - r)f(0) + rf(1)$. In other words, the cube root of the volume of members of a linear array is a concave function of the parameter of the array. When K_0 and K_1 are both three-dimensional, the equality holds iff K_0 is homothetic to K_1.

PROOF   Suppose $V(K_1) = 0$, and suppose K_0 and K_1 both contain the origin. Then $K_r = (1 - r)K_0 + rK_1 \supset (1 - r)K_0$. Therefore $V(K_r) \geq (1 - r)^3 V(K_0)$, and $f(r) \geq (1 - r)f(0) = (1 - r)f(0) + rf(1)$. A similar result holds for $V(K_0) = 0$.

Suppose both K_0 and K_1 have positive volume. We can assume that K_0 and K_1 are positioned so that each contains the origin O. Let B_{r_0} and

B_{r_1} be balls such that $V(B_{r_0}) = V(K_0)$ and $V(B_{r_1}) = V(K_1)$. Let $\{K_0{}^i\}$ be a sequence of successive symmetrals of K_0 such that $K_0{}^i \to B_{r_0}$, and similarly let $K_1{}^i \to B_{r_1}$. Given $\epsilon > 0$ we have $K_0{}^i + B_\epsilon \supset B_{r_0}$ for i large enough. Therefore there is a finite number N such that $K_0{}^N \supset B_{r_0-\epsilon}$.

Similarly the sequence $\{K_1{}^{N+1}, K_1{}^{N+2}, K_1{}^{N+3}, \ldots\}$ converges to B_{r_1} so that $K_1{}^{N+N'} \supset B_{r_1-\epsilon}$ for some N'. Since $\overline{A + B} \supset \overline{A} + \overline{B}$ and $\overline{A} + \overline{B} \supset \overline{A} + \overline{B}$, it follows that $(1 - r)K_0{}^i + rK_1{}^i \supset (1 - r)K_0{}^{i+1} + rK_1{}^{i+1} = K_r{}^{i+1}$, and therefore $V(K_r) \geq V(K_r{}^i) \geq V(K_r{}^{i+1})$. In particular we have $V(K_r) \geq V(K_r{}^{N+N'}) \geq V[(1 - r)B_{r_0-\epsilon} + rB_{r_1-\epsilon}]$. Since this is true for arbitrary ϵ we have $V(K_r) \geq V[(1 - r)B_{r_0} + rB_{r_1}] = V[B_{(1-r)r_0 + rr_1}]$. Therefore $f(r) \geq (4\pi/3)^{1/3}[(1 - r)r_0 + rr_1]$, and $f(r) \geq (1 - r)f(0) + rf(1)$.

It remains to show when the equality holds. If K_0 is homothetic to K_1, then we can assume that $K_0 = \lambda K_1$. Therefore $V(K_0) = V(\lambda K_1) = \lambda^3 V(K_1)$, and $f(0) = \lambda f(1)$. But then $K_r = (1 - r)\lambda K_1 + rK_1 = [(1 - r)\lambda + r]K_1$, and $f(r) = [(1 - r)\lambda + r]f(1) = (1 - r)f(0) + rf(1)$. Suppose K_0 is not homothetic to K_1. Then by Theorem 21.6 $V(K_r) > V(K_r{}^i)$. Therefore $V(K_r) > (4\pi/3)^{1/3}[(1 - r)r_0 + rr_1]$, and $f(r) > (1 - r)f(0) + rf(1)$. This completes the proof.

An immediate consequence of the Brunn-Minkowski theorem is the following relation between mixed volumes.

21.8 Minkowski's inequality If K and L are convex bodies, then $V^3(K,K,L) \geq V^2(K)V(L)$, where equality holds iff K is homothetic to L. In particular $A^3(K) \geq 3^3 V^2(K)(4\pi/3)$, where equality holds iff K is a ball.

PROOF From Theorem 21.7 we have $V(K + \epsilon L) \geq [V^{1/3}(K) + \epsilon V^{1/3}(L)]^3 \geq V(K) + 3V^{2/3}(K)\epsilon V^{1/3}(L)$. Therefore we have $[V(K + \epsilon L) - V(K)]/\epsilon \geq 3V^{2/3}(K)V^{1/3}(L)$ and $V(K,K,L) \geq V^{2/3}(K)V^{2/3}(L)$.

It follows that among all convex bodies with a given surface area the ball, and only the ball, has maximum volume. This is not quite as satisfactory as the solution we obtained for the plane, since we are restricted to convex bodies. However, if we consider Jordan-measurable sets M for which $\lim_{\epsilon \to 0} [V(M + \epsilon B_1) - V(M)]/\epsilon$ exists, then we can use the limit to define surface area. It can be shown that the Brunn-Minkowski theorem holds (with the same conditions for equality) for a wide class of sets which includes, for example, all closed bounded measurable sets.[1] It follows that among all members of this extended collection of sets the ball, and only the ball, has maximum volume.

We conclude this section with the following generalization of Theorem 17.5.

21.9   Theorem   Let Π and Π' be distinct polyhedra with the same set of unit exterior normals to their faces. If $A(\Pi) = A(\Pi')$ and Π' is circumscribed to a sphere, then $V(\Pi') > V(\Pi)$.

PROOF   Let F_i be the faces of Π and let $\overrightarrow{OU_i}$ be the corresponding unit exterior normals. According to Theorem 19.15 we have $3V(\Pi,\Pi,\Pi') = \sum H(U_i)|F_i|$, where H is the support function of Π'. Let Σ be the polyhedron circumscribed to the unit sphere having exterior normals $\overrightarrow{OU_i}$. If $\Pi' = r\Sigma$ is the homothety of Σ which has surface area equal to $A(\Pi)$, then $3V(\Pi,\Pi,\Pi') = \sum r|F_i| = rA(\Pi)$. From Minkowski's inequality we have $rA(\Pi) \geq 3V^2(\Pi)V(\Pi')$, where equality holds iff Π is homothetic to Π'. Therefore $3V(\Pi') = rA(\Pi')/V^2(\Pi') \leq rA(\Pi)/V^2(\Pi)$. Since $A(\Pi') = A(\Pi)$, we have $V(\Pi') \geq V(\Pi)$, and equality holds iff $\Pi = \Pi'$.

Exercises

21.1   Prove parts (b) and (c) of Theorem 21.3.

21.2   Let f be a real-valued function differentiable on the interval $[a,b]$. Show that f is convex on $[a,b]$ iff f' is nondecreasing on $[a,b]$. (Hint: Use the mean-value theorem of differential calculus.)

21.3   Use Exercise 18.11 and the definition of Jordan measure to show that the volume of a convex body always exists.

21.4   Complete the proof of Theorem 21.5.

21.5   State and prove the two-dimensional analog to Theorem 21.6.

21.6   State and prove the Brunn-Minkowski theorem for a linear array in the plane.

21.7   State and prove Minkowski's inequality for two-dimensional convex bodies.

21.8   Let K^* be the reflection of the three-dimensional convex body K with respect to any fixed point. Prove that $V(K + K^*) \geq 2^3 V(K)$, and determine necessary and sufficient conditions for the equality to hold.

21.9   Show that the distance function and the support function of a convex body are each convex functions.

21.10   Show that each of the following functions is convex over all of 3-space:
   a. $f(x,y,z) = |x|$
   b. $f(x,y,z) = |x| + |y| + |z|$
   c. $f(x,y,z) = \max \{|x|,|y|,|z|\}$

21.11   Show that the sum of two convex functions is also a convex function.

21.12   Let $\{f_\alpha\}$ be a collection of convex functions with the same domain D and assume that $f(P) = \sup f_\alpha(P)$ exists for each $P \varepsilon D$. Show that f is a convex function.

21.13   Use Exercises 21.11 and 21.12 to solve Exercise 21.10 (note that $|x| = \max\{-x,x\}$).

21.14   According to Exercise 20.9 the sphere is a solution to the isodiametric problem. Let K be an arbitrary solution to this problem and use Exercise 21.8 to show that the sphere is the only solution.

21.15   Use Theorem 21.9 to show that if polyhedra Π and Π' have the same unit exterior normals and if each face of Π has the same area as the corresponding face of Π', then Π' is a translate of Π.

21.16   Use Exercise 21.15 to show that whenever a polyhedron Π has faces which occur in parallel pairs, then Π has a center.

22   GEOMETRIC INEQUALITIES

In this section we shall discuss extremum problems which involve various numerical quantities associated with a convex body. Some of these are quite easy to solve. For others the existence of a solution can often be shown using Blaschke's selection theorem, but sometimes the construction of a solution is extremely difficult. Many such problems are still unsolved today. Throughout this section we shall use the following notation. $D(K) =$ diameter of K, $R(K) =$ circumradius of K, $r(K) =$ inradius of K, and $\Delta(K) =$ thickness of K (see Theorem 10.8 and Exercise 10.15).

22.1   The **thickness** $\Delta(K)$ of a convex body K is the minimum width of K.

First we discuss the following type of problem. Of all convex bodies with a fixed value of one numerical quantity, which ones have the maximum or minimum value of a second numerical quantity? The isoperimetric problem is an extremum problem of this type. To each such problem there corresponds an inequality between the quantities involved. For example, the isoperimetric problem corresponds to Minkowski's inequality. Another example is given by Exercise 21.14. Of all convex bodies with the same diameter the ball and only the ball has the maximum volume. If K is any convex body with diameter D, we then have $V(K) \leq V(B) = \pi D(K)/6$. Summarizing the solutions of these two problems in both the plane and 3-space, we have

22.2   Theorem   (*a*) For any convex body K in 3-space, $A^3(K) \geq 36\pi V^2(K)$ and $D^3(K) \geq 6V(K)/\pi$, where equality holds only for a ball. (*b*) For any convex body K in the plane, $L^2(K) \geq 4\pi V(K)$ and $D^2(K) \geq 4V(K)/\pi$, where equality holds only for a disk.

Suppose we ask ourselves the following question. Of all convex bodies with the same surface area which ones have minimum volume? Let K be the convex body bounded by a right circular cylinder with radius r

and height h. Then $A(K) = 2\pi rh + 2\pi r^2 = 2V(K)r + 2\pi r^2$ and $r^3 - A(K)r/2\pi + V(K)/\pi = 0$. It can be shown using standard methods from the theory of equations that for any fixed $A(K)$ and all $V(K)$ small enough this equation always has positive solutions for r. This means that we can find convex bodies with fixed surface area which have arbitrarily small volume. In other words, if we restrict ourselves to three-dimensional convex bodies, then there is no solution to the problem. If we also consider convex bodies K with dimension less than 3, then $A(K) = 3V(K,K,B_1) = 2|K|$, where $|K|$ is the two-dimensional Jordan measure of K. In this case a solution would be any convex body K of dimension less than 3 with $|K| = A/2$. A similar result holds for convex bodies of the same diameter.

We turn now to a comparison of the diameter and circumradius of a convex body. For a fixed circumradius the largest possible diameter is obviously twice the circumradius, so that $D(K) \leq 2R(K)$. We also have the following.

22.3   Theorem   If M is any closed bounded set in 3-space, then $R(M) \leq D(M)\sqrt{\frac{3}{8}}$, and equality holds if M is a regular tetrahedron. If M is any closed bounded set in the plane, then $R(M) \leq D(M)/\sqrt{3}$, and equality holds if M is an equilateral triangle.

PROOF   We shall only prove the theorem for 3-space. If M is not convex, then its convex cover K has the same diameter and $R(M) \leq R(K)$. Therefore $D(M)/R(M) \geq D(K)/R(K)$, and it suffices to determine the minimum value of $D(K)/R(K)$ for convex bodies K. Let K be a convex body, let S be its circumsphere, and suppose that the center of S is the origin O. We assert that the convex cover of $S \cap K$ contains O. Suppose the contrary; then there is a closed half space with exterior unit normal $\overrightarrow{OU}$ whose boundary contains O and which does not contain $S \cap K$. Translate S in the direction $\overrightarrow{OU}$ to S' so that S' still contains K. S and S' intersect in a circle C with radius smaller than $R(K)$. If S'' is the sphere generated by revolving C about its diameter, then S'' also contains K. But this contradicts the fact that S is the circumsphere of K and proves the assertion. It follows from Theorem 9.7 (Carathéodory's theorem) that there are four or fewer points belonging to $S \cap K$ such that O belongs to their convex cover. Suppose there are four points and let T be the tetrahedron spanned by them. Since $R(K) = R(T)$ and $D(K) \geq D(T)$, it follows that $D(K)/R(K) \geq D(T)/R(T)$. Consequently we need only determine the minimum value of $D(M)/R(M)$ for tetrahedra. Since the diameter of a tetrahedron is the length of its longest side, it remains to show that of all tetrahedra inscribed to the same sphere the regular tetra-

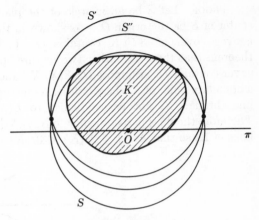

Fig. 22.1

hedron has the minimum length for its largest side. Let $X_i, i = 1, \ldots,$
4 be the vertices of a tetrahedron inscribed to a fixed sphere with center at
the origin and radius R. Since O lies in the convex cover of $\{X_i\}$, we
have $O = \sum\limits_{i=1}^{4} \lambda_i X_i,\ \lambda_i \geq 0,\ \sum\limits_{i=1}^{4} \lambda_i = 1$ (see Exercise 22.6). Now let $D =$
max $|X_i X_j|$. From the law of cosines we get $|X_i X_j|^2 = 2R^2 - 2X_i \cdot X_j$.
Therefore $(1 - \lambda_j)D^2 = \sum\limits_{i=1}^{4} \lambda_i D^2 - \lambda_j D^2 \geq \sum\limits_{i=1}^{4} \lambda_i |X_i X_j|^2 = \sum\limits_{i=1}^{4} 2\lambda_i$
$(R^2 - X_i \cdot X_j) = 2R^2 - 2\left(\sum\limits_{i=1}^{4} \lambda_i X_i \right) \cdot X_j = 2R^2$. Summing over j we
get $\sum\limits_{j=1}^{4} (1 - \lambda_j)D^2 = 3D^2 \geq 8R^2$. Since equality holds for a regular
tetrahedron, the theorem is proved when the number of points determined
by Carathéodory's theorem is four. If the number of points is three, the
above argument can be applied to give us the fact that of all triangles inscribed to the same circle the equilateral triangle has the minimum length
of its largest side, and $D/R \geq \sqrt{3}$. If the number of points is two, then
$D/R \geq 2$. Since $2 > \sqrt{3} > \sqrt{\frac{8}{3}}$ and since the circumcircle and circumsphere of a triangle or line segment have the same radius, it follows that
$D(M)/R(M) \geq \sqrt{\frac{8}{3}}$ for every closed bounded set in 3-space.

A problem very similar to the preceding is to find bounds for the ratio
$\Delta(K)/r(K)$ for convex bodies K. For a fixed thickness the largest possible
inradius is half the thickness, so that $2r(K) \leq \Delta(K)$. This gives us a
lower bound for $\Delta(K)/r(K)$. The next two theorems give us an upper
bound.

22.4   Theorem   If K is a convex body in the plane, then $\Delta(K) \leq 3r(K)$.
Equality holds iff K is an equilateral triangle.

PROOF   Let S be an incircle of the plane convex body K and let the center of S be the origin O.   As shown in the proof of Theorem 10.11 the convex cover of $S \cap K$ contains O.   It follows from Carathéodory's theorem that there are either two or three points of $S \cap K$ whose convex cover contains O.   Suppose $O \in S[X_1,X_2]$ and $X_1,X_2 \in S \cap K$.   Since X_1 is a boundary point of K, there is at least one supporting line to K at X_1.   Any line through X_1 not perpendicular to $L(X_1,X_2)$ separates points of S.   Therefore the lines perpendicular to $S[X_1,X_2]$ at X_1 and X_2 are supporting lines of K, so that $\Delta(K) \leq 2r(K) < 3r(K)$.

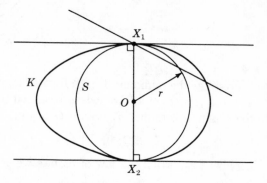

Fig. 22.2

Suppose O lies in the interior of the convex cover of three points of $S \cap K$.   The supporting lines to K at these points form a triangle $\triangle ABC$. Let a, b, and c be the lengths of the sides opposite vertices A, B, and C respectively, and suppose $a \geq b \geq c$.   If h is the length of the perpendicular dropped from A to the opposite side, it follows from the fact that S is also the incircle of $\triangle ABC$ that $V(\triangle ABC) = ha/2 = r(a + b + c)/2$. Therefore $\Delta(K) \leq h = (1 + b/a + c/a)r(K) \leq 3r(K)$.   We leave it to the reader to determine when the equality holds.

22.5   Theorem   If K is a convex body in 3-space, then $\Delta(K) \leq 2\sqrt{3}\,r(K)$. Equality holds if K is a regular tetrahedron.

PROOF   Let S be an insphere of the convex body K and let the center of S be the origin O.   As in the proof of Theorem 22.4 the origin lies in the convex cover of four or fewer points of $S \cap K$.   Suppose O lies in the interior of the convex cover of four points of $S \cap K$.   The supporting planes to K at these points form a tetrahedron T whose insphere is also S.   Since $\Delta(K)/r(K) \leq \Delta(T)/r(T)$, it follows that we need only determine the

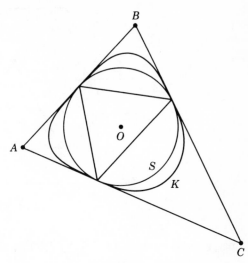

Fig. 22.3

maximum of $\Delta(K)/r(K)$ for tetrahedra. Let π and π' be parallel support-ing planes of tetrahedron T. If π contains exactly one vertex of T and π' contains three or fewer vertices, we can rotate π' slightly about an edge and rotate π about the vertex to a parallel position, so that the distance between them is decreased. It follows that $\Delta(T)$ is the minimum distance between parallel supporting planes of T each of which contains two vertices of T.

Let $F_1, \ldots, F_4$ be the faces of tetrahedron T and let $\overrightarrow{OU_1}, \ldots, \overrightarrow{OU_4}$ be the unit exterior normals to these faces. Given a unit vector $\overrightarrow{OU}$ the projection of some set of three of the faces of T onto a plane perpendicular to $\overrightarrow{OU}$ will exactly cover the projection of the fourth face. It follows that

$$U \cdot \sum_{i=1}^{4} |F_i| U_i = 0.$$ Since U is arbitrary, we have $\sum_{i=1}^{4} |F_i| U_i = O$. There-fore $\left(\sum_{i=1}^{4} |F_i| U_i \right)^2 = 0 = \sum_{i=1}^{4} |F_i|^2 + 2 \sum_{i<j} |F_i||F_j| U_i \cdot U_j$. Also since the geometric mean of a pair of numbers is less than the arithmetic mean, we have $\left(\sum_{i=1}^{4} |F_i| \right)^2 = \sum_{i=1}^{4} \sum_{j=1}^{4} |F_i||F_j| \leq \frac{1}{2} \sum_{i=1}^{4} \sum_{j=1}^{4} \left(|F_i|^2 + |F_j|^2 \right) = 4 \sum_{i=1}^{4} |F_i|^2$. Therefore $\sum_{i=1}^{4} |F_i| \leq 2 \left(\sum_{i=1}^{4} |F_i|^2 \right)^{1/2}$. Now let $S_{ij} = |F_i| U_i + |F_j| U_j$ and let X_i be the vertex of T opposite to face F_i. If π and π' are parallel supporting planes of T a distance h apart and if π contains X_i and X_j while π' contains the remaining two vertices, then $V(T) = h|S_{ij}|/3$.

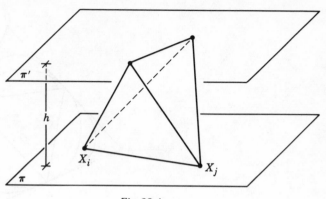

Fig. 22.4

Since we also have $V(T) = \frac{1}{3} \sum\limits_{i=1}^{4} r(T)|F_i|$, it follows that

$$h = \frac{r(T)\left(\sum\limits_{i=1}^{4} |F_i|\right)}{|S_{ij}|} \leq 2r(T)\left(\sum\limits_{i=1}^{4} |F_i|^2\right)^{1/2}|S_{ij}|$$

Therefore we have $\min h \leq 2r(T)\left(\sum\limits_{i=1}^{4} |F_i|^2\right)^{1/2}/\max |S_{ij}|$. But $\sum\limits_{i<j} |S_{ij}|^2 = 2\sum\limits_{i=1}^{4} |F_i|^2$ and $\max |S_{ij}| \geq \left(\sum\limits_{i<j} |S_{ij}|^2/6\right)^{1/2} = \left(\sum\limits_{i=1}^{4} |F_i|^2/3\right)^{1/2}$. Therefore $\Delta(T) = \min h \leq 2\sqrt{3}\, r(T)$. Since equality holds for a regular tetrahedron, our theorem holds when the center of the insphere lies in the convex cover of four points of $S \cap K$. Suppose O lies in the convex cover of three or fewer points of $S \cap K$ and let π be the plane containing O and these points. If we apply Theorem 22.4 to $K \cap \pi$, we get $\Delta(K) \leq \Delta(K \cap \pi) \leq 3r(K) < 2\sqrt{3}\, r(K)$, and our proof is complete.

The remainder of this section will be devoted to some improvements and applications of the Brunn-Minkowski theorem. If we restrict our sets to those pairs of convex bodies which have projections of equal area in at least one direction, then not only is $[V((1-r)K_0 + rK_1)]^{1/3}$ a concave function of r, but so is $V[(1-r)K_0 + rK_1]$ itself.

22.6   Theorem   Let K_0 and K_1 be three-dimensional convex bodies and let σ_0 and σ_1 be the orthogonal projections of K_0 and K_1 onto plane π. Let $|M|$ be the two-dimensional measure of set M. If $|\sigma_0| = |\sigma_1|$, then $V(K_r) = V[(1-r)K_0 + rK_1] \geq (1-r)V(K_0) + rV(K_1)$ for $0 \leq r \leq 1$.

PROOF   First suppose that σ_0 is a translate of σ_1 and translate K_1 so that $\sigma_0 = \sigma_1$. Let $P \epsilon \sigma_0$ and let l_P be the line through P perpendicular to

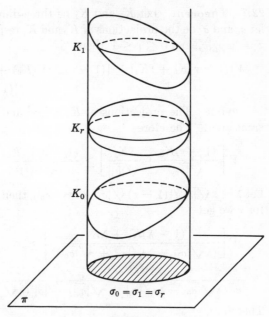

$$\sigma_0 = \sigma_1 = \sigma_r$$

Fig. 22.5

π. Since $|l_P \cap K_r| \geq (1 - r)|l_P \cap K_0| + r|l_P \cap K_1|$, we have

$$V(K_r) = \int_{\sigma_0} |l_P \cap K_r| \, dA_p \geq (1 - r)\int_{\sigma_0} |l_P \cap K_0| \, dA_p$$
$$+ r\int_{\sigma_0} |l_P \cap K_1| \, dA_p = (1 - r)V(K_0) + rV(K_1)$$

(see the proof of Theorem 21.5).

Now suppose that σ_0 is not a translate of σ_1, and translate K_0 and K_1 so that σ_0 and σ_1 both contain the origin O. According to the two-dimensional form of Theorem 20.6 there is a sequence of symmetrizations $\sigma_0{}^i$ of σ_0 about lines l_i in π passing through O such that $\sigma_0{}^i \rightarrow D$. D is the disk in π with center O and area equal to $|\sigma_0|$. Let $\bar{K}_0$ be the symmetrization of K_0 with respect to π. If π_i is the plane through l_i perpendicular to π, then we let $\bar{K}_0{}^i$ be the symmetral of $\bar{K}_0$ with respect to π_i. By Blaschke's selection theorem we can find a subsequence $\bar{K}_0{}^j$ which converges to a convex body K_0' such that $V(K_0') = V(K_0)$ and the projection of K_0' onto π is D. Similarly we construct K_1' with $V(K_1') = V(K_1)$ such that the projection of K_1' onto π is also D. It follows from Theorem 20.3 and the first part of this proof that $V[(1 - r)K_0 + rK_1] \geq V[(1 - r)K_0' + rK_1'] \geq (1 - r)V(K_0') + rV(K_1') = (1 - r)V(K_0) + rV(K_1)$, and our proof is complete.

An immediate consequence of the preceding theorem is the following sharpening of the Brunn-Minkowski theorem.

22.7   Theorem   Let K_0 and K_1 be three-dimensional convex bodies and let σ_0 and σ_1 be the projections of K_0 and K_1 respectively onto a plane π. If $x^2 = |\sigma_0|/|\sigma_1|$ and $0 \leq r \leq 1$, then

$$V[(1 - r)K_0 + rK_1] \geq [(1 - r)x^{-2}V(K_0) + rV(K_1)][(1 - r)x + r]^2 \geq [(1 - r)V^{1/3}(K_0) + rV^{1/3}(K_1)]^3$$

PROOF   The projections of $K_0/\sqrt{|\sigma_0|}$ and $K_1/\sqrt{|\sigma_1|}$ onto π have the same area.   Therefore

$$V\left[\frac{(1 - r)K_0}{\sqrt{|\sigma_0|}} + \frac{rK_1}{\sqrt{|\sigma_1|}}\right] \geq \frac{(1 - r)V(K_0)}{(\sqrt{|\sigma_0|})^3} + \frac{rV(K_1)}{(\sqrt{|\sigma_1|})^3}$$

Let $\lambda = r\sqrt{|\sigma_0|}/[(1 - r)\sqrt{|\sigma_1|} + r\sqrt{|\sigma_0|}]$, then $0 \leq \lambda \leq 1$, and substituting for r we get

$$V\left[\frac{(1 - \lambda)K_0 + \lambda K_1}{(\lambda\sqrt{|\sigma_1|} - \lambda\sqrt{|\sigma_0|} + \sqrt{|\sigma_0|})^3}\right] \geq$$

$$\frac{(1 - \lambda)V(K_0)}{|\sigma_0|(\lambda\sqrt{|\sigma_0|} - \lambda\sqrt{|\sigma_0|} + \sqrt{|\sigma_0|})} + \frac{\lambda V(K_1)}{|\sigma_1|(\lambda\sqrt{|\sigma_1|} - \lambda\sqrt{|\sigma_0|} + \sqrt{|\sigma_0|})}$$

Therefore,

$$V[(1 - \lambda)K_0 + \lambda K_1] \geq \left[\frac{(1 - \lambda)V(K_0)}{|\sigma_0|} + \frac{\lambda V(K_1)}{|\sigma_1|}\right]$$

$$[\lambda\sqrt{|\sigma_1|} - \lambda\sqrt{|\sigma_0|} + \sqrt{|\sigma_0|}]^2 = [(1 - \lambda)x^{-2}V(K_0) + \lambda V(K_1)][\lambda + x(1 - \lambda)]^2$$

To complete the proof we shall need the following inequality.   If a and b are nonnegative real numbers and $0 \leq \theta \leq 1$, then $[(1 - \theta)a^{1/3} + \theta b^{1/3}]^3 \leq (1 - \theta)^3a + \theta^3b \leq (1 - \theta)a + \theta b$.   Now let $a = V(K_0)$, $b = x^3V(K_1)$, and $\theta = \lambda/[(1 - \lambda)x + \lambda]$.   Then

$$\frac{(1 - \lambda)xV^{1/3}(K_0) + \lambda xV^{1/3}(K_1)}{(1 - \lambda)x + \lambda} \leq \frac{(1 - \lambda)xV(K_0) + \lambda x^3V(K_1)}{(1 - \lambda)x + \lambda}$$

Multiplying both sides by $[(1 - \lambda) + \lambda x^{-1}]^3$, we get the desired result.

The preceding theorem also has its counterpart in the plane.   We leave the proof as an exercise for the reader.

22.8   Theorem   Let K_0 and K_1 be two-dimensional convex bodies in the plane and let $\sigma_0(U)$ and $\sigma_1(U)$ be the projection of K_0 and K_1 respectively on a line perpendicular to the direction $\overrightarrow{OU}$.   If $x = |\sigma_0(U)|/|\sigma_1(U)|$ and $0 \leq r \leq 1$, then

$$V[(1 - r)K_0 + rK_1] \geq [(1 - r)x^{-1}V(K_0) + rV(K_1)][(1 - r)x + r]$$

$$\geq [(1 - r)V^{1/2}(K_0) + rV^{1/2}(K_1)]^2$$

The projection of a convex body K onto a plane is closely related to the surface area of K. In fact Cauchy showed that the surface area is in a sense the arithmetic mean of the projections in all directions. Together with the preceding theorem this can be used to show that not only is $V^{1/3}(K_r)$ a concave function of r but so is $A^{1/2}(K_r)$.

22.9   Cauchy's formula   Let $\sigma(K,U)$ be the projection of convex body K onto a plane with unit normal $\overrightarrow{OU}$, then $A(K) = \pi^{-1}\int_\Omega |\sigma(K,U)|\, dS$, where dS is an element of surface area of the unit sphere Ω with unit exterior normal $\overrightarrow{OU}$.

PROOF   First suppose that K is a polyhedral region with faces F_i and unit exterior normals $\overrightarrow{OU_i}$, $i = 1, \ldots, k$.   Then

$$2\int_\Omega |\sigma(K,U)|\, dS = \sum_{i=1}^{k} \int_\Omega ||F_i|U_i \cdot U|\, dS = \sum_{i=1}^{k} |F_i|\int_\Omega |U_i \cdot U|\, dS$$

$$= \sum_{i=1}^{k} |F_i|2\pi = 2\pi A(K)$$

Since both $\int_\Omega |\sigma(K_i,U)|\, dS \to \int_\Omega |\sigma(K,U)|\, dS$ and $A(K_i) \to A(K_i)$ whenever $K_i \to K$, and since any convex body can be expressed as the limit of a sequence of polyhedral regions, it follows that the formula also holds for arbitrary convex bodies.

22.10   Theorem   If K_0 and K_1 are three-dimensional convex bodies and $0 \le r \le 1$, then $A^{1/2}[(1-r)K_0 + rK_1] \ge (1-r)A^{1/2}(K_0) + rA^{1/2}(K_1)$.

PROOF   Since $\sigma(K_r,U) = (1-r)\sigma(K_0,U) + r\sigma(K_1,U)$, we can apply Theorem 22.8 to get

$$|\sigma(K_r,U)| \ge [(1-r)x^{-1}(N,U)|\sigma(K_0,U)| + r|\sigma(K_1,U)|]$$
$$[(1-r)x(N,U) + r]$$

If $\omega_0(N)$ and $\omega_1(N)$ are the width of K_0 and K_1 respectively in the direction $\overrightarrow{ON}$, then $x(N,U) = \omega_0(N)/\omega_1(N)$ for any unit vector $\overrightarrow{ON}$ perpendicular to $\overrightarrow{OU}$.   We assert that there is a number y such that given any direction $\overrightarrow{OU}$ we can always find a direction $\overrightarrow{ON}$ perpendicular to $\overrightarrow{OU}$ such that $x(N,U) = y$.   To see this let $S(U)$ be the interval of real numbers which is the range of the function $x(N,U)$ for fixed U.   Given any two directions $\overrightarrow{OU_1}$ and $\overrightarrow{OU_2}$ there is always at least one number in $S(U_1) \cap S(U_2)$.   For if $\overrightarrow{ON}$ is perpendicular to both $\overrightarrow{OU_1}$ and $\overrightarrow{OU_2}$, then $x(N,U_1) = x(N,U_2)$. It follows from Helly's theorem that there is a point y belonging to the intersection of all the segments $S(U)$. Therefore

$$|\sigma(K_r,U)| \geq [(1 - r)y^{-1}|\sigma(K_0,U)| + r|\sigma(K_1,U|][(1 - r)y + r]$$

Integrating both sides of this inequality with respect to an element of surface area over the unit sphere and applying Cauchy's formula we get $A(K_r) \geq [(1 - r)y^{-1}A(K_0) + rA(K_1)][(1 - r)y + r]$.

To complete the proof we use the following inequality. If a and b are nonnegative real numbers and $0 \leq \theta \leq 1$, then

$$[(1 - \theta)a^{1/2} + \theta b^{1/2}]^2 \leq (1 - \theta)^2 a + \theta^2 b \leq (1 - \theta)a + \theta b$$

If we let $a = A(K_0)$, $b = y^2 A(K_1)$, and $\theta = r/[(1 - r)y + r]$, then we get

$$[(1 - r)y^{-1}A(K_0) + rA(K_1)][(1 - r)y + r]$$
$$\geq [(1 - r)A^{1/2}(K_0) + rA^{1/2}(K_1)]^2$$

and we have finished.

For fixed convex bodies K_0 and K_1 and $0 \leq r \leq 1$ the function $f(r) = V^{1/3}[(1 - r)K_0 + rK_1]$ is a polynomial in r, and therefore f possesses derivatives of all orders. Since the Brunn-Minkowski theorem asserts that f is a concave function, it follows from Exercise 21.2 that $f''(r) \leq 0$ for $0 \leq r \leq 1$. We conclude this section with the following consequence of this result.

22.11 Theorem If K_0 and K_1 are convex bodies, then

    a. $V(K_0)V(K_0,K_1,K_1) \leq V^2(K_0,K_0,K_1)$ and
    b. $V(K_1)V(K_1,K_0,K_0) \leq V^2(K_1,K_1,K_0)$

PROOF Let $f(r) = V^{1/3}[(1-r)K_0+rK_1]$, then $f^3(r) = (1-r)^3 V(K_0) + 3(1 - r)^2 r V(K_0,K_0,K_1) + 3(1 - r)r^2 V(K_0,K_1,K_1) + r^3 V(K_1)$. It follows that

$$D_r[f^3(0)] = 3[V(K_0,K_0,K_1) - V(K_0)]$$

and

$$D_r^2[f^3(0)] = 6[V(K_0) - 2V(K_0,K_0,K_1) + V(K_0,K_1,K_1)]$$

Since $f(r) = [f^3(r)]^{1/3}$, we also have

$$3D_r[f(r)] = [f^3(r)]^{-2/3}D_r[f^3(r)]$$

and

$$9D_r^2(f(r)) = 2[f^3(r)]^{-5/3}D_r[f^3(r)] + 3[f^3(r)]^{-2/3}D_r^2[f^3(r)]$$

Therefore,

$$D_r^2[f(0)] = 2V^{-5/3}(K_0)[V(K_0,K_1,K_1) - V^2(K_0,K_0,K_1)] \leq 0$$

and part (*a*) follows immediately. If we interchange the roles of K_0 and K_1, part (*b*) follows, and the proof is complete.

Exercises

22.1 Determine upper and lower bounds whenever possible of the following ratios for convex bodies in the plane: (*a*) r/R; (*b*) r/D; (*c*) R/Δ; (*d*) L/D; (*e*) r/V; (*f*) R/V.

22.2 Determine upper and lower bounds whenever possible of the following ratios for convex bodies in 3-space: (*a*) r/R; (*b*) r/D; (*c*) R/Δ; (*d*) A/D; (*e*) r/V; (*f*) R/V.

22.3 Determine when equality holds for the inequalities in Exercise 22.1.

22.4 Determine when equality holds for the inequalities in Exercise 22.2

22.5 Show that the diameter of a tetrahedron is the length of its longest side. Do the same for a triangle.

22.6 Let $P_1, \ldots, P_4$ be vertices of a tetrahedron T and let $X \varepsilon T$. Show that there are real numbers $\lambda_i \geq 0$ such that $X = \sum_{i=1}^{4} \lambda_i P_i$ and $\sum_{i=1}^{4} \lambda_i = 1$.

22.7 Use Exercise 22.6 to show that whenever X lies in convex body K, then $X = \sum_{i=1}^{4} \lambda_i P_i, \lambda_i \geq 0, \sum_{i=1}^{4} \lambda_i = 1$, where $P_i \varepsilon K$.

22.8 Complete the proof of Theorem 22.3 for closed bounded sets in the plane.

22.9 Prove **Jung's Theorem**: Every set of diameter D is contained in a sphere of radius $D\sqrt{\frac{3}{8}}$.

22.10 Determine when equality holds in Theorem 22.4.

22.11 Prove **Blaschke's Theorem**: Every convex body in 3-space of thickness Δ contains a sphere of radius $\Delta/2\sqrt{3}$.

22.12 Give examples of convex bodies K other than regular tetrahedra for which $\Delta(K) = 2\sqrt{3}\,r(K)$.

22.13 Prove Theorem 22.8.

22.14 State and prove the two-dimensional analog to Cauchy's formula for surface area. Use this result to show that every convex set of constant width ω has length $\pi\omega$.

22.15 Using the notation of Theorem 22.9, show that $\int_\Omega |\sigma(K_i,U)|\,dS \to \int_\Omega |\sigma(K,U)|\,dS$ whenever $K_i \to K$.

22.16 Let K_0 and K_1 be convex bodies in 3-space and suppose $0 \leq r \leq 1$. If $f(r) = V^{1/3}[(1 - r)K_0 + rK_1]$, show that $f'(0) \geq f(1) - f(0)$. Use this result to prove Minkowski's inequality.

22.17   Show that the two-dimensional analog to Theorem 22.11 reduces to Minkowski's inequality in the plane.

22.18   Use Theorem 22.11 to show that:

   a. $V(K)V(K,B,B) \leq A^2(K)$
   b. $4\pi A(K) \leq 3V^2(K,B,B)$

Now use these results to show that:

   c. $36\pi V^2(K) \leq A^3(K)$ (Minkowski's inequality)
   d. $(36\pi)^2 V(K) \leq V^3(K,B,B)$

22.19   Show that for all convex bodies K in the plane, $\Delta(K) \leq \sqrt{3}\ V(K)$ where equality holds if K is an equilateral triangular region.

22.20   Show that the plane convex body K of least area containing a segment of unit length which can be rotated inside K through a complete revolution is the equilateral triangular region of unit thickness.

INTRODUCTION

5

**EUCLIDEAN
n-DIMENSIONAL SPACE**

In this chapter we generalize the concepts of the preceding chapters to n-dimensional euclidean space E^n. First we define E^n and determine how the postulates for E^3 can be extended to E^n. The notion of an r-flat is introduced, and its basic properties are developed. Next we define angular measurement in E^n along with parallelism and perpendicularity. Volume is generalized to E^n by introducing Jordan n-measure. In Sec. 25 supporting r-flats are defined, and extreme points are characterized. The theorems of Radon, Helly, and Carathéodory are all carried over to E^n. The motions and similarities of E^n are defined and categorized in Sec. 26. The final section of the chapter is devoted to applying the results of the

175

preceding sections to develop necessary and sufficient conditions for a linear programming problem to have a solution.

Results from linear algebra or analysis could be used to shorten the proofs of many of the theorems in this chapter considerably. However, we have avoided the use of these properties in favor of geometric properties in order to illustrate the use of the geometric concepts involved.

23   DEFINITION OF E^n

Descartes was the first mathematician to make extensive use of coordinates in geometry. They proved to be an extremely valuable tool and paved the way for the differential and integral calculus. Postulates 3 and 4 of Appendix 1 could be called the coordinate postulates, and they provide us with the means to set up a rectangular coordinate system for the plane or for 3-space. In 3-space this gives us a one-to-one correspondence between the points of 3-space and the set of all ordered triples of real numbers.

It was not until the middle of the nineteenth century that mathematicians first carried this process one step further and actually identified points in the plane with ordered pairs of real numbers and points of 3-space with ordered triples of real numbers. Instead of treating geometry as an axiomatic system built up from the undefined concepts of point, line, plane, etc., we can construct geometry from the real-number system by defining a point to be an ordered triple of real numbers, a plane to be the solution set $\{(x,y,z)\}$ of a linear equation $ax + by + cz + d = 0$, and a line to be the solution set of a pair of linear equations. Besides making available a wealth of algebraic techniques, this treatment has the advantage of reducing the problem of showing the consistency of euclidean geometry to the problem of showing that the real-number system is consistent. In order to bring out the distinction between attaching coordinates to points of euclidean space and the pure coordinate geometry of ordered triples, the reader should verify the fact that all the postulates in Appendix 1 are satisfied by the system of all ordered triples of real numbers (see the exercises at the end of Secs. 23 and 24).

Another important advantage of the geometry of ordered triples is that it can easily be generalized to higher dimensions. We now proceed to do just that.

23.1   n-dimensional euclidean space, E^n, is the set R^n of all ordered n-tuples of real numbers $\{(x_1, \ldots ,x_n)\}$ together with a distance defined on R^n as follows: If $X = (x_1, \ldots ,x_n)$ and $Y = (y_1, \ldots ,y_n)$, then the distance between X and Y is $|XY| = [(x_1 - y_1)^2 + \cdots + (x_n - y_n)^2]^{1/2}$. The elements of R^n are called **points of** E^n.

We note that when $n = 1, 2,$ or 3, the distance defined in 23.1 reduces to ordinary euclidean distance. From now on we shall identify the euclidean plane with E^2 and euclidean 3-space with E^3.

The following definitions and properties of E^n are easily generalized from E^2 and E^3.

23.2 We use capital letters to stand for points of E^n and small letters to stand for real numbers.

a. If $A = (a_1, \ldots, a_n)$, $B = (b_1, \ldots, b_n)$, and k is any real number, then we define the **dot product**, $A \cdot B = \sum_{i=1}^{n} a_i b_i$, the **sum of A and B**, $A + B = (a_1 + b_1, \ldots, a_n + b_n)$, and the **product of a point and a scalar**, $kA = (ka_1, \ldots, ka_n)$. $O = (0, \ldots, 0)$ is called the **null point**.

b. If $A \neq O$, then the set of all points X such that $A \cdot X = b$ is called a **hyperplane**. Two hyperplanes are called **parallel** if they do not intersect.

c. Points $A_1, \ldots, A_s$ are called **linearly independent** if $c_1 A_1 + \cdots + c_s A_s = 0$ implies that $c_1 = \cdots = c_s = 0$. The intersection of $n - r$ hyperplanes $A_i \cdot X = b_i$; $i = 1, \ldots, n - r$, where $\{A_i\}$ are linearly independent, is called an **r-flat**. Using linear algebra it can be shown that this definition is equivalent to the following. An r-flat is the set of all points $X \in E^n$ such that

$$X = \mu_1 B_1 + \cdots + \mu_r B_r + B; \; - \infty < \mu_i < \infty, i = 1, \ldots, r$$

where $B_1, \ldots, B_r$ are linearly independent.

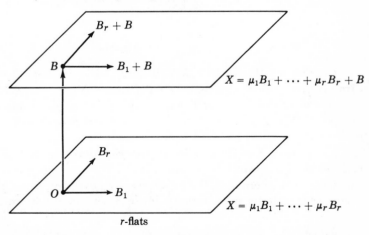

r-flats

Fig. 23.1

d. A 1-flat is called a **line.**   If P, Q, and R are any three points on the line $X = \mu B_1 + B$ so that $P = pB_1 + B$, $Q = qB_1 + B$, and $R = rB_1 + B$, $p \neq q$, then $B_1 = (P - Q)/(p - q)$ and $B = R - (P - Q)r/(p - q)$. Therefore the equation of the line can be written $X = (P - Q)(\mu - r)/(p - q) + R = t(P - Q) + R$, $- \infty < t < + \infty$. If $R = Q$, then the equation becomes $X = tP + (1 - t)Q$, $- \infty < t < + \infty$.

e. The set of all points $X \,\varepsilon\, E^n$ such that $X = (1 - t)P + tQ$, $0 \leq t \leq 1$, is called the **segment** $S[P,Q]$ joining P to Q. We note that $X = \mu B_1 + B$, $0 \leq \mu \leq 1$, is the equation of $S[B, B + B_1]$. We generalize this to r-dimensional segments as follows. An **r-dimensional parallelotope** $S[B, B + B_1, \ldots, B + B_r]$ is defined to be all points $X \,\varepsilon\, E^n$ such that $X = \mu_1 B_1 + \cdots + \mu_r B_r + B$; $0 \leq \mu_i \leq 1$, $i = 1, \ldots, r$, where $B_1, \ldots, B_r$ are linearly independent.

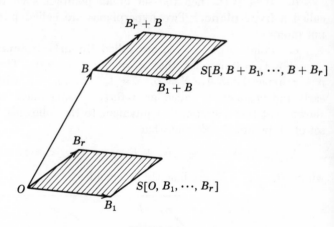

Fig. 23.2

f. The set of all points X such that $|XP| = r$ is called the $(n-1)$-**dimensional sphere** with center P and radius r. $N(P,r) = \{X \,\varepsilon\, E^n | |PX| < r\}$ is the **neighborhood** of P with radius r and is called an **open ball.** $\bar{N}(P,r) = \{X \,\varepsilon\, E^n | |PX| \leq r\}$ is the **closed neighborhood** of P with radius r and is called a **closed ball.**

g. A point X of E^n is called an **interior point** of set S iff there is a neighborhood of X which is contained in S. If there is a neighborhood of X which does not intersect S, then X is called an **exterior point** of S. If X is neither an exterior nor interior point of S, we call X a **boundary point** of S.

h. A set S in E^n is called **open** iff it consists entirely of interior points. S is called **closed** iff it contains all its boundary points. If for

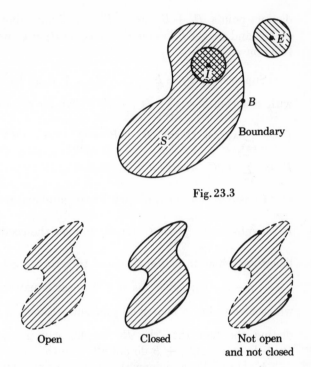

Fig. 23.3

Open   Closed   Not open
                                    and not closed

Fig. 23.4

every two points of S there is a curve joining them which is contained in S, then we call S **connected**. A **curve** is defined in E^n exactly as in E^3 (see 2.1).

It is an easy exercise for the reader to verify that Postulates 1 through 4 of Appendix 1 are satisfied in E^n. Postulates 5 through 8 also hold after a few modifications are made.

23.3 Theorem a. Every hyperplane in E^n contains at least n points not all lying in the same $(n-2)$-flat.

b. E^n contains at least $n+1$ points all of which are not contained in the same hyperplane.

c. If two points lie in an r-flat, then the line joining them lies in the same r-flat.

d. Any n points lie in a hyperplane, and any n points which do not all lie in an $(n-2)$-flat determine a hyperplane.

PROOF **a.** Let the parametric equation of the hyperplane π be $X = \mu_1 B_1 + \cdots + \mu_{n-1} B_{n-1} + B$, where $\{B_i\}$ are linearly independent. Letting all the μs except one be zero and the remaining μ be one, we get the distinct points $B_1 + B, \cdots, B_{n-1} + B$ all lying in π. Set $\mu_i = 0$ for each i, and we get B lies on π. Since no $B_i = O$, we have n distinct points lying on π.

Suppose $B, B_1 + B, \ldots, B_{n-1}, + B$ all lie in the same $(n-2)$-flat with equation $X = \sum\limits_{i=1}^{n-2} \mu_i C_i + C$. Then for certain constants λ_i we have

$B = \sum\limits_{i=1}^{n-2} \lambda_i C_i + C$ and $B_j + B = \sum\limits_{i=1}^{n-2} \lambda_i{}^j C_i + C$. Substituting we get

$B_j = \sum\limits_{i=1}^{n-2} b_i{}^j C_i$, where $b_i{}^j = \lambda_i{}^j - \lambda$.

Consider now an arbitrary linear combination of the Bs, $\sum\limits_{i=1}^{n-1} k_i B_i$.

If we substitute $\sum\limits_{i=1}^{n-2} b_i{}^j C_i$ for B_j and set the coefficients of the resulting linear combination of the Cs equal to zero, we get $\sum\limits_{i=1}^{n-1} k_i b_j{}^i = 0$, $j = 1$,

$\cdots, n-2$. This gives us $n - 2$ linear equations in $n - 1$ unknowns, which always has a nontrivial solution. But then $\sum\limits_{i=1}^{n-1} k_i B_i = O$, contradicting the fact that the Bs are linearly independent. Therefore B, $B_1 + B, \ldots, B_{n-1} + B$ do not all lie in the same $(n-2)$-flat.

b. Let E_i be the point with the ith coordinate 1 and the remaining coordinates 0. The Es are linearly independent. For suppose $\sum\limits_{i=1}^{n} c_i E_i = O$, then setting the ith coordinate of the sum equal to 0 we get $c_i = 0$ for each i. The points $O, E_1, \cdots, E_n$ are $n + 1$ distinct points of E^n. The proof that they do not all lie in the same hyperplane is exactly the same as the proof of part (a).

c. Let the r-flat π_r have the equation $X = \mu_1 B_1 + \cdots + \mu_r B_r + B$, and let $P, Q \in \pi_r$. Then if $R = (1 - t)P + tQ$, $P = \mu_1{}^1 B_1 + \cdots + \mu_r{}^1 B_r + B$, and $Q = \mu_1{}^2 B_1 + \cdots + \mu_r{}^2 B_r + B$, we have $R = [(1 - t)\mu_1{}^1 + t\mu_1{}^2]B_1 + \cdots + [(1 - t)\mu_r{}^1 + t\mu_r{}^2]B_r + (1 - t + t)B$. Therefore $R \in \pi_r$.

d. Let $B_1, \ldots, B_{n-1}, B$ be n points of E^n. If $B_1 - B, \ldots, B_{n-1} - B$ are linearly independent, then $X = \mu_1(B_1 - B) + \cdots + \mu_{n-1}(B_{n-1} - B) + B$ is the equation of a hyperplane containing $B_1, \ldots, B_{n-1}$ and B. If they are not linearly independent, let $B_1 - B, \ldots, B_r - B$ be the largest subset of $B_1 - B, \ldots, B_{n-1} - B$ which is linearly independent. The equation $X = \mu_1(B_1 - B) + \cdots + \mu_r(B_r - B) + B$ represents an r-flat π_r containing $B_1, \ldots, B_{n-1}, B$. To see this suppose that $B_j - B = c_1(B_1 - B) + \cdots + c_r(B_r - B)$, then $B_j = c_1(B_1 - B) + \cdots +$

$c_r(B_r - B) + B$ and $B_j \in \pi_r$. Since an r-flat is the intersection of $n - r$ hyperplanes, our proof is complete.

Exercises

23.1   Show that E^3 satisfies Postulates 1 through 4.

23.2   Without using Theorem 23.3 show directly that E^3 satisfies Postulates 5 through 8.

23.3   Show that E^n satisfies Postulates 1 through 4.

23.4   Prove that the two ways of defining a 2-flat in E^5 given in Definition 23.2 are equivalent.

23.5   Prove that the two ways of defining an r-flat in Definition 23.2 are equivalent.

23.6   Prove the following generalization of 23.2 part (**d**): If $C_0, X_1, \ldots, X_r$ lie in the r-flat π_r and if $C_i = X_i - C_0$ are linearly independent, then $\pi_r = \{ X | X = C_0 + \sum_{i=1}^{r} \mu_i C_i, - \infty < \mu_i < \infty \}$.

23.7   Complete the proof of part (**b**) of Theorem 23.3.

23.8   Prove that every r-flat contains at least $r + 1$ points not all lying in an $(r-1)$-flat.

23.9   Show that any $r + 1$ points lie in at least one r-flat and that any $r + 1$ points not all lying in an $(r-1)$-flat determine an r-flat.

23.10   Show that the set of all n-tuples of real numbers R^n forms a vector space if we use part (**a**) of Definition 23.2.

23.11   Generalize from 3-space to define the following concepts in E^n: (**a**) a hypersurface, (**b**) a simple closed hypersurface.

23.12   State the n-dimensional form of Theorem 5.8. Use this to prove the n-dimensional analog to Theorem 5.9.

23.13   Given r and s, what is the minimum value of t such that an r-flat and an s-flat will always be contained in a t-flat?

24   MEASUREMENT IN E^n

One of the properties of real numbers which proves most useful in our development of E^n is the following.

24.1   The Cauchy-Schwarz inequality

$$\left(\sum_{i=1}^{n} a_i b_i \right)^2 \leq \left(\sum_{i=1}^{n} a_1{}^2 \right) \left(\sum_{i=1}^{n} b_i{}^2 \right)$$

where equality holds iff there is a real number t such that $a_i + tb_i = 0$ for each $i = 1, \ldots, n$. If we let $|A| = |AO|$ be the distance from point A

to the null point, this is equivalent to the inequality $|A \cdot B| \leq |A||B|$, where $A \cdot B = |A||B|$ iff $A = tB$ for some real number t.

PROOF Let t be a real parameter. Then

$$0 \leqslant \sum_{i=1}^{n} (a_i + tb_i)^2 = \left(\sum_{i=1}^{n} a_1{}^2 \right) + \left(\sum_{i=1}^{n} a_i b_i \right) 2t + \left(\sum_{i=1}^{n} b_1{}^2 \right) t^2$$

Since a quadratic with positive leading coefficient is positive iff its discriminant is negative, it follows that $4 \left(\sum_{i=1}^{n} a_i b_i \right)^2 - 4 \left(\sum_{i=1}^{n} a_i{}^2 \right) \left(\sum_{i=1}^{n} b_i{}^2 \right) < 0$ unless the quadratic has a zero. But a nonnegative quadratic has a zero t_0 iff its discriminant is zero. Therefore

$$4 \left(\sum_{i=1}^{n} a_i b_i \right)^2 - 4 \left(\sum_{i=1}^{n} a_i{}^2 \right) \left(\sum_{i=1}^{n} b_i{}^2 \right) = 0 \text{ iff } a_i + t_0 b_i = 0$$

for $i = 1, \ldots, n$.

We now proceed to define angular measurement and perpendicularity in E^n. We make the following definition.

24.2 A **ray** $R[P,Q]$ is the set of points $X = (1 - t)P + tQ$; $0 \leq t$. An **angle** $\angle BAC$ is the union of two rays $R[A,B)$ and $R[A,C)$ having the same initial point A, called the **vertex** of the angle.

From our knowledge of analytic geometry we know that in E^3 the formula $B \cdot C = |B||C| \cos \angle BOC$ holds for arbitrary points B and C. The Cauchy-Schwarz inequality enables us to generalize this to define angular measurement in E^n.

24.3 Definition $\cos \angle AOB = A \cdot B/|A||B|$, and in general

$$\cos \angle ABC = \frac{(A - B) \cdot (C - B)}{(|A - B||C - B|)}$$

24.4 Theorem To each angle $\angle BAC$ there corresponds a unique real number $m \angle BAC$ between 0 and π called the **measure** of $\angle BAC$.

PROOF Let $m \angle BAC = \text{Arc cos } (\cos \angle ABC)$. Since $-1 \leq \cos \angle ABC \leq 1$ by the Cauchy-Schwarz inequality, it follows that $m \angle BAC$ exists and lies between 0 and π. It remains to show that $m \angle BAC = m \angle B'AC'$ whenever $R[A,B) = R[A,B')$ and $R[A,C) = R[A'C')$. Since B' lies on $R[A,B)$ and C' lies on $R[A,C)$, we have $B' = (1 - t)A + tB$ and $C' = (1 - s)A + sC$ for positive numbers t and s. Therefore $B' - A = t(B - A)$, $C' - A = s(C - A)$, and $\cos \angle B'AC' = t(B - A) \cdot s(C - A)/(|t(B - A)||s(C - A)|) = \cos \angle BAC$. This follows from the fact that $|rX| = r|X|$ for any point X and any positive number r.

The following theorem tells us that if two lines l_1 and l_2 intersect at A so that one angle with vertex A and sides on l_1 and l_2 respectively has measure $\pi/2$, then all four such angles have measure $\pi/2$.

24.5 Theorem Let $B' \varepsilon L(A,B)$, $B' \neq A$ and $C' \varepsilon L(A,C)$, $C' \neq A$. If $m \angle BAC = \pi/2$, then $m \angle B'AC' = \pi/2$.

PROOF By assumption $B' = A + t(B - A)$, $t \neq 0$, and $C' = A + s(C - A)$, $s \neq 0$. Therefore

$$\cos \angle B'AC' = \frac{(B' - A) \cdot (C' - A)}{(|B' - A||C' - A|)}$$

$$= \frac{ts(B - A) \cdot (C - A)}{(|ts||B - A||C - A|)} = 0$$

Therefore $m \angle B'AC' = \pi/2$.

24.6 If $m \angle BAC = \pi/2$, then lines $L(B,A)$ and $L(C,A)$ are said to be **perpendicular**. A useful fact is that $(B - A) \cdot (C - A) = 0$ iff $L(B,A)$ is perpendicular to $L(C,A)$ $(B \neq A, C \neq A)$.

We note that Theorem 24.5 shows that this definition is independent of the choice of point B on $L(B,A)$ and point C on $L(C,A)$.

In E^3 we know that the locus of all points on lines perpendicular to a fixed line at a fixed point on the line is a plane. A similar situation holds in E^n. Let $L(P,Q)$ be any line in E^n. Then $(X - Q) \cdot (P - Q) = 0$ is the equation of the locus of all points X on lines passing through Q perpendicular to $L(P,Q)$. Since the distributive and commutative laws for the dot product hold in E^n this equation can be written $(P - Q) \cdot X = Q \cdot (P - Q)$. This is the equation of a hyperplane. We make the following definition.

24.7 Line l is called **perpendicular** to hyperplane π iff l is perpendicular to every line in π passing through $l \cap \pi$.

The next few theorems give us a number of relations between lines and hyperplanes.

24.8 Theorem Through a given point P not on hyperplane π there passes exactly one line perpendicular to π.

PROOF Let the equation of π be $A \cdot (X - X_0) = 0$, and consider the point $Y_0 = P - A[(P - X_0) \cdot A]/A \cdot A$. Since $A \cdot Y_0 = A \cdot P -$

$(P - X_0) \cdot A = A \cdot X_0$, it follows that $Y_0 \, \varepsilon \, \pi$.   We assert that $L(P,Y_0)$ is perpendicular to π.   Let $X \, \varepsilon \, \pi$.   Then

$$(P - Y_0) \cdot (X - Y_0)$$

$$= A \cdot \left\{ X - P + \frac{(P - X_0) \cdot A}{A \cdot A} \, A \right\} \quad \frac{(P - X_0) \cdot A}{A \cdot A}$$

$$= A \cdot (X - X_0) \, \frac{(P - X_0) \cdot A}{A \cdot A} = 0$$

Therefore $L(P,Y_0)$ is perpendicular to π.

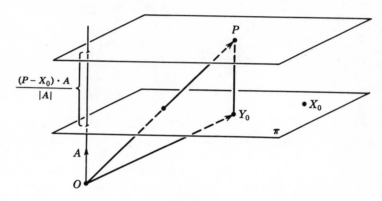

Fig. 24.1

We now show that no other line through P is perpendicular to π. Since the equation of $L(P,Y_0)$ can be written $X = P + t(P - Y_0) = P + t[(P - X_0) \cdot A/A \cdot A]A = P + sA, \, - \infty < s, t < + \infty$, we see that $L(P,Y_0)$, and therefore Y_0, is independent of which point $X_0 \, \varepsilon \, \pi$ we use to construct Y_0.   Let X_0 be an arbitrary point of π, $X_0 \neq Y_0$.   Then

$$(P - X_0) \cdot (Y_0 - X_0) = (P - X_0) \cdot \left\{ (P - X_0) - \frac{(P - X_0) \cdot A}{A \cdot A} \, A \right\}$$

$$= |P - X_0|^2 - \frac{[(P - X_0) \cdot A]^2}{|A|^2}$$

$$\geq |P - X_0|^2 - \frac{|P - X_0|^2 |A|^2}{|A|^2} = 0$$

By 24.1, the Cauchy-Schwarz inequality, equality holds iff $(P - X_0) = kA$ for some real number k.   If equality holds, $X_0 = P - kA$ and $X_0 \, \varepsilon \, L(P,Y_0)$.   This means that $L(P,Y_0)$ intersects π in two distinct points X_0

and Y_0 and therefore lies entirely in π. But then $P \in \pi$, contrary to assumption. Therefore equality does not hold and $(P - X_0) \cdot (Y_0 - X_0) > 0$. It follows that $L(P,X_0)$ is not perpendicular to π and $L(P,Y_0)$ is the only line through P perpendicular to π.

24.9   Theorem   Let X_0 be an arbitrary point on the hyperplane π with equation $A \cdot X = b$. Then $L(A + X_0,X_0)$ is the unique line through X_0 perpendicular to π.

   PROOF $(A + X_0 - X_0) \cdot (X - X_0) = A \cdot X - A \cdot X_0 = 0$ for every $X \in \pi$. Therefore $L(A + X_0,X_0)$ is perpendicular to π.

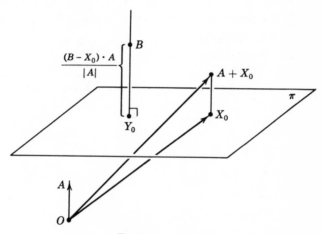

Fig. 24.2

   Suppose that $B \notin \pi$ and let $Y_0 = B - [(B - X_0) \cdot A/A \cdot A]A$. According to the proof of Theorem 24.8, $L(B,Y_0)$ is the unique line through B perpendicular to π, and the equation of $L(B,Y_0)$ can be written $X = Y_0 + sA$, $-\infty < s < +\infty$. If $X_0 = Y_0$, it follows that $L(B,X_0)$ has the equation $X = X_0 + sA$. But this is also an equation for $L(A + X_0,X_0)$. If $X_0 \neq Y_0$, then $L(B,X_0)$ is not perpendicular to π and $L(A + X_0,X_0)$ is the only line through X_0 perpendicular to π.

24.10   Theorem   Let π_1 and π_2 be two distinct hyperplanes with equations $A_1 \cdot X = a_1$, $A_2 \cdot X = a_2$ respectively. π_1 and π_2 are parallel iff $A_1 = kA_2$ for some nonzero real number k.

   PROOF   Suppose $A_1 = kA_2$, $k \neq 0$. If $X \in \pi_1$, then $A_1 \cdot X = a_1 = kA_2 \cdot X$, and $A_2 \cdot X = a_1/k$. If $a_1/k = a_2$, then $\pi_1 = \pi_2$, contrary to assumption. Therefore $A_2 \cdot X = a_1/k \neq a_2$, $X \notin \pi_2$, and π_1 is parallel to π_2.

Suppose $A_1 \neq kA_2$ for any k. If $a_1 = a_2 = 0$, then $O \in \pi_1 \cap \pi_2$ and π_1 is not parallel to π_2. Suppose not both a_1 and a_2 are zero, and let $A_1 \cdot X = c_1 x_1 + \cdots + c_n x_n$ and $A_2 \cdot X = d_1 x_1 + \cdots + d_n x_n$. If $c_i : d_i = c_j : d_j$ for each pair of subscripts i and j, then $A_1 = kA_2$, contrary to assumption. It follows that there is at least one pair of subscripts p, q such that $\begin{vmatrix} c_p & c_q \\ d_p & d_q \end{vmatrix} \neq 0$. Since not both a_1 and a_2 are zero, the pair of equations $c_p x_p + c_q x_q = a_1$, $d_p x_p + d_q x_q = a_2$ has a unique solution $(\bar{x}_p, \bar{x}_q)$. The point X with its pth coordinate equal to $\bar{x}_p$, its qth coordinate equal to $\bar{x}_q$, and all other coordinates zero lies in $\pi_1 \cap \pi_2$. Therefore π_1 and π_2 are not parallel.

24.11   Theorem   If line l is perpendicular to hyperplane π_1 and π_1 is parallel to hyperplane π_2, then l is perpendicular to π_2.

PROOF   We may assume that π_1 and π_2 have equations $A \cdot X = a$, $A \cdot X = b$ respectively. Let $P = l \cap \pi_1$; then by Theorem 24.9 the equation of l can be written $X = P + tA$. If $t_0 = (b - A \cdot P)/A \cdot A$, we then have $l \cap \pi_2 = Q = P + t_0 A$. Since $Q \in l$, the equation of l can be written $X = Q + sA$. According to Theorem 24.9 this is also the equation of the line through Q perpendicular to π_2.

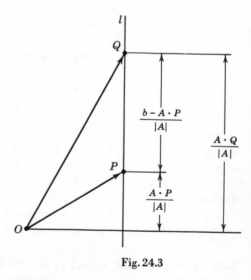

Fig. 24.3

24.12   Theorem $L(P,Q)$ is perpendicular to hyperplane π at point Q iff $|PX|^2 = |PQ|^2 + |QX|^2$ for all $X \in \pi$.

PROOF $|PX|^2 = (P - X) \cdot (P - X)$
$$= [(P - Q) + (Q - X)] \cdot [(P - Q) + (Q - X)]$$
$$= |PQ|^2 + |QX|^2 + 2(P - Q) \cdot (Q - X)$$

Since $L(P,Q)$ is perpendicular to $L(Q,X)$ iff $(P - Q) \cdot (Q - X) = 0$, the theorem follows.

Besides showing that the perpendicular distance from a point P to a hyperplane π is the shortest distance between P and points of π, we have also shown that the Pythagorean theorem is valid in E^n.

We now turn to a discussion of length, volume, and surface area in E^n. The length of a curve in E^n is easily taken care of with the following remark. If the reader will consider all the points discussed in Sec. 2 as points in E^n, then all the definitions and results of Sec. 2 hold in E^n.

In order to discuss n-dimensional volume we need to generalize triangle and tetrahedron as well as rectangle and rectangular parallelepiped to E^n. To do this we shall use a generalization of the space separation axiom. A convex set in E^n is defined exactly as in E^3.

24.13   Theorem   Let π be a hyperplane in E^n.   Then E^n is the union of π and two convex sets H_1 and H_2 such that whenever $P \varepsilon H_1$ and $Q \varepsilon H_2$, then $S(P,Q) \cap \pi \neq \emptyset$. H_1 and H_2 are called the **half spaces** with boundary hyperplane π.

    PROOF   Let $A \cdot X = b$ be the equation of π, and define $H_1 = \{X \varepsilon E^n | A \cdot X < b\}$ and $H_2 = \{X \varepsilon E^n | A \cdot X > b\}$.   We prove only that H_1 is convex.   The proof that H_2 is convex is similar.   Suppose $P, Q \varepsilon H_1$ and consider any point $R = (1 - t)P + tQ, 0 \leq t \leq 1$.   We have $R \cdot A = [(1 - t)P + tQ] \cdot A = (1 - t)P \cdot A + tQ \cdot A < (1 - t)b + tb = b$. Therefore $R \varepsilon H_1$, and H_1 is convex.

    To complete the proof let $P \varepsilon H_1$ and $Q \varepsilon H_2$.   Since $P \cdot A < b$ and $Q \cdot A > b$, the real number $t_0 = (b - P \cdot A)/(Q \cdot A - P \cdot A)$ exists, and $0 \leq t_0 \leq 1$.   If $R = (1 - t_0)P + t_0Q$, then $R \cdot A = b$ and $R \varepsilon S(P,Q) \cap \pi$.

    As in the preceding chapters we use the notation $H(\pi,P)$ for the half space with boundary hyperplane π which contains point P, and $H[\pi,P)$ for the closed half space $H(\pi,P) \cup \pi$.

We now make the following definitions.

24.14   Let $B_1 - B_0, \ldots, B_n - B_0$ be n independent points in E^n.   For fixed i let H_i be the closed half space containing B_i and bounded by the hyperplane containing the remaining points $B_j, j \neq i$.   We call $\overset{n}{\underset{i=0}{\cap}} H_i$ an n-**simplex** T with **vertices** $B_0, \ldots, B_n$.

24.15   A rectangular n-dimensional parallelotope, or more simply an n-**box**, is an n-dimensional parallelotope $S[B, B + B_1, \ldots, B + B_n]$ in

which $L(B,B + B_i)$ is perpendicular to the hyperplane H_i with equation
$$X = B + \sum_{j \neq i} \mu_j B_j,$$

In an n-simplex $T(B_0,B_1, \ldots ,B_n)$ let h_i be the perpendicular distance from vertex B_i to the hyperplane containing T_i, the simplex spanned by the remaining vertices B_j, $j \neq i$. In E^2 a triangle has area $|T_i|h_i/2$, and in E^3 a tetrahedron has volume $|T_i|h_i/3$. We generalize this with the following recursive definition.

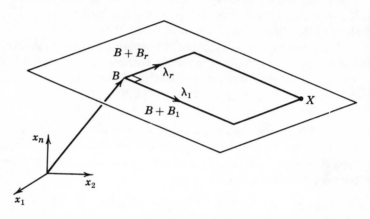

Fig. 24.4

24.16   The **n-volume** of an n-simplex T is $|T| = |T_i|h_i/n$.

In Theorem 28.8 we show that it is possible to identify an r-flat with E^r. This means that we can always find an equation of an r-flat of the form
$$X = \sum_{i=1}^{r} \lambda_i B_i + B \text{ such that } B_i \cdot B_j = 0 \text{ for } i \neq j \text{ and } |B_i| = 1 \text{ for each } i.$$
The λs act as coordinates of point X, and we can identify X with the point $(\lambda_1, \ldots ,\lambda_r)$ of E^r. All the metric properties of E^r including our definition of r-volume are preserved under this correspondence. We use these results in the following discussion.

Let $T(O,B_1, \ldots ,B_n)$ be a simplex in E^n, let $B_i = (b_{i1}, \ldots ,b_{in})$, and let det (b_{ij}) be the determinant of the matrix with elements b_{ij}. In E^2 we know that $|T| = |\text{det } (b_{ij})|/2$ and that $|\text{det } (b_{ij})|$ remains invariant under a rotation of coordinate axes about the origin. We assert that $|T(O,B_1, \ldots ,B_n)| = |\text{det } (b_{ij})|/n!$ for arbitrary n and that $|\text{det } (b_{ij})|$ is invariant under a change of coordinates which keeps the origin fixed. Suppose the assertion is true for any $(n-1)$-simplex and let $T = T(O,B_1, \ldots ,B_n)$ be an n-simplex.

First we show that $|\text{det } (b_{ij})|$ is invariant under a change of coordinates keeping the origin fixed. To see this let $C_i \cdot C_j = 0$ for $i \neq j$ and

$|C_i| = 1$ for $i = 1, \ldots, n$. Then $\det (c_{ij}) \det (c_{ij}) = 1$, and $\det (c_{ij}) = \pm 1$. Choose Cs with these properties so that $O, B_1, \ldots, B_{n-1}$ and $O, C_1, \ldots, C_{n-1}$ span the same hyperplane (see Theorem 28.8), and let $B_i = \mu_{i1}C_1 + \cdots + \mu_{in}C_n$, $i = 1, \ldots, n$. Then $\det (b_{ij}) = \det (\mu_{ij}) \det (c_{ij})$ and $|\det (b_{ij})| = |\det (\mu_{ij})|$.

Now choose coordinate axes with O the origin so that the x_n axis is perpendicular to $T(O, B_1, \ldots, B_{n-1})$. Then $h_n = \pm b_{nn}$ and

$$
\frac{\det (b_{ij})}{n!} = \frac{1}{n!}
\begin{vmatrix}
b_{11} & \cdots & b_{1(n-1)} & 0 \\
\cdots\cdots\cdots\cdots\cdots\cdots\cdots \\
b_{(n-1)1} & \cdots & b_{(n-1)(n-1)} & 0 \\
b_{n1} & \cdots & b_{n(n-1)} & b_{nn}
\end{vmatrix}
$$

$$
= \frac{1}{n} b_{nn} \frac{1}{(n-1)!}
\begin{vmatrix}
b_{11} & \cdots & b_{1(n-1)} \\
\cdots\cdots\cdots\cdots\cdots\cdots \\
b_{(n-1)1} & \cdots & b_{(n-1)(n-1)}
\end{vmatrix}
$$

$$
= \pm \frac{1}{n} h_n |T_n|
$$

Therefore $|T| = |\det (b_{ij})|/n!$. Besides giving us a convenient formula for computing the volume of a simplex, this result also shows that Definition 24.16 is independent of which base and corresponding altitude are used.

In order to be a good definition of n-volume it should give rise to a reasonable generalization for the n-volume of n-boxes. This turns out to be the case.

24.17 Theorem Let $e_i = |B_i|$ be the lengths of the edges of an n-box $S = S[B, B + B_1, \ldots, B + B_n]$. Then the n-volume of S is $|S| = e_1 \cdots e_n$.

PROOF Let P be the center of S (that is, the intersection of the n hyperplanes each midway between a pair of parallel faces of S), and consider the $2n$ pyramids with vertex P and base an $(n-1)$-face of S. The base of a pyramid can be partitioned into $(n-1)$-simplexes each of which, together with P, determines an n-simplex. All these simplexes have the same height, and their union is the whole pyramid. Therefore the n-volume of each pyramid is $1/n$ times the $(n-1)$-volume of the base times the height. Let S_i be the $(n-1)$-face of S through B which does not contain $B + B_i$. Let S_{ij} be the $(n-2)$-face of S through B which does not contain $B + B_i$ and $B + B_j$. Define S_{ijk} in a similar manner. We have

$$
|S| = \frac{1}{n} (e_1|S_1| + \cdots + e_n|S_n|)
$$

We can now repeat the process on each $(n-1)$-box S_i. For example,

$$|S_1| = \frac{1}{(n-1)} (e_2|S_{12}| + \cdots + e_n|S_{1n}|)$$

Continuing this process we eventually get

$$|S| = \frac{1}{n!} (n!e_1e_2 \cdots e_n)$$

This completes the proof.

Polyhedra are the basic elements used to define Jordan measure in E^3. We therefore use n-dimensional polyhedra to define n-dimensional Jordan measure.

24.18

    a. A function f with domain A in E^m and range in E^n is called **continuous** at P iff given $\epsilon > 0$ there is a $\delta > 0$ such that $f[N(P,\delta) \cap A] \subset N[f(P),\epsilon]$. If the inverse relation f^{-1} is a continuous function, then f is called **bicontinuous**.

    b. A **hypersurface** is a continuous function of an $(n-1)$-box into E^n. We also allow the domain to be all of E^{n-1}. We use the word hypersurface to stand for both the function itself and the range of the function.

    c. The bicontinuous image of an $(n-1)$-sphere in E^n is called a **simple closed hypersurface**.

    d. A simple closed hypersurface which is the union of $(n-1)$-simplexes, no one containing interior points of any other, is called an n-**polyhedron**. An n-polyhedron together with its interior is called an n-**polyhedral region**.

It can be shown that the Jordan-curve theorem holds in E^n as well as in E^3, so that part (***d***) makes sense.[1]

As in E^3, the n-volume of an n-polyhedron Π is obtained by partitioning Π into n-simplexes and summing up the volumes of the n-simplexes (see Exercises 24.11 and 24.12).

24.19 Let A be a set of points in E^n and let $V(\Pi)$ stand for the n-volume of n-polyhedron Π. If A contains no finite union of nonoverlapping n-polyhedra Π, we define $m_i(A) = 0$. If not we let $m_i(A) = \sup_{\Pi \subset A} V(\Pi)$. $m_i(A)$ is called the **inner** n-**measure** of A. Let $m_0(A) = \inf_{\Pi \supset A} V(\Pi)$ and

[1] See D. W. Hall and G. L. Spencer, "Elementary Topology," John Wiley & Sons, Inc., New York, 1955.

call $m_0(A)$ the **outer n-measure** of A. If $m_0(A) = m_i(A)$, we denote the common value by $|A|_J^m$ and call it the **Jordan n-measure** or n-volume of A.

All the properties of Jordan measure developed in Sec. 3 and Sec. 4 can be carried over to E^n.

Surface area in E^n can be developed in terms of n-volume exactly the same way as in Chap. 4.[1]

Exercises

24.1 If P, $Q \in E^n$ and $|X| = |OX|$, show that $|P + Q| \leq |P| + |Q|$.

24.2 Use Exercise 24.1 to show that whenever P, Q, $R \in E^n$, then $|PQ| \leq |PR| + |RQ|$. Determine when the equality holds.

24.3 Show that Postulates 11 through 14 in Appendix 1 hold when Theorem 24.4 is used to define the measure of an angle in E^n.

24.4 Show that the law of sines and the law of cosines both hold for triangles in E^n.

24.5 In E^n we call r-flat π_r perpendicular to $(n-r)$-flat $\pi_{(n-r)}$ iff $\pi_r \cap \pi_{(n-r)}$ is a point P and every line in π_r through P is perpendicular to every line in $\pi_{(n-r)}$ through P. Show that through each point of a 2-flat F in E^4 there passes exactly one 2-flat F' perpendicular to F.

24.6 Extend Exercise 24.5 to r-flats in E^n.

24.7 Let π be a hyperplane in E^n and suppose that $L(P,Q)$ is perpendicular to π at Q. Show that $\{X \in E^n | m \angle PQX < \pi/2\}$ and $\{X \in E^n | m \angle PQX > \pi/2\}$ are the two half spaces in E^n bounded by π.

24.8 Find the volume of the n-simplex whose vertices are the origin and E_i, $i = 1$, $\ldots$, n, where E_i is the point whose ith coordinate is 1 and all others are 0.

24.9 If $P = (x_1, x_2, x_3)$, $Q = (y_1, y_2, y_3)$, $R = (z_1, z_2, z_3)$, and the origin O form a tetrahedron T in E^3, show directly that

$$|T| = \pm\tfrac{1}{6}\begin{vmatrix} x_1 & x_2 & x_3 \\ y_1 & y_2 & y_3 \\ z_1 & z_2 & z_3 \end{vmatrix}$$

24.10 In Definition 24.14 show that $\{B_i - B_j; i \neq j, j \text{ fixed}\}$ are linearly independent whenever $\{B_i - B_0, i = 1, \ldots, n\}$ are linearly independent.

24.11 Generalize Theorem 4.5 to E^n.

24.12 Generalize Theorem 4.6 to E^n.

24.13 If $T = T(O, B_1, \ldots, B_n)$ is an orthogonal simplex, i.e., if $L(O, B_i)$ is perpendicular to the $(n-1)$-simplex with vertices O and B_j, $j \neq i$, show that $|T| = |B_1| \cdots |B_n|/n!$.

[1] For a detailed discussion see H. G. Eggleston, "Convexity," Cambridge University Press, London, 1958.

24.14 Show that an n-dimensional parallelotope $S[O,B_1, \ldots ,B_n]$ has n-volume equal to the absolute value of the determinant of the matrix whose ith row is composed of the components of B_i.

24.15 Generalize Theorems 3.13 and 3.14 to E^n.

25 CONVEXITY IN E^n

A nonempty closed bounded convex set in E^n is called a **convex body.** The reader can verify that Theorems 6.7, 6.8, 6.9, and 11.9 all carry over directly to E^n with minor changes in wording. These properties will be used throughout the following.

25.1 Let S be a set of points in E^n. Hyperplane π is called a **supporting hyperplane** of S iff π contains at least one boundary point of S and S lies entirely in one of the closed half spaces bounded by π. The closed half space bounded by π which contains S is called a **supporting half space** of S. If F is an r-flat which contains boundary points of the n-dimensional convex set K but no interior points of K, then F is called a **supporting r-flat** of K.

We note that a supporting r-flat of S is not defined in E^n unless S is **n-dimensional,** that is, S contains at least one $(n-1)$-dimensional sphere.

Just as in E^3 an n-dimensional closed convex set is identical with the intersection of all its supporting half spaces. This will be proved by the following theorems.

25.2 Theorem If K_1 is a closed convex set and K_2 is a convex body which does not intersect K_1, then there exists a hyperplane separating K_1 from K_2.

PROOF Let P_1 and P_2 be points of K_1 and K_2 such that $|P_1P_2| = \inf_{Q_i \varepsilon K_i} |Q_1Q_2|$. It can be shown that such a pair of points will always exist (see Appendix 2). Let π_1 and π_2 be the hyperplanes through P_1 and P_2 perpendicular to $L(P_1,P_2)$. Suppose there is a point $Q \varepsilon K_1$ on the same side of π_1 as P_2. In the 2-flat spanned by P_2, P_1, and Q drop a perpendicular from P_2 to $L(P_1,Q)$ with foot F. If $F \varepsilon S(P_1,Q)$, then $|P_2F| < |P_2P_1|$, contrary to assumption. If $Q \varepsilon S(P_1,F)$, then $|P_2Q| < |P_2P_1|$, also contrary to assumption. Therefore all of K_1 lies on one side of π_1 and π_1 is a supporting hyperplane of K_1. Similarly π_2 supports K_2, and any hyperplane between π_1 and π_2 will separate K_1 from K_2.

25.3 Theorem Let Σ be a simple hypersurface which partitions E^n into three disjoint sets. Σ bounds a convex set K iff through each point of Σ there passes at least one supporting plane of K.

PROOF   First we use induction on n to prove the "only if" part of the theorem.   The statement is true for $n = 2$ (see Theorem 7.6).   Suppose the theorem is true for $n = 2, \ldots, k - 1$.   Let I be a fixed interior point of K and B be an arbitrary boundary point of K.   Let π_{k-1}, π_2 be a $(k-1)$-flat and 2-flat respectively containing $L(B,I)$, $\pi_2 \not\subset \pi_{k-1}$. $\pi_2 \cap K$ is a convex set with boundary point B, so by the induction hypothesis there is a supporting line l to $\pi_2 \cap K$ at B.   Now let K' be the projection of K

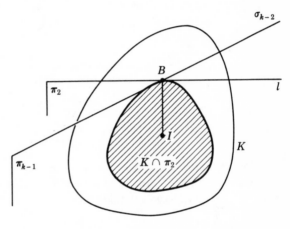

Fig. 25.1

parallel to l onto π_{k-1}.   That is, through each point P of K draw the line p parallel to l in the 2-flat spanned by P and l, and let $P' = p \cap \pi_{k-1}$ be the projection of P. K' is convex.   For let P', $Q' \in K'$ and let P, $Q \in K$ be in their preimages. $L(B,P')$, $L(B,Q')$, and l span a 3-flat (or 2-flat) π_3 which contains $L(P,P')$ and $L(Q,Q')$.   Since $L(P,P')$ and $L(Q,Q')$ are parallel to l and all lie in π_3, it follows that $L(P,P')$ is parallel to $L(Q,Q')$. If $R' \in S(P',Q')$, then the line through R' parallel to $L(P',P)$ in the 2-flat spanned by $L(P,P')$ and $L(Q,Q')$ intersects $S(P,Q)$ in a point R. R' is the image of R under the projection.   Therefore K' is convex.   By the induction hypothesis there is a supporting $(k-2)$-flat σ_{k-2} to K' at its boundary point B.   Let σ be the hyperplane spanned by σ_{k-2} and l.   We assert that σ is a supporting hyperplane of K.   Suppose the contrary.   Then there is an interior point X of K on σ.   But the projection of X onto π_{k-1} parallel to l will be an interior point of K' lying on σ_{k-2}.   This contradicts the choice of σ_{k-2} and proves one half of the theorem.

The proof of the converse is exactly the same as in E^3 and is left to the reader (see Theorem 8.10).

Let K be an n-dimensional closed convex set and let M be the intersection of all its supporting half spaces.   If $X \notin K$, then there is a point

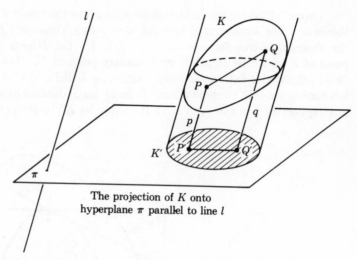

The projection of K onto
hyperplane π parallel to line l

Fig. 25.2

P of K a minimum distance from X, and the hyperplane through P perpendicular to $L(X,P)$ separates X from K. Therefore $X \notin M$ and $M \subset K$. Since $K \subset M$, we have the following.

25.4   Theorem   An n-dimensional closed convex set is identical to the intersection of all its supporting hyperplanes.

Both **convex cover** and **extreme points** are defined in E^n exactly as in E^3 (see 8.12 and 8.13). We now generalize a number of theorems taken from Secs. 8 and 9.

25.5   Theorem   A convex n-polyhedral region Π is the convex cover K of the set Y of its extreme points.

PROOF   We use induction on n. The theorem is true for $n = 2$ and 3 (see Theorem 8.14). Suppose the theorem is true for $(n-1)$-polyhedral regions and consider the $(n-1)$-faces of Π. We can assume that no two $(n-1)$-polyhedra on the boundary hypersurface of Π lie in the same hyperplane. If there are two such polyhedra, let their union be considered as a single $(n-1)$-polyhedron. With this stipulation the set of vertices of Π coincides with Y. Let Π' be an $(n-1)$-face of Π, Y' be its set of extreme points, and let K' be the convex cover of Y'. By the induction hypothesis $\Pi' = K'$. Since $Y' \subset Y$, this means that every $(n-1)$-face of Π is contained in K. Since any line through an interior point of Π intersects its boundary in two points of K, it follows that the interior of Π is also contained in K. Therefore $\Pi \subset K$. Since $Y \subset \Pi$ and Π is convex, we also have $K \subset \Pi$. Therefore $\Pi = K$, and we have finished.

25.6 Theorem The convex cover K of a finite set of points $S = \{P_1, \ldots, P_k\}$ is equal to $M = \{X|X = \sum_{i=1}^{k} \mu_i P_i, \mu_i \geq 0, \sum_{i=1}^{k} \mu_i = 1\}$.

PROOF We prove the theorem by induction on k. If $k = 1$, then $M = \{P_1\} = S = K$. Suppose the theorem is true for $(k - 1)$ points, and let $X \varepsilon M$, $X = \sum_{i=1}^{k} \mu_i P_i$, $\mu_i \geq 0$, $\sum_{i=1}^{k} \mu_i = 1$. If $\mu_k = 1$, then $X = P_k \varepsilon K$. Suppose $\mu_k < 1$. Then $\lambda = 1 - \mu_k > 0$, and we can write $X = \lambda(\mu_1 P_1/\lambda + \cdots + \mu_{k-1} P_{k-1}/\lambda) + \mu_k P_k$. By the induction hypothesis the point in parentheses belongs to the convex cover of $\{P_1, \ldots, P_{k-1}\}$ and therefore also to K. Since $\lambda + \mu_k = 1$ and K is convex, it follows that $X \varepsilon K$. Therefore $M \subset K$. It remains to show that $K \subset M$. This will follow once we have shown that M is convex. Let $A = \sum_{i=1}^{k} \alpha_i P_i$, $\alpha_i \geq 0$, $\sum_{i=1}^{k} \alpha_i = 1$, and let $B = \sum_{i=1}^{k} \beta_i P_i$, $\beta_i \geq 0$, $\sum_{i=1}^{k} \beta_i = 1$. If $X = (1 - t)A + tB$, $0 \leq t \leq 1$, then $X = (1 - t)\left(\sum_{i=1}^{k} \alpha_i P_i\right) + t\left(\sum_{i=1}^{k} \beta_i P_i\right) = \sum_{i=1}^{k} [(1 - t)\alpha_i + t\beta_i]P_i$. Since $(1 - t)\alpha_i + t\beta_i \geq 0$ and $\sum_{i=1}^{k} [(1 - t)\alpha_i + t\beta_i] = 1$, it follows that $X \varepsilon M$ and M is convex. This completes the proof.

25.7 Theorem The convex cover K of any set of points S is equal to the set M of all points of the form $X = \sum_{i=1}^{k} \mu_i P_i$, $\mu_i \geq 0$, $\sum_{i=1}^{k} \mu_i = 1$, where $P_i \varepsilon S$ and k is some positive integer.

PROOF Let $X \varepsilon M$, $X = \sum_{i=1}^{k} \mu_i P_i$, $\mu_i \geq 0$, $\sum_{i=1}^{k} \mu_i = 1$. By Theorem 25.6, X belongs to the convex cover of $\{P_1, \ldots, P_k\}$. Therefore $X \varepsilon K$ and $M \subset K$. It remains to show that $K \subset M$. Let $A = \sum_{i=1}^{j} \alpha_i P_i, \alpha_i \geq 0$, $\sum_{i=1}^{j} \alpha_i = 1$, and let $B = \sum_{i=1}^{k} \beta_i Q_i$, $\beta_i \geq 0$, $\sum_{i=1}^{k} \beta_i = 1$. If $\{R_1, \ldots, R_m\} = \{P_i\} \cup \{Q_i\}$, then we can write

$A = \sum_{i=1}^{m} \alpha_i' R_i$, $\alpha_i' \geq 0$, $\sum_{i=1}^{m} \alpha_i' = 1$ and $B = \sum_{i=1}^{m} \beta_i' R_i$, $\beta_i' \geq 0$, $\sum_{i=1}^{m} \beta_i' = 1$

where $\alpha_i' = \alpha_i$ if $R_i = P_i$, otherwise $\alpha_i' = 0$ and $\beta_i' = \beta_i$ if $R_i = Q_{i+j}$, otherwise $\beta_i = 0$. Exactly as in the proof of Theorem 25.6, if $X = (1 - t)A + tB, 0 \le t \le 1$, we can show that $X = \sum\limits_{i=1}^{m} \mu_i R_i$, $\mu_i \ge 0$, $\sum\limits_{i=1}^{m} \mu_i = 1$. Therefore $X \in M$, and M is convex. It follows that $K \subset M$, and we have finished.

25.8   Radon's Theorem   Let $S = \{P_1, \ldots, P_k\}$ be a finite set of points in E^n. If $k \ge n + 2$, then S can be partitioned into two sets whose convex covers intersect.

PROOF   Consider the following system of $n + 1$ homogeneous linear equations, $\sum\limits_{i=1}^{k} \mu_i = 0$, $\sum\limits_{i=1}^{k} \mu_i p_{ij} = 0$, $1 \le j \le n$, where p_{ij} is the jth coordinate of P_i. Since $k > n + 1$, there is a nontrivial solution $\bar{\mu}_i, i = 1, \ldots, k$, common to these equations. Let $M = \{P_i \,|\, \bar{\mu}_i \ge 0\}$, and let $N = \{P_i \,|\, \bar{\mu}_i < 0\}$. Let $\mu > 0$ be the sum of all the nonnegative $\bar{\mu}_i$. If $P = \sum\limits_{P_i \in M} \mu_i P_i / \mu$ and $Q = \sum\limits_{P_i \in N} -\mu_i P_i / \mu$, then according to Theorem 25.6 P lies on the convex cover of M and Q lies on the convex cover of N. But $P = Q$ since $\sum\limits_{i=1}^{k} \bar{\mu}_i P_i = O$. This completes the proof.

25.9   Helly's theorem   Let $K = \{K_1, \ldots, K_k\}$ be k convex sets lying in E^n, $k \ge n + 1$. If every $n + 1$ of these sets have a nonempty intersection, then the intersection of all the sets is not empty.

PROOF   Suppose $k = n + 2$. Let S_i be a point in the intersection of all $K_j, j \ne i$. According to Theorem 25.8 $S = \{S_1, \ldots, S_{n+2}\}$ can be partitioned into two sets M and N such that their convex covers contain at least one common point P. By suitable numbering we can assume that M is the convex cover of $S_1, \ldots, S_k$ and N is the convex cover of $S_{k+1}, \ldots, S_{n+2}$. According to Theorem 25.6 we can write:

a. $P = \sum\limits_{i=1}^{k} \mu_i S_i, \mu_i \ge 0, \sum\limits_{i=1}^{k} \mu_i = 1$

b. $P = \sum\limits_{i=k+1}^{n+2} \lambda_i S_i, \lambda_i \ge 0, \sum\limits_{i=k+1}^{n+2} \lambda_i = 1$

Since $S_i \in K_j$, $j \ne i$, it follows from (a) that $P \in K_j, j \ne 1, \ldots, k$. Similarly it follows from (b) that $P \in K_j, j \ne k + 1, \ldots, n + 2$. This implies that $P \in \bigcap\limits_{i=1}^{n+2} K_i$, and our proof for $k = n + 2$ is complete.

The induction proof for $k > n + 2$ is exactly the same as in Theorem 9.2 and is left to the reader.

25.10   Carathéodory's theorem   If X is any point on the convex cover
of a set S in E^n, then there is a set of q points $M = \{P_1, \ldots ,P_q\}$,
$q \leq n + 1$, contained in S such that X belongs to the convex cover of M.

PROOF.   Let X belong to the convex cover of S.   According to
Theorem 25.7, $X = \sum\limits_{i=1}^{k} \mu_i X_i$, $\mu_i \geq 0$, $\sum\limits_{i=1}^{k} \mu_i = 1$, $X_i \varepsilon S$.   Let k be the
smallest integer such that X can be so represented and suppose $k \geq n + 2$.
By the proof of Theorem 25.8 there exist $\bar{\mu}_i$ not all zero such that $\sum\limits_{i=1}^{k} \bar{\mu}_i = 0$,
$\sum\limits_{i=1}^{k} \bar{\mu}_i X_i = 0$.   Consider all the negative $\bar{\mu}_i$ and let $\mu_{i_0}/\bar{\mu}_{i_0}$ have the largest
ratio.   Then we can write $X = \sum\limits_{i=1}^{k} [\mu_i - (\mu_{i_0}/\bar{\mu}_{i_0})\bar{\mu}_i]X_i$.   Since $\mu_i -$
$(\mu_{i_0}/\bar{\mu}_{i_0})\bar{\mu}_i \geq 0$, $\sum\limits_{i=1}^{k} [\mu_i - (\mu_{i_0}/\bar{\mu}_{i_0})\bar{\mu}_i] = 1$ and the coefficient of X_{i_0} is zero,
it follows that X can be represented as a combination of $k - 1$ points of S.
This contradicts the choice of k and proves the theorem.

25.11   Theorem   The convex cover K of a finite set of points
$S = \{P_1, \ldots ,P_k\}$ in E^n is a convex polyhedral region.

PROOF   We use induction on n.   The theorem is true for a finite set of
points in E^2 or E^3 (see Theorem 8.15).   Suppose the theorem is true for a
finite set of points in E^{n-1}.   By the induction hypothesis we may assume
that not all points of S lie in the same hyperplane.   This implies that
$k \geq n + 1$.

Suppose $k = n + 1$.   Any r points of S must span an $(r-1)$-flat,
otherwise all $n + 1$ points lie in a hyperplane.   By the induction
hypothesis it follows that the convex cover of any n points of S is an
$(n-1)$-polyhedral region.   We assert that the boundary of K is precisely
the union of these polyhedral regions.   Let Π' be any $(n-1)$-polyhedral
region determined by n points of S.   The hyperplane σ containing Π' is a
supporting hyperplane of K, since all points of S lie on one side of σ and
therefore K lies on one side of σ.   It follows that Π' consists entirely of
boundary points of K.   Suppose $X \varepsilon K$ and X does not lie on the convex
cover of n or fewer points of S.   It follows from Theorem 25.6 that X lies
on a line segment joining P_n to the convex cover of $\{P_1, \ldots ,P_{n-1}\}$.
Let Y be the intersection of $L(P_n,X)$ with the polyhedron Π'' spanned by
$\{P_1, \ldots ,P_{n-1}\}$. Y must be an interior point of Π'', otherwise Y would
lie on some $(n-2)$-face of Π'' which together with P_n would determine an
$(n-1)$-polyhedron containing X.   Let N be a neighborhood of Y which
lies in Π''.   The cone with vertex P_n and base N belongs to K and contains
a spherical neighborhood of X.   Therefore X is an interior point of K.
This proves the assertion.

If $k > n + 1$, Theorem 25.10 tells us that every point of K lies on the convex cover Π' of $n + 1$ or fewer points of S. We may assume that Π' is an n-polyhedral region. For if Π' is contained in some hyperplane σ, we can form the convex cover of Π' and some point of S not in σ to increase its dimension by 1. Let the union of all these n-polyhedral regions be the set Σ. $\Sigma \subset K$, since each member of Σ is contained in K. Also every point of K lies on a member of Σ. Therefore $K = \Sigma$. Since the boundary of K consists of the union of $(n-1)$-polyhedral regions, K is an n-polyhedral region.

Exercises

25.1 Complete the proof of Theorem 25.3.

25.2 Prove that any two lines in E^n which are parallel to the same line are parallel to each other (Hint: Use Exercise 23.6 and Theorem 24.9).

25.3 Two 2-flats which lie in the same 3-flat and do not intersect are called parallel. Prove that in E^n any two 2-flats parallel to the same 2-flat are parallel to each other.

25.4 Generalize Exercise 25.3 to r-flats in E^n.

25.5 Show that there is exactly one hyperplane π' parallel to a given hyperplane π passing through a given point not on π. Is this true for r-flats in general instead of just hyperplanes?

25.6 Complete the proof of Theorem 25.9.

25.7 Generalize Theorems 8.6 and 8.7 to E^n.

25.8 Generalize Theorem 8.9 to E^n.

25.9 Extend Exercises 8.14 and 8.15 to E^n.

25.10 Generalize Theorems 9.3 and 9.4 to E^n.

25.11 Extend Exercises 9.7 and 9.8 to E^n.

25.12 Generalize Theorems 10.3, 10.4, and 10.5 to E^n.

25.13 Show that a point of a convex body in E^n a maximum distance from the origin is an extreme point.

25.14 Prove that the diameter of a simplex in E^n is the length of its longest side.

25.15 The centroid of a finite set of points $S = \{P_1, \ldots, P_k\}$ in E^n is defined to be the point $C = (P_1 + \cdots + P_k)/k$. Show that the centroid of S lies in the interior of the convex cover of S.

25.16 Let $S = \{P_1, \ldots, P_k\}$ be a finite set of points in E^n with centroid C and diameter D. If S' is a nonempty subset of S with centroid C', show that $|CC'| \leq (k - 1)D/k$.

26   TRANSFORMATIONS IN E^n

We devote this section to a generalization to E^n of some results in Chap. 3. The basic concepts presented in Sec. 11, including Theorem 11.9, all carry over directly to E^n with minor changes in wording, and the details are left to the reader. We shall use these results throughout the section.

26.1   Theorem   (a)   The image of an r-flat under a motion f is an r-flat.   **(b)**   If line L is perpendicular to hyperplane π, then $f(L)$ is perpendicular to $f(\pi)$.

PROOF   In order to prove part (a) we shall show that if π_r has equation $X = B_0 + \sum_{i=1}^{r} \mu_i(B_i - B_0)$ and f is a motion, then $f(\pi_r)$ is an r-flat with   equation $f(X) = f(B_0) + \sum_{i=1}^{r} \mu_i[f(B_i) - f(B_0)]$.   Let $X = B_0 + \mu(B - B_0)$ be the equation of a line l and let $Y = f(B_0) + \mu[f(B) - f(B_0)]$ be the equation of line l'.   Suppose $f(X)$ does not lie on l', so that $f(B_0)$, $f(B)$, and $f(X)$ form a triangle.   Then the sum of the lengths of two sides would equal the length of the third side, which is impossible (see Exercise 24.2).   Therefore $f(X) \in l'$ and $f(X) = f(B) + \lambda[f(B) - f(B_0)]$.   We assert that $\lambda = \mu$.   For if μ is positive, so that $X \in R[B_0,B)$, then $f(X) \in R[f(B_0),f(B))$, and λ is also positive.   But then solving for μ we get

$$\mu = \frac{|X\,B_0|}{|B\,B_0|} = \frac{|f(X)\,f(B_0)|}{|f(B)\,f(B_0)|}$$
$$= \lambda$$

A similar argument holds for μ negative, so that $f(l)$ is precisely the line with equation $f(X) = f(B_0) + \mu[f(B) - f(B_0)]$.

Suppose the assertion is true for $(r-1)$-flats, and let π_r be an arbitrary r-flat with equation $X = B_0 + \sum_{i=1}^{r} \mu_i(B_i - B_0)$.   If we write this in the form $X = [B_0 + \mu_r(B_r - B_0)] + \sum_{i=1}^{r-1} \mu_i(B_i - B_0)$ and fix μ_r, it follows from the induction hypotheses that $f(X) = f[B_0 + \mu_r(B_r - B_0)] + \sum_{i=1}^{r-1} \mu_i[f(B_i) - f(B_0)]$, where $f(B_i) - f(B_0)$, $i = 1, \ldots, r - 1$, are linearly independent. From the above assertion for lines we also get that $f[B_0 + \mu_r(B_r - B_0)] = f(B_0) + \mu_r[f(B_r) - f(B_0)]$.   Therefore $f(X) = f(B_0) + \sum_{i=1}^{r} \mu_i[f(B_i) - f(B_0)]$

Suppose   that $Y = f(B_0) + \sum_{i=1}^{r} \lambda_i[f(B_i) - f(B_0)]$.   Then $Y = f(B_0) +$

$\lambda_r[f(B_r) - f(B_0)] + \sum\limits_{i=1}^{r-1} \lambda_i[f(B_i) - f(B_0)]$. Applying the induction hypothesis to f^{-1} we get $f^{-1}(Y) = B_0 + \lambda_r(B_r - B_0) + \sum\limits_{i=1}^{r-1} \lambda_i(B_i - B_0)$ and $f^{-1}(Y) \varepsilon \pi_r$. It follows that the equation of $f(\pi_r)$ is $f(X) = f(B_0) + \sum\limits_{i=1}^{r} \mu_i[f(B_i) - f(B_0)]$.

If $f(\pi_r)$ is an s-flat, $s < r$, then by the induction hypothesis on f^{-1} we have that $f^{-1}[f(\pi_r)] = \pi_r$ is an s-flat, giving a contradiction. Therefore $f(\pi_r)$ is an r-flat.

It remains to prove part (**b**). According to Theorem 24.12 we can write the equation of a hyperplane π as all X such that $|PX|^2 = |PQ|^2 + |QX|^2$, where $L(P,Q)$ is perpendicular to π at Q. Let $X' = f(X)$ and consider the locus of points Y such that $|P'Y|^2 = |P'Q'|^2 + |Q'Y|^2$. This is precisely $f(\pi)$ and is also the hyperplane π' perpendicular to $L(P',Q')$ at Q'. According to part (**a**) $f[L(P,Q)] = L(P',Q')$, and our theorem is proved.

We note that Theorem 26.1 implies that perpendicular lines are carried onto perpendicular lines under an arbitrary motion.

We now make the following definitions.

26.2   Let P be an arbitrary point in E^n. The transformation T_P such that $T_P(X) = X + P$ is called the **translation** of E^n in the direction $\overrightarrow{OP}$. Just as in E^3, $\overrightarrow{AB}$ stands for the vector determined by the directed line segment from A to B.

26.3   Let π be a fixed hyperplane in E^n. For each $X \varepsilon E^n$ let π be the perpendicular bisector of $S(X,X')$. The transformation R_π, such that $R_\pi(X) = X$ if $X \varepsilon \pi$ and $R_\pi(X) = X'$ otherwise, is called the **reflection about hyperplane** π.

26.4   Let $A_i = (a_{i1}, \ldots, a_{in})$, $i = 1, \ldots, n$, be an orthonormal set of points in E^n, that is, $A_i \cdot A_j = 0$ for $i \neq j$ and $|A_i| = 1$. Let x_i stand for the ith coordinate of point X and let $X' = \sum\limits_{i=1}^{n} x_i A_i$. The transformation which sends X into X' is called a **rotation about the origin.** The matrix $A = (a_{ij})$ is called the **matrix of the rotation,** and we denote the rotation with matrix A by R^A. In matrix notation the equation of the rotation can be written $X' = XA$. If $\det A = 1$, the rotation R^A is called **proper.** If $\det A = -1$, the rotation R^A is called **improper.**

26.5   Theorem   Translations, reflections, and rotations about the origin are all motions of E^n.

PROOF

a.   If $P' = P + T$ and $Q' = Q + T$, then $|P'Q'|^2 = (P' - Q') \cdot (P' - Q') = (P - Q) \cdot (P - Q) = |PQ|^2$, so that a translation preserves distance. Since a translation is also a one-to-one map of E^n onto itself, it is a motion.

b.   Consider the reflection R_π. R_π is a one-to-one map of E^n onto itself. If $P, Q \, \varepsilon \, \pi$, then $P = P'$, $Q = Q'$, and distance is preserved. If $P \, \varepsilon \, \pi$, $Q \, \xi \, \pi$, let $X = L(Q,Q') \cap \pi$. In the 2-flat spanned by $L(P,X)$ and $L(Q,Q')$, $\triangle PQX$ is congruent to $\triangle PXQ'$ and $|PQ| = |P'Q'|$. If $P \, \xi \, \pi$, $Q \, \xi \, \pi$, let $P_0 = L(P,P') \cap \pi$ and $Q_0 = L(Q,Q') \cap \pi$. If the equation of π is $A \cdot X = b$, then by Theorem 24.9 the equation of $L(P,P')$ is $X = P_0 + tA$, and the equation of $L(Q,Q')$ is $X = Q_0 + sA$. If $P_0 = Q_0$, then $|PQ| = |P'Q'|$. If $P_0 \neq Q_0$, then the equation of the 2-flat spanned by $L(P,P')$ and $L(P_0,Q_0)$ can be written

$$X = P_0 + sA + t(Q_0 - P_0)$$
$$= sA + (1 - t)P_0 + tQ_0 \qquad -\infty < s, t < +\infty$$

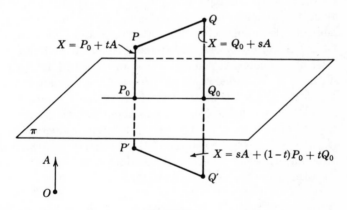

Fig. 26.1

In a similar way we can show that this is also the equation of the 2-flat spanned by $L(Q,Q')$ and $L(P_0,Q_0)$. Since $L(P,P')$ and $L(Q,Q')$ lie in the same 2-flat and are perpendicular to the same line, they are therefore parallel. Using familiar properties of plane euclidean geometry the reader can now easily show that $|PQ| = |P'Q'|$.

c.   Using the same notation as in 26.4 let R^A be a rotation about the origin with matrix A. Let p_i, q_i be the ith coordinates of P and Q respectively. Then $P' = \sum_{i=1}^{n} p_i A_i$, $Q' = \sum_{i=1}^{n} q_i A_i$, and $|P'Q'|^2 = (P' - Q') \cdot$

$(P' - Q') = \left[\sum_{i=1}^{n} (p_i - q_i)A_i \right] \cdot \left[\sum_{i=1}^{n} (p_i - q_i)A_i \right] = \sum_{i=1}^{n} (p_i - q_i)^2 =$

$|PQ|^2$. The fact that $X' = XA$, $X = X'A^T$ and $\det A = \det A^T = \pm 1$
guarantees that R^A is a one-to-one map of E^n onto E^n. A^T is the transpose
of A.

26.6   Theorem   The following sets of transformations of E^n form transformation groups:

   a. All translations
   b. All rotations about the origin
   c. All proper rotations about the origin
   d. The set G of all finite products of reflections

   PROOF   **a.**   If T_P and T_Q are any two translations, then $T_P T_Q =$
T_{P+Q} is also a translation. T_0 is the identity transformation, and
$T_P T_{(-P)} = T_0$. Therefore $T_P^{-1} = T_{(-P)}$ is also a translation.
   b. Let A be the matrix of the rotation R^A. The fact that the rows
of A form a set of orthonormal points is equivalent to the property that A
satisfies the matrix equation $AA^T = I$. I is the identity matrix with 1s
along the diagonal and 0s elsewhere. A^T is the transpose of A. If we
multiply this equation on the left by A^T and on the right by A, we get
$(A^TA)(A^TA) = (A^TA)$. Therefore $A^TA = \text{I}$, and the rows of A^T form
a set of orthonormal points. Since we have $(R^{A^T}R^A)(X) = R^{A^T}(XA) =$
$X(AA^T) = X$, it follows that $R^{A^T}R^A = I$. This shows that every rotation
about the origin has an inverse which is also a rotation about the origin.
Now let R^A and R^B be two rotations about the origin with matrices A and B
respectively. Let $C = AB$ be the matrix product of A and B. Then
$(R^B R^A)(X) = R^B(XA) = X(AB)$. We assert that the rows of C form an
orthonormal set of points, and therefore $R^B R^A = R^{AB}$ is a rotation about
the origin. This follows from the fact that $CC^T = (AB)(AB)^T =$
$ABB^TA^T = AA^T = I$.
   c. If A is the matrix of rotation R^A, $\det A = 1$, and B is the matrix
of rotation R^B, $\det B = 1$, then $\det A^T = 1$, where A^T is the matrix of
$(R^A)^{-1} = R^{A^T}$, and $\det (AB) = 1$, where AB is the matrix of $R^B R^A = R^{AB}$.
This means that the inverse of a proper rotation is a proper rotation and
the product of two proper rotations is a proper rotation.
   d. Let R_π be a reflection. By construction $R_\pi R_\pi = I$. Therefore
R_π is its own inverse. If $R \,\epsilon\, G$, then $R = R_{\pi_1} \cdots R_{\pi_k}$ and $R^{-1} = R_{\pi_k} \cdots$
R_{π_1} is also a finite product of reflections. The product of two finite products
of reflections is also a finite product of reflections. Therefore G is a group.

Henceforth we shall refer to the points E_i, with ith coordinate 1 and all other coordinates 0, as the **natural orthonormal set** of points. Using the same notation as in 26.4, if $A_{i_1} = E_{i_1}$, then R^A is called a **rotation about the line** $L(O, E_{i_1})$. In general if $A_{i_j} = E_{i_j}, j = 1, \ldots , r < n - 1$, then R^A is called a **rotation about the r-flat** spanned by O and E_{i_j}, $j = 1, \ldots , r$. If $r = n - 1$, say $A_i = E_i$, $i = 1, \ldots , n - 1$, then either $A_n = E_n$ or $A_n = -E_n$. If $A_n = E_n$, R^A is the identity. If $A_n = -E_n$, then R^A is the reflection about the hyperplane spanned by $O, E_1, \ldots , E_{n-1}$. These considerations lead to the following.

26.7 Theorem   An improper rotation about the origin is the product of a proper rotation about the origin and a reflection about a hyperplane.

PROOF   Let A be the matrix of an improper rotation R^A. Let $A'_i = A_i$, $i = 1, \ldots , n - 1$ and $A'_n = -A_n$, and let A' be the matrix with rows A'_i. Then det $A' = -$ det $A = +1$, and $R^{A'}$ is a proper rotation about the origin. If π is the hyperplane spanned by $O, E_1, \ldots , E_{n-1}$, then $R^A = R^{A'} R_\pi$. This completes the proof.

26.8 Theorem   Every motion f of E^n which leaves the origin fixed is a rotation about the origin.

PROOF   Let E_i, $i = 1, \ldots , n$, be the natural orthonormal set. Since f is a motion, the points $A_i = f(E_i)$ are all of unit distance from the origin. According to Theorem 26.1, perpendicularity is preserved under an arbitrary motion. Therefore the points A_i form an orthonormal set. Let R^A be the rotation about the origin determined by the points A_i. We assert that $f = R^A$. To see this let $X' = f(X)$. Since the proof of Theorem 26.1 applies directly to all of E^n as well as to r-flats, it follows that if $X = \sum_{i=1}^{n} x_i E_i$ and $f(O) = O$, then $X' = f(X) = \sum_{i=1}^{n} x_i f(E_i) = \sum_{i=1}^{n} x_i A_i$. In matrix notation this can be written $X'A^T = X$. But then $f(X) = X' = XA = R^A(X)$ for every X, and $f = R^A$.

26.9 Theorem   Every motion f of E^n can be written as a product of a translation and a rotation about the origin.

PROOF   Let $Z = f(O)$. The product of two motions is a motion, therefore $T_{-Z}f$ is a motion which leaves the origin fixed. According to Theorem 26.8, $T_{-Z}f = R^A$ for some rotation about the origin. But then $f = T_Z R^A$, and we have finished.

26.10 Theorem   The group G of all finite products of reflections coincides with the group of all motions of E^n.

PROOF   Let π and π' be hyperplanes through O and $P/2$ perpendicular to $L(O,P)$. Then $T_P = R_{\pi'}R_{\pi}$.

Let R^A be an arbitrary rotation about the origin and let $A_i = (a_{i1}, \ldots, a_{in})$ be formed from the rows of A. Let E_i be the natural orthonormal set. We shall now describe a certain sequence of reflections. Let P^k stand for the image of P under the product of the first k reflections of this sequence. First we reflect about the perpendicular bisector of $S(E_1,A_1)$. Then $E_1^1 = A_1$. Since the perpendicular bisector of $S(E_1,A_1)$ is the locus of all points equidistant from E_1 and A_1, and since $|OE_1| = |OA_1|$, we also have $O^1 = O$. Since $L(O,E_1^1)$ is perpendicular to the hyperplane σ spanned by O, $E_2^1, \ldots, E_n^1$, it follows that $E_2^1, \ldots, E_n^1, A_2, \ldots, A_n, O$ all lie in σ. Let the second reflection be about the perpendicular bisector of $S(E_2^1,A_2)$. $\triangle A_1OE_2^1$ is congruent to $\triangle A_1OA_2$. Therefore $|A_1E_2^1| = |A_1A_2|$, and it follows that $E_1^2 = A_1$ as well as $E_2^2 = A_2$. As before, we also have $O^2 = O$. Now reflect about the perpendicular besector of $S(E_3^2,A_3)$.

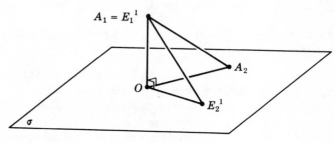

Fig. 26.2

Using congruent triangles again we get $O^3 = O$, $E_1^3 = A_1$, $E_2^3 = A_2$, and $E_3^3 = A_3$. Repeating this process we eventually get $O^{n-1} = O$, $E_1^{n-1} = A_1, \ldots, E_{n-1}^{n-1} = A_{n-1}$. Now either $A_n = E_n^{n-1}$ or $A_n = -E_n^{n-1}$. In the latter case a reflection about the hyperplane spanned by O, $A_1, \ldots, A_{n-1}$ gives $E_i^n = A_i$, $i = 1, \ldots, n$. In either case we arrive at a product of reflections Π which leaves the origin fixed and sends E_i into A_i, $i = 1, \ldots, n$. According to Theorem 26.8, Π is a rotation about the origin R^B. Since $R^B(E_i) = A_i$, we also have the matrix equations $E_iB = A_i$, $i = 1, \ldots, n$. This implies that $A = B$ and $\Pi = R^A$.

We have now shown that every rotation about the origin and every translation is a finite product of reflections. By Theorem 26.9 it follows that every motion is a finite product of reflections, and our theorem is proved.

We now turn to a discussion of transformations of E^n which do not preserve distance. **Similarity** and **homothety** are defined in E^n exactly as in 13.1 and 13.3. If the center of the homothety is the origin O, then

$H(O,r)(P) = rP$. As in Chaps. 3 and 4, we will let $rM = \{X | X = H(O,r)(P), P \, \varepsilon \, M, O$ the origin$\}$. Since the proofs of Theorems 13.4 and 13.6 carry over directly to E^n, we have the following.

26.11   Theorem   **(a)** A homothety in E^n is a similarity which maps each line either onto itself or onto a parallel line. **(b)** Every similarity in E^n which is not a motion has exactly one fixed point.

We shall use these results to prove the next two theorems.

26.12   Theorem   Every similarity f of E^n with ratio $r \neq 1$ which leaves the origin fixed is a product of a rotation and homothety about the origin.

PROOF   Let H be the homothety about O with ratio $1/r$. Since Hf keeps O fixed and preserves distances, it follows from Theorem 26.8 that $Hf = R^A$ for some rotation about O. Therefore $f = H(O,r)R^A$, and our proof is complete.

If we consider $T_P R^A T_{-P}$ as a **rotation about point** P, then the following holds.

26.13   Theorem   Every similarity f of E^n with ratio $r \neq 1$ is a product of a homothety and a rotation about its fixed point F.

PROOF   The product of two similarities is a similarity, therefore $T_{(-F)} f T_F$ is a similarity which leaves the origin fixed. By Theorem 26.12 we have $T_{(-F)} f T_F = H(O,r)R^A$ for some rotation and homothety about O. Therefore

$$f = T_F H(O,r) R^A T_{(-F)} = H(F,r)(T_F R^A T_{(-F)})$$

which is what we set out to prove.

We hope that by now the reader has developed sufficient techniques to generalize from E^3 to E^n. Most of the remaining results in Chaps. 3 and 4 can be carried over to E^n, but we shall not do so here.

Exercises

26.1   Generalize Theorem 11.9 to E^n.

26.2   Show that perpendicular lines are carried onto perpendicular lines under an arbitrary motion of E^n.

26.3   Show that Definition 26.4 reduces to the usual definition of a rotation about the origin in the plane when $n = 2$.

26.4   If lines $l_1, \ldots, l_k$ are each perpendicular to the same hyperplane in E^n, show that l_i and l_j are parallel for $i \neq j$.

26.5 Let H_2 and H_2' be 2-flats in E^4 which are each perpendicular to the same 2-flat H_2''. Show that H_2 and H_2' are parallel (see Exercise 25.3).

26.6 Generalize Exercise 26.5 to two r-flats in E^n each perpendicular to the same $(n-r)$-flat (see Exercise 24.5).

26.7 Show that the rows of an $n \times n$ matrix A form a set of orthonormal points in E^n iff $AA^T = I$.

26.8 Prove Theorem 26.11.

26.9 Generalize Theorems 12.10 and 12.11 to E^n.

26.10 Generalize Theorem 12.15 to E^n.

26.11 Extend Exercise 13.4 to E^n.

26.12 Generalize Exercise 13.7 to E^n.

26.13 Generalize Theorems 14.4 and 14.5 to E^n.

26.14 Generalize Theorems 14.7 and 14.8 to E^n.

26.15 Extend Exercises 14.14 and 14.15 to E^n.

26.16 Generalize Theorem 15.1 to E^n.

26.17 Generalize Theorem 15.4 to E^n.

26.18 Generalize Theorems 15.6 and 15.7 to E^n.

26.19 If A is a nonsingular $n \times n$ matrix, i.e., det $A \neq 0$, and if $B \varepsilon E^n$, the transformation $X' = AX + B$ for $X \varepsilon E^n$ is called an **affine transformation** of E^n. Show that every motion and similarity of E^n is an affine transformation.

26.20 Show that the image of a convex set under an affine transformation of E^n is a convex set (see Exercise 26.19).

26.21 Use Exercise 26.12 to show that $V(rK) = r^n V(K)$.

27 LINEAR PROGRAMMING

In recent years the theory of convex sets has found wide application to linear programming. There are many good books on this subject, and it is hoped that after this very brief introduction the reader will refer to them for more detailed study. We shall give a few applications of the preceding sections to illustrate the ideas involved. First we define a linear programming problem.

27.1 Let all terms involved be real numbers, and let

$$a_{11}x_1 + \cdots + a_{1n}x_n \le b_1$$
$$\cdots \cdots \cdots \cdots \cdots$$
$$a_{m1}x_1 + \cdots + a_{mn}x_n \le b_m$$

be m inequalities subject to the restrictions $x_i \ge 0$, $i = 1, \ldots, n$. If $f = c_1x_1 + \cdots + c_nx_n$, then a **linear programming problem** is to find a set of real numbers $\{x_i\}$ which maximizes f and satisfies all the inequalities.

A typical linear programming problem can be formulated as follows. There are n products each made on the same m machines in a given factory. Let a_{ij} be the time spent on the ith machine producing one unit of the jth product. Let x_j be the number of units of the jth product produced per day. Then $\sum\limits_{j=1}^{n} a_{ij}x_j$ represents the total time spent on the ith machine in one day. If b_i represents the amount of time the ith machine is available for production each day and c_i represents the profit obtained on the sale of one unit of the ith product, then f represents the total profit per day. The problem is then to maximize the profit subject to the given time limitations.

In order to bring into play the geometry of E^n, a linear programming problem can be recast in the following manner. Let $X = (x_1, \ldots, x_n)$, $C = (c_1, \ldots, c_n)$, and $A_i = (a_{i1}, \ldots, a_{in})$, $i = 1, \ldots, m$. Let M be the intersection of the half spaces $A_i \cdot X \leq b_i$, $i = 1, \ldots, m$ and $x_i \geq 0$, $i = 1, \ldots, m$. Any point of M is called a **feasible point,** and M is called the **feasible set** of the problem. Since M is the intersection of convex sets, M is either a convex set or the null set. If $C \cdot X_0 = \max\limits_{X \epsilon M} C \cdot X$, then X_0 is called a **solution.** The problem then is to find a solution if one exists.

Using the preceding notation we can prove the following.

27.2   Theorem   If the feasible set M of a linear programming problem is a convex body, then there is an extreme point of M which is a solution.

PROOF   Suppose I is an interior point of M. If every point of M lies in the hyperplane π with equation $X \cdot C = I \cdot C$, then every point of M is a solution including all its extreme points. If not all points of M lie in π, then π separates points of M and there are points P and Q of M such that $P \cdot C < I \cdot C < Q \cdot C$. Therefore I cannot be a solution. Let π_1 with

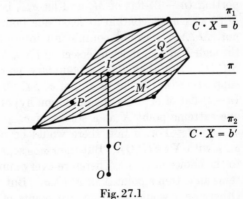

Fig. 27.1

equation $C \cdot X = b$ and π_2 with equation $C \cdot X = b'$, $b \geq b'$, be the supporting hyperplanes of M perpendicular to $L(O,C)$. Any point on $\pi_1 \cap M$ is a solution. But every supporting hyperplane σ of M contains at least one extreme point, since M is a polyhedral region and therefore M is the convex cover of its extreme points. If σ contained no extreme points of M, it would then contain no points of the convex cover of the extreme points and could not be a supporting hyperplane of M. This completes the proof.

27.3 Theorem If a solution to a linear programming problem exists, then there must be at least one extreme point of its feasible set M which is a solution.

PROOF Let X_0 be a solution. As in the proof of Theorem 27.2, X_0 lies on a supporting hyperplane π of M with equation $C \cdot X = C \cdot X_0$. We assert that every supporting hyperplane of M contains at least one extreme point of M. Since every point of $\pi \cap M$ is a solution, our theorem will then be proved.

If M is bounded, then it is a polyhedral region and is the convex cover of its extreme points. Since every supporting hyperplane of the convex cover of a finite number of points must contain at least one of the given points, the assertion holds for bounded M.

Suppose M is not bounded. We assert that every supporting i-flat σ_i, $0 \leq i \leq n - 1$, of M contains at least one extreme point of $\sigma_i \cap M$ considered as a subset of σ_i. To show this we use induction on i. The assertion is trivially true for $i = 0$. Suppose σ_1 is a supporting line of M. Any line possesses a point with some negative coordinates. Therefore $\sigma_1 \cap M$ is a ray $R[A,B)$ or a segment $S[A,B]$. But then A is an extreme point of $\sigma_1 \cap M$ as a subset of σ_1. Suppose that the assertion is true for any supporting $(n - 2)$-flat of M, and let σ_{n-1} be a supporting $(n-1)$-flat of M. $M \cap \sigma_{n-1}$ must contain at least one boundary point relative to σ_{n-1}. If not, $M \cap \sigma_{n-1}$ would contain an interior point I. As above, any line through I in σ_{n-1} must intersect $M \cap \sigma_{n-1}$ in some ray $R[C,D)$ or segment $S[C,D]$. But then C is a boundary point of $M \cap \sigma_{n-1}$. Let σ_{n-2} be a supporting $(n-2)$-flat in σ_{n-1} of $\sigma_{n-1} \cap M$ at C. σ_{n-2} is also a supporting $(n-2)$-flat of M. By the induction hypothesis $\sigma_{n-2} \cap M$ contains at least one extreme point X as a subset of σ_{n-2}. X is also an extreme point of $\sigma_{n-1} \cap M$. For, if not, there would be points P, Q on $\sigma_{n-1} \cap M$ not on σ_{n-2}, with $X \in S(P,Q)$. But then σ_{n-2} separates P from Q in σ_{n-1}, contrary to the choice of σ_{n-2}. Therefore every supporting hyperplane σ of M contains an extreme point X of $M \cap \sigma$. But X is also an extreme point of M. Otherwise σ would separate two points of M. This completes the proof.

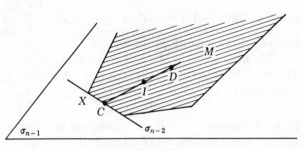

Fig. 27.2

Since a feasible set M is the intersection of a finite number of half spaces, and extreme points cannot lie interior to any r-face of M, $r > 0$, there can only be a finite number of extreme points of M. Therefore in order to determine a solution, when a solution exists, all we need to do is compute $C \cdot X_i$ for each extreme point and pick one which maximizes $C \cdot X$. A number of things prevent this from being a practical scheme. First of all, it is no easy matter to find all the extreme points or even to determine whether a solution exists. Also, the number of extreme points may be extremely large and cause the examination of each extreme point to be too time-consuming.

One method of finding a solution which circumvents these objections and has proved to be very practical is the so called "simplex method." Roughly speaking, the simplex method consists of the following: (**a**) An extreme point X_0 of M is selected.   (**b**) All 1-faces emanating from X_0 are examined for extreme points, and one is selected, Y_0, which gives the greatest improvement in f. If none of these extreme points increase f, then X_0 is a solution.   (**c**) If an unbounded 1-face emanates from X_0 and f increases beyond bounds along this edge, then there is no solution.   (**d**) The process is repeated, starting with Y_0, until a solution is obtained.

It turns out that finding a solution to a linear programming problem is closely related to finding a solution to another problem called its dual. The use of matrix notation will help to simplify the following discussion considerably. Let the linear programming problem be $A_i \cdot X \leq b_i$, $i = 1, \ldots, m$, $x_i \geq 0$, $i = 1, \ldots, m$, maximize $f = C \cdot X$. In matrix notation we write $AX \leq B$, $x_i \geq 0$, maximize $f = CX$, where A is the matrix (a_{ij}). Matrix M is less than or equal to matrix N iff they have the same number of rows and the same number of columns and each element of M is less than or equal to the corresponding element of N. A point in E^n will be considered either as a $1 \times n$ matrix or an $n \times 1$ matrix, whichever is convenient.

27.4   If $AX \leq B$, $X \geq O$, $\max\limits_{X} f = CX$ is a given linear programming problem, then $-YA \leq -C$, $Y \geq O$, $\max_Y f' = -BY$ is called the **dual linear programming problem.**

We note that the dual to the dual problem is the original problem. The dual is obtained by replacing A, B, and C by $-A$, $-C$, and $-B$ respectively.

27.5   Theorem   If M is the feasible set of a linear programming problem and M' is the feasible set of its dual, then

> ***a.*** $X \varepsilon M$, $Y \varepsilon M'$ implies $CX \leq BY$.
>
> ***b.*** $X_0 \varepsilon M$, $Y_0 \varepsilon M'$ and $CX_0 = BY_0$ implies that X_0 is a solution to the original problem and Y_0 is a solution to the dual.
>
> ***c.***   If M and M' are not empty then both problems have a solution.

PROOF   ***a.*** $AX \leq B$ implies $YAX \leq YB$. $C \leq YA$ implies $XC \leq YAX$. Therefore $XC \leq YAX \leq YB$.

b.   By part (a), $CX \leq BY_0 = CX_0$ for every $X \varepsilon M$, and $BY \geq CX_0 = BY_0$ for every $Y \varepsilon M'$.

c.   Let $Y_0 \varepsilon M'$. If $X \varepsilon M$, then by (a) $CX \leq BY_0$. Since the set of real numbers $\{CX | X \varepsilon M\}$ is bounded from above, it has a least upper bound R_0. Let π be the hyperplane with equation $CX = R_0$ and let H be the half space containing M bounded by π. In order to show that the original problem has a solution it remains only to show that π is a supporting hyperplane of M.

Let Σ be the finite set of hyperplanes which are the boundaries of the half spaces which define M. Each boundary point B of M lies on the intersection Π of a finite number of distinct independent hyperplanes of Σ. If $n - r$ is the largest number of such hyperplanes, $n \geq r$, B is called an interior point of $F_r = \Pi \cap M$, and F_r is called an r-face of M. If $r = n$, then B is an extreme point of M. Consider the finite number of distances from the faces of M to π. If face F_r is parallel to π, its distance is the perpendicular distance from F_r to π. If F_r is not parallel to π, we assert that it contains an s-face F_s, $0 \leq s < r$, such that the distance from F_r to π equals the distance from F_s to π. To see this we notice that F_r cannot contain an entire line, otherwise M would not lie in H. Therefore the boundary of F_r is not empty. The distance from F_r to π cannot be taken on by an interior point of F_r. Since every boundary point of F_r lies on some face $F_s \subset F_r$, $s < r$, the assertion is proved. If we continue the above process until either $s = 0$ or F_s is parallel to π, we conclude that the distances from faces of M to π are all well defined and the minimum such distance d exists. If $d > 0$, then the half space with equation $CX \leq R_0 - d$ contains all the faces of M and therefore contains M. But this contradicts the choice of

R_0. Therefore $d = 0$, π contains some point of M, and π is a supporting hyperplane of M. This shows that the original problem has a solution.

In order to show that the dual problem has a solution let $X_0 \varepsilon M$, $X_0 \geq O$, $AX_0 \leq B$. If $Y \varepsilon M'$, then $BY \geq CX_0$ by (a), and the set $\{BY | Y \varepsilon M'\}$ has a greatest lower bound R_0'. The remainder of the proof follows the pattern of the preceding part and is left to the reader.

To obtain necessary and sufficient conditions for a problem to have a solution it will help to bring in the notion of the lagrangian form $\Phi(X,Y)$.

27.6   Theorem X_0 is a solution to a linear programming problem iff there exists $Y_0 \geq O$ such that $\Phi(X,Y_0) \leq \Phi(X_0,Y_0) \leq \Phi(X_0,Y)$ for all $X \geq O$ and all $Y \geq O$. $\Phi(X,Y) = XC + Y(B - AX)$ is called the **lagrangian form** of the problem, and (X_0,Y_0) is called a **saddle point** of Φ.

PROOF   Suppose (X_0,Y_0) is a saddle point of Φ. Then $X_0C + Y_0(B - AX_0) \leq X_0C + Y(B - AX_0)$, and $Y_0(B - AX_0) \leq Y(B - AX_0)$ for $Y \geq O$. If $Y_0 = O$, then $Y_0(B - AX_0) = 0$. If $Y_0 \neq O$, choose Y' so that $O \leq Y' \leq Y_0$, where at least one coordinate of Y' is smaller than the corresponding coordinate of Y_0. Then $Y'(B - AX_0) < Y_0(B - AX_0)$, contrary to assumption, unless $B - AX_0 = O$. If $B - AX_0 = O$, then $Y_0(B - AX_0) = 0$.   We   now   have $XC + Y_0(B - AX) \leq X_0C + Y_0(B - AX_0) = X_0C$ for all $X \geq O$. It follows that whenever $B - AX \geq O$, then $XC \leq X_0C$. Therefore X_0 is a solution to the original problem.

To prove the converse, suppose X_0 is a solution and consider the following transformation T from E^n into E^{m+1}. Let

$$B' = \left(b_1, \ldots, b_m, \sum_{i=1}^{n} c_i x_i^0\right)$$

$$X_0 = (x_1^0, \ldots, x_n^0)$$

$$Z = (z_1, \ldots, z_{m+1})$$

and

$$A' = \begin{bmatrix} a_{11} & \cdots & a_{1n} \\ \cdots & \cdots & \cdots \\ a_{m1} & \cdots & a_{mn} \\ c_1 & \cdots & c_n \end{bmatrix}$$

Then $T(X) = Z = B' - A'X$. Let $S = \{Z | Z = T(X), X \geq O\}$. Since a linear transformation maps half spaces onto half spaces (in general of different dimensions), S is a convex set in E^{m+1}. Also, if K is the set of all points in E^{m+1} with all coordinates positive, then $K \cap S$ is empty. For if $\bar{Z} \varepsilon S$ and $\bar{Z} = B' - A'\bar{X} \varepsilon K$, then $B - A\bar{X} > O$ and the $(m + 1)$th coordinate of $\bar{Z}$ would be nonpositive, contrary to assumption. Let $\bar{K}$ be the closure of K. $\bar{K} \cap S$ is not empty, since $Z_0 = B' - A'X_0$ belongs to $\bar{K} \cap S$. We now consider two possibilities. Either $\bar{K} \cap S = O$ or $\bar{K} \cap S \neq O$. We assert that in either case there is a point $\bar{Z} = (\bar{z}_1, \ldots, \bar{z}_m, 1)$, $\bar{Z} \geq O$, such that $\bar{Z}Z \leq 0$ for $Z \varepsilon S$.

Suppose $\bar{K} \cap S = O$. Since S lies in a convex cone C such that $C \cap K$ is empty, we can apply Exercise 27.9 to find a point

$$P = (p_1, \ldots, p_{m+1}) > O$$

such that $PZ \leq 0$ for $Z \varepsilon C$ and therefore for $Z \varepsilon S$. If we let $\bar{Z} = P/p_{m+1}$, then $\bar{Z} = (\bar{z}_1, \ldots, \bar{z}_{m+1}, 1) \geq O$ and $\bar{Z}Z \leq 0$ for $Z \varepsilon S$.

Suppose $\bar{K} \cap S \neq O$ and let $P \varepsilon \bar{K} \cap S$, $P \neq O$, $P = (p_1, \ldots, p_m, 0)$. We shall show that the hyperplane with equation $z_{m+1} = 0$ is a supporting hyperplane of S. Suppose the contrary; then there is a point

$$Q = (q_1, \ldots, q_{m+1}) \varepsilon S$$

such that $q_{m+1} > 0$. Every point $R = (1 - t)P + tQ$, $0 \leq t \leq 1$, belongs to S since S is convex. But then if t is chosen sufficiently small, R will have

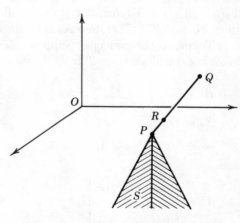

Fig. 27.3

all coordinates positive and $S \cap K$ is not empty. This contradiction shows that $z_{m+1} = 0$ is a supporting hyperplane of S. It follows that if $\bar{Z} = (0, \ldots, 0, 1)$, then $\bar{Z} \geq O$ and $\bar{Z}Z \leq 0$ for all $Z \varepsilon S$.

To complete the proof of the theorem let $Y_0 = (\bar{z}_1, \ldots, \bar{z}_m)$. Then $\bar{Z}Z = Y_0(B - AX) + C(X - X_0) \leq 0$, for all $X \geq O$. Since $AX_0 \leq B$ and $Y_0 \geq O$, we have $Y_0(B - AX_0) = 0$ and $Y(B - AX_0) \geq 0$ for $Y \geq O$.

Therefore

$$XC + Y_0(B - AX) \leq X_0C + Y_0(B - AX_0) \leq X_0C + Y(B - AX_0)$$

for all $X \geq O$, $Y \geq O$, and our proof is complete.

27.7 Theorem If a linear programming problem has a solution X_0, then its dual has a solution Y_0, and $CX_0 = BY_0$.

PROOF According to Theorem 27.6, there exists $Y_0 \geq O$ such that $XC + Y_0(B - AX) \leq X_0C + Y_0(B - AX_0) \leq X_0C + Y(B - AX_0)$. The lagrangian form of the dual problem is

$$\Phi(Y,X) = -YB + (YA - C)X$$

and if there exists $\bar{X} \geq O$ such that $\Phi(Y,\bar{X}) \leq \Phi(\bar{Y},\bar{X}) \leq \Phi(\bar{Y},X)$, then $\bar{Y}$ is a solution to the dual problem. But $\Phi(Y,X) = -\Phi(X,Y)$. Therefore $\Phi(Y,X_0) \leq \Phi(Y_0X_0) \leq \Phi(Y_0,X)$, and Y_0 is a solution to the dual problem. It remains to show that $CX_0 = BY_0$. In the inequality $\Phi(X,Y_0) \leq \Phi(X_0,Y_0)$ if we let $X = O$, we get $0 \leq X_0(C - AY_0)$. Since $C - AY_0 \leq O$ and $X_0 \geq O$, we have $X_0(C - AY_0) = 0$. Similarly in the inequality $\Phi(X_0,Y_0) \leq \Phi(X_0,Y)$ if we let $Y = O$, we get $Y_0(B - AX_0) = 0$. Since $B - AX_0 \geq O$ and $Y_0 \geq O$, we have $Y_0(B - AX_0) = 0$. But then $X_0C - X_0AY_0 = Y_0B - Y_0AX_0$ and $X_0C = Y_0B$.

Exercises

27.1 Find all solutions to the following linear programming problems:
  a. $x_1 \geq 0$, $x_2 \geq 0$, $x_1 + x_2 \leq 1$; maximize $2x_1 - 3x_2$.
  b. $x_1 \geq 0$, $x_2 \geq 0$, $x_1 + x_2 \leq 1$, $x_1 \leq \frac{1}{2}$; maximize $2x_1 + 3x_2$.
  c. $x_1 \geq 0$, $x_2 \geq 0$, $x_1 + x_2 \leq 1$, $x_1 \leq \frac{1}{2}$; maximize $2x_1 + 2x_2$.
  d. $x_1 \geq 0$, $x_2 \geq 0$, $x_1 - x_2 \leq 1$; maximize $2x_1 - 3x_2$.
  e. $x_1 \geq 0$, $x_2 \geq 0$, $x_1 + x_2 \leq -1$; maximize $2x_1 + 2x_2$.

27.2 Find all solutions to the following linear programming problems:
  a. $x_1 \geq 0$, $x_2 \geq 0$, $x_3 \geq 0$, $x_1 + x_2 + x_3 \leq 1$; maximize x_1.
  b. $x_1 \geq 0$, $x_2 \geq 0$, $x_3 \geq 0$, $x_1 + x_2 + x_3 \leq 1$; maximize $x_1 + 2x_2 + 3x_3$.
  c. $x_1 \geq 0$, $x_2 \geq 0$, $x_3 \geq 0$, $x_1 \leq 1$, $x_2 \leq 1$; maximize $x_1 - x_2$.

27.3 Suppose $x_i \geq 0$, $i = 1, \ldots, n$, and let f_j, $j = 1, \ldots, m$ be linear functions of the x_i each $\leq b_j$, $\geq b_j$, or $= b_j$ for $j = 1, \ldots, m$. If we are either to maximize or minimize a function f linear in the x_i subject to these constraints, show that any such problem can be formulated as a linear programming problem.

27.4 Two machines M_1 and M_2 produce three products P_1, P_2, and P_3. Machine M_1 produces one unit of P_1, two units of P_2, and six units of P_3 each day, and M_2 produces two units of each product each day. It costs \$400 a day to run M_1 and \$300 a day to run M_2. How should the machines be utilized to produce eight units of P_1, ten units of P_2, and six units of P_3 at minimum cost to the producer?

27.5 State the dual to the problem in Exercise 27.4.

27.6 Complete the proof of Theorem 27.5.

27.7 Generalize Theorems 16.2 and 16.3 to E^n.

27.8 Generalize Theorems 16.5 and 16.6 to E^n.

27.9 Generalize Theorems 16.8, 16.9, and 16.11 to E^n.

27.10 Generalize Theorem 16.12 to E^n.

27.11 Prove Theorem 16.12 and its generalization to E^n directly without using the polar dual.

27.12 Let M be the feasible set of the linear programming problem $AX \leq B$, $X \geq O$, $\max_X f = CX$, and let M' be the feasible set of the dual problem. Show that the original problem and its dual each have a solution if (a) $B \geq O$ and M' is not empty; (b) $A \geq O$ and $B \geq O$.

27.13 Using the same notation as in Exercise 27.12 show that whenever $C \leq O$ and M is not empty, then the original linear programming problem has a solution.

INTRODUCTION

6

**MINKOWSKI
GEOMETRY**

So far we have restricted ourselves to euclidean geometry. However, a great deal of the theory of convex bodies and of other branches of euclidean geometry does not depend on the fact that we work in euclidean space and thus can be carried over to other geometries. In this chapter we investigate a generalization of euclidean geometry called Minkowski geometry. For those familiar with the terminology used by analysts, we note that an n-dimensional Minkowski space is also called an n-dimensional Banach space. We use the term Minkowski space since this is the one most frequently used by geometers and we wish to emphasize the geometric aspects of these spaces.

First we introduce the concept of a

215

metric space and give various examples. Then topologically equivalent metric spaces and isometric metric spaces are defined. We show that every r-flat in E^n is isometric to E^r and also that every metric line in E^n is an ordinary line. The remainder of Sec. 28 is devoted to a brief discussion of spherical two-dimensional space.

Next, the Minkowski plane $\mathfrak{M}^2$ is defined and it is shown that $\mathfrak{M}^2$ is euclidean iff its unit circle is an ellipse. The fact that perpendicularity in $\mathfrak{M}^2$ is in general not symmetric is discussed, and the Minkowski planes which do have symmetric perpendicularity are characterized. The notions of rectangles and area in $\mathfrak{M}^2$ are then investigated.

Minkowski n-space $\mathfrak{M}^n$ is defined and characterized in terms of normed linear spaces. We then show that any two n-dimensional Minkowski spaces are topologically equivalent. The remainder of Sec. 30 is devoted to an investigation of volume and surface area in $\mathfrak{M}^3$. In particular the solution to the isoperimetric problem in $\mathfrak{M}^3$ is described and its relation to the existence of transversals discussed.

28 METRIC SPACES

In Sec. 18 we introduced the distance $D(K_1,K_2)$ between two convex bodies in E^3. Theorem 18.5 shows that D has many properties in common with ordinary euclidean distance between points in E^n. It turns out that both are examples of the more general notion of a metric space.

28.1 A **metric space** $\mathfrak{M}$ is an ordered pair (M,ρ), where M is a set of points and ρ is a real-valued function of two variables. Each variable has domain M, and the following properties hold:

  a. $\rho(X,Y) \geq 0$, where equality holds iff $X = Y$.
  b. $\rho(X,Y) = \rho(Y,X)$.
  c. The **triangle inequality**: $\rho(X,Y) + \rho(Y,Z) \geq \rho(X,Z)$.

The elements of M are called the **points of** $\mathfrak{M}$, and ρ is called the **metric of** $\mathfrak{M}$.

The following examples illustrate the wide variety of metric spaces.

28.2 Theorem The following ordered pairs $\mathfrak{M} = (M,\rho)$ are all metric spaces:

  a. $M = R^n$, the set of all n-tuples of real numbers, and

$$\rho(X,Y) = \left[\sum_{i=1}^{n} (x_i - y_i)^2 \right]^{1/2}$$

b. M is the set of all closed bounded subsets of E^3, and $\rho(X,Y) = D(X,Y) = \inf \{\epsilon \geq 0 | X \subset N(Y,\epsilon)$ and $Y \subset N(X,\epsilon)\}$.

c. M is an arbitrary nonempty set, and $\rho(X,Y) = 1$ if $X \neq Y$, while $\rho(X,Y) = 0$ if $X = Y$.

d. $M = R^n$ and $\rho(X,Y) = \max_{1 \leq i \leq n} |x_i - y_i|$.

e. M is the set of all continuous real-valued functions defined on the interval $[0,1]$ of real numbers, and $\rho(X,Y) = \sup_{0 \leq t \leq 1} |X(t) - Y(t)|$.

PROOF   The proof of (**b**) is the content of Theorem 18.5.   Parts (**c**) and (**d**) are quite easy to prove, and their proofs are left to the reader.   It remains to prove (**a**) and (**e**).

a. Let $X = (x_1, \ldots, x_n)$, $Y = (y_1, \ldots, y_n)$,   and $Z = (z_1, \ldots, z_n)$ be any three points of $\mathfrak{M}$.   Using Theorem 24.1, we have

$$\rho^2(X,Z) = \sum_{i=1}^{n} (x_i - z_i)^2 = \sum_{i=1}^{n} [(x_i - y_i) + (y_i - z_i)]^2$$

$$= \rho^2(X,Y) + \rho^2(Y,Z) + 2 \sum_{i=1}^{n} (x_i - y_i)(y_i - z_i)$$

$$\leq \rho^2(X,Y) + \rho^2(YZ,) + 2\rho(X,Y)\rho(Y,Z)$$

$$= [\rho(X,Y) + \rho(Y,Z)]^2$$

where equality holds iff $(X - Y) = t(Y - Z)$ for some real number t. The remaining properties follow directly from the definition of ρ.

e. Suppose $\rho(X,Y) = \sup_{0 \leq t \leq 1} |X(t) - Y(t)| = 0$.   Then $X(t) = Y(t)$ for $0 \leq t \leq 1$, and $X = Y$.   Conversely, if $X = Y$, then $\rho(X,Y) = 0$. Now let X, Y, and Z be any three points of $\mathfrak{M}$.

$$\rho(X,Z) = \sup_{0 \leq t \leq 1} |X(t) - Z(t)|$$

$$= \sup_{0 \leq t \leq 1} |[X(t) - Y(t)] + [Y(t) - Z(t)]|$$

$$\leq \sup_{0 \leq t \leq 1} |X(t) - Y(t)| + \sup_{0 \leq t \leq 1} |Y(t) - Z(t)|$$

$$= \rho(X,Y) + \rho(Y,Z)$$

The symmetry of the definition of ρ gives us the remaining property.

Parts (**a**) and (**d**) of the preceding theorem illustrate the important fact that a set of points may have more than one metric placed upon it.   It is important, therefore, not only to specify the points when discussing a metric space but to also specify the metric.

In the sequel to Definition 11.8 we defined the topology of a space S to be the geometry associated with the group of bicontinuous transformations of S onto itself. Up to now we have only been concerned with euclidean spaces, so that no mention of the metric was necessary when we defined continuity. For arbitrary metric spaces we make the following definitions.

28.3   Let $\mathfrak{M} = (M,\rho)$ and $\mathfrak{M}' = (M',\rho')$ be two metric spaces.

a.   A spherical **neighborhood** of P in $\mathfrak{M}$ with radius r is the set $N(P,r) = \{X \varepsilon \mathfrak{M}|\rho(X,P) < r\}$. We shall occasionally use the notation $N\rho(P,r)$ to indicate the metric used.

b.   A transformation f of $\mathfrak{M}$ onto $\mathfrak{M}'$ is called **continuous** iff for each point $f(P)$ and each positive number ϵ there is a positive number δ such that $f[N(P,\delta)] \subset N'[f(P),\epsilon]$, where N' stands for a neighborhood in $\mathfrak{M}'$.

c. $\mathfrak{M}$ is called **topologically equivalent** to $\mathfrak{M}'$ iff there is a bicontinuous transformation of $\mathfrak{M}$ onto $\mathfrak{M}'$.

Interior, boundary, and exterior points are defined in a metric space exactly as in E^n. The same holds true for open and closed sets.

If $\mathfrak{M}'$ is topologically equivalent to $\mathfrak{M}$ under f, and g is a bicontinuous transformation of $\mathfrak{M}$ onto itself, then $g' = fgf^{-1}$ is a bicontinuous transformation of $\mathfrak{M}'$ onto itself. It follows that f induces an isomorphism between the group G of bicontinuous transformations of $\mathfrak{M}$ onto itself and the group G' of bicontinuous transformations of $\mathfrak{M}'$ onto itself. Therefore the invariants of G correspond in a unique manner to invariants of G'. This means that $\mathfrak{M}$ and $\mathfrak{M}'$ have the same topological properties and justifies our definition of topologically equivalent metric spaces.

28.4   Theorem   Let $\mathfrak{M} = (M,\rho)$ and $\mathfrak{M}' = (M,\rho')$ be two metric spaces over the same set M. If every open set of $\mathfrak{M}$ is open in $\mathfrak{M}'$ and conversely, then $\mathfrak{M}$ is topologically equivalent to $\mathfrak{M}'$.

PROOF   Suppose every open set of $\mathfrak{M}$ is open in $\mathfrak{M}'$ and conversely, and let f be the identity map of M onto itself. We assert that f is bicontinuous and therefore $\mathfrak{M}$ is topologically equivalent to $\mathfrak{M}'$. To see this let $P \varepsilon M$ and let $N'(P,\epsilon)$ be a neighborhood of P in $\mathfrak{M}'$. Since $N'(P,\epsilon)$ is open in $\mathfrak{M}'$, it is also open in $\mathfrak{M}$. Therefore there is a neighborhood $N(P,\delta)$ in $\mathfrak{M}$ such that $N(P,\delta) \subset N'(P,\epsilon)$. Since P is an arbitrary point of $\mathfrak{M}'$, this implies that f is continuous. A similar argument gives us that f^{-1} is continuous and completes the proof.

28.5   Theorem   Let D^n be the metric space (R^n,ρ), where $\rho(X,Y) = \max_{1 \le i \le n} |x_i - y_i|$. Then D^n is topologically equivalent to E^n.

PROOF   The following inequalities hold for arbitrary n-tuples X, $Y \varepsilon R^n$:

$$\max_{1 \le i \le n} |x_i - y_i| \le \left[\sum_{i=1}^{n} (x_i - y_i)^2 \right]^{1/2} \le n \max_{1 \le i \le n} |x_i - y_i|$$

If we let ρ' stand for the euclidean metric, this can be written $\rho(X,Y) \le \rho'(X,Y) \le n\rho(X,Y)$. Let S be an open set in E^n and let $P \varepsilon S$. Since S is open, there is an $\epsilon > 0$ such that $N_{\rho'}(P,\epsilon) \subset S$. If $\rho(P,X) \le \epsilon/n$, then $\rho'(P,X) \le n\rho(P,X) \le \epsilon$, so that $N_\rho(P,\epsilon/n) \subset S$. Therefore S is open in D^n. Now suppose that S' is open in D^n and let $P' \varepsilon S'$. Since S' is open, there is an $\epsilon' > 0$ such that $N_\rho(P',\epsilon') \subset S'$. If $\rho'(P',X) \le \epsilon'$, then $\rho(P',X) \le \rho'(P',X) \le \epsilon'$. Therefore $N_{\rho'}(P',\epsilon') \subset S'$, and S' is open in E^n.

In Sec. 11 we defined congruent or isometric subsets of E^3. We generalize this idea to arbitrary metric spaces.

28.6   Two metric spaces $\mathfrak{M} = (M,\rho)$ and $\mathfrak{M}' = (M',\rho')$ are **isometric** iff there is a one-to-one mapping f of M onto M' such that $\rho'[f(X),f(Y)] = \rho(X,Y)$ for every X, $Y \varepsilon \mathfrak{M}$. f is called an **isometry** of $\mathfrak{M}$ onto $\mathfrak{M}'$. If $\mathfrak{M} = \mathfrak{M}'$, then f is called a **motion.**

We remind ourselves that the metric geometry of a space is the study of all those properties of the space which are invariant under motions (see Sec. 11).

28.7   Theorem   If $\mathfrak{M} = (M,\rho)$ and $\mathfrak{M}' = (M',\rho')$ are two isometric spaces, then the group G of motions of $\mathfrak{M}$ is isomorphic to the group G' of motions of $\mathfrak{M}'$. Thus the metric geometry of $\mathfrak{M}$ is the same as the metric geometry of $\mathfrak{M}'$.

PROOF   Since $\mathfrak{M}$ is isometric to $\mathfrak{M}'$, there is a one-to-one mapping F of M onto M' such that $\rho'[F(X),F(Y)] = \rho(X,Y)$ for X, $Y \varepsilon \mathfrak{M}$. Let $g \varepsilon G$ and consider the mapping $g' = FgF^{-1}$. g' is a one-to-one mapping of M' onto itself, and distance is preserved, since F^{-1} is an isometry whenever F is. Therefore $g' \varepsilon G'$. On the other hand every element of G' is of this form. For suppose $h' \varepsilon G'$. Then $h = F^{-1}h'F \varepsilon G$, and it follows that $h' = FhF^{-1}$. Consider the mapping I from G into G', where $I(g) = FgF^{-1}$. I is one-to-one onto, and $I(gh) = FghF^{-1} = FgF^{-1}FhF^{-1} = I(g)I(h)$. Therefore I is an isomorphism, and our proof is complete.

The following is a property of E^n which is often used but seldom proved.

28.8   Theorem   Let F^r be a metric space whose points form an r-flat in E^n and whose metric is the metric of E^n. Then F^r is isometric to E^r.

PROOF   Suppose that the equation of F^r is $X = \mu_1 B_1 + \cdots + \mu_r B_r$, $-\infty < \mu_i < +\infty$, where the B_i are linearly independent. We assert that F^r has an equation $X = \lambda_1 C_1 + \cdots + \lambda_r C_r$, $-\infty < \lambda_i < +\infty$, where the C_i are orthonormal. To see this we first note that no B_i is O, otherwise the B_i would not be linearly independent. Let $C_1 = B_1/|OB_1|$ and let $C_2 = B_2 - (B_2 \cdot C_1)C_1$. Since $C_2 \cdot C_1 = B_2 \cdot C_1 - B_2 \cdot C_1 = 0$, if we normalize C_2 by dividing by its distance from the origin, we obtain a pair of orthonormal points C_1, C_2. Now let $C_3 = B_3 - (B_3 \cdot C_1)C_1 - (B_3 \cdot C_2)C_2$. Then $C_3 \cdot C_2 = B_2 \cdot C_2 - B_3 \cdot C_2 = 0$ and $C_3 \cdot C_1 = B_3 \cdot C_1 - B_3 \cdot C_1 = 0$, and after normalizing C_3 we obtain three orthonormal points C_1, C_2, C_3. In general let $C_k = B_k - (B_k . C_1)C_1 - \cdots - (B_k \cdot C_{k-1})C_{k-1}$. This gives us a set of orthonormal points C_i, $i = 1, \ldots, r$. By construction each C_i is a linear combination of the B_is. Suppose $C_i = k_1 B_1 + \cdots + k_r B_r$, and consider the equation

$$\begin{aligned}
X &= \mu_1 B_1 + \cdots + \mu_i(k_1 B_1 + \cdots + k_r B_r) + \cdots + \mu_r B_r \\
&= (\mu_1 + \mu_i k_1)B_1 + \cdots + \mu_i k_i B_i + \cdots + (\mu_r + \mu_i k_r)B_r \\
&= \lambda_1 B_1 + \ldots + \lambda_r B_r
\end{aligned}$$

If each μ_i ranges over all real numbers, it follows that each λ_i ranges over all the real numbers, and conversely. Therefore $X = \mu_1 B_1 + \cdots + \mu_i C_i + \cdots + \mu_r B_r$, $-\infty < \mu_i < +\infty$, is an equation of F^r. If we substitute C_i for B_i, $i = 1, \ldots, r$, we get $X = \mu_1 C_1 + \cdots + \mu_r C_r$, $-\infty < \mu_i < +\infty$, for an equation of F^r, and our assertion is proved.

We now prove the theorem for an arbitrary r-flat F^r passing through the origin. We may suppose that the equation of F^r is $X = \mu_1 C_1 + \cdots + \mu_r C_r$, $-\infty < \mu_i < +\infty$, where the C_i are orthonormal. Let the mapping f from F^r onto E^r be defined as follows: $f(X) = X' = (\mu_1, \ldots, \mu_r)$. We assert that f is an isometry. f is easily seen to be one-to-one onto. Let $P = p_1 C_1 + \cdots + p_r C_r$ and $Q = q_1 C_1 + \cdots + q_r C_r$ both lie on F^r, and let ρ_n and ρ_r stand for the metric in E^n and E^r respectively. Then

$$\begin{aligned}
\rho_n{}^2(P,Q) &= (P - Q) \cdot (P - Q) \\
&= \left[\sum_{i=1}^{r} (p_i - q_i)C_i \right] \cdot \left[\sum_{i=1}^{r} (p_i - q_i)C_i \right] \\
&= \sum_{i=1}^{r} (p_i - q_i)^2 = \rho_r{}^2(P',Q')
\end{aligned}$$

Therefore f is an isometry of F^r onto E^r.

If the equation of the r-flat F^r is $X = \mu_1 B_1 + \cdots + \mu^r B^r + B$, $-\infty < \mu_i < +\infty$, then $T_{-B}(F^r)$ is an r-flat passing through the origin. Let f be an isometry of $T_{-B}(F^r)$ onto E^r. Then fT_{-B} is an isometry of F^r onto E^r, and our proof is complete.

We conclude this section with some properties of metric lines and segments in various metric spaces.

28.9   Let $\mathfrak{M} = (M,\rho)$ be an arbitrary metric space.

   a.   If f is an isometry of E^1 onto a subset of $\mathfrak{M}$, then $f(E^1)$ is called a **metric line in** $\mathfrak{M}$.

   b.   If f is an isometry of an interval $[a,b]$ of E^1 onto a subset of $\mathfrak{M}$, then $f([a,b])$ is called a **metric segment** joining $f(a)$ to $f(b)$.

   c.   A subset K of $\mathfrak{M}$ is called **convex** iff **every** segment joining points of K lies entirely in K.

In general more than one segment can be found which joins two points of a metric space (see Theorem 28.11).   However, this is not the case in E^n.

28.10   Theorem   In E^n every metric line (metric segment) is an ordinary line (ordinary segment), and conversely.

PROOF   Suppose L is an ordinary line.   According to Theorem 28.8, L is isometric to E^1 and L is a metric line.   If S is an ordinary segment, let L be the line containing S.   There is an isometry f of L onto E^1. f restricted to S is an isometry of S onto an interval of E^1.   Therefore S is a metric segment.

Suppose S is a metric segment in E^n and let P', Q' be the end points of S.   We assert that $S = S[P',Q']$.   Let P, Q be the isometric images of P', Q' respectively on E^1 and let R' be an arbitrary point of S coming from R on E^1.   Since $P < R < Q$, we have $|P - R| + |R - Q| = |P - Q|$, and therefore $|P'R'| + |R'Q'| = |P'Q'|$.   According to the proof of part (**a**) of Theorem 28.2 this occurs iff $(P' - R') = t(R' - Q')$ for some real number t.   Therefore $R' = sP' + (1 - s)Q'$ for some real number $0 \leq s \leq 1$,

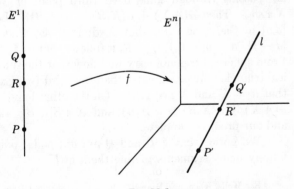

Fig. 28.1

$R' \varepsilon S[P',Q']$ and $S \subset S[P',Q']$. Suppose $R' \varepsilon S[P',Q']$. Then $(P' - R')$ = $t(R' - Q')$ for some real number t. Let X be chosen so that $(P - X)$ = $t(X - Q)$. Then $|P - X| + |X - Q| = |P - Q|$. But then $|P'X'| +$ $|X'Q'| = |P'Q'|$ and $(P' - X') = t(X' - Q')$. Therefore $R' = X' \varepsilon S$, and $S[P',Q'] \subset S$.

Applying the preceding considerations to the case $P < Q < R$ and the case $R < P < Q$ will show that every metric line is an ordinary line. This completes the proof.

There is a convenient metric that can be placed on the unit sphere in E^3 which has a close relationship to the theory of convex cones. The following can be extended to E^n, but we restrict ourselves to E^3 for simplicity. Let S^2 be the unit sphere in E^3 with center at the origin, and let $P, Q \varepsilon S^2$. Let $\alpha(P,Q)$ be the euclidean length of the shortest arc of a great circle of S^2 containing P and Q. The first two properties of a metric follow directly from the definition of α, while the third is a well-known property of spherical triangles.[1]

28.11   Theorem $U^2 = (S^2, \alpha)$ is a metric space called **spherical 2-dimensional space**. The segments of U^2 are precisely the arcs of great circles on S^2 with length less than or equal to π.

PROOF   Suppose $\widehat{AB}$ is an arc of a great circle in S^2 with euclidean length $l \leq \pi$. Consider the interval $[0,l]$ of real numbers. If $r \varepsilon [0,l]$, let $f(r)$ be the point R on $\widehat{AB}$ such that the length of $\widehat{AR}$ equals r. f is an isometry of $[0,l]$ into U^2. Therefore $\widehat{AB}$ is a segment.

Suppose $S[A,B]$ is a segment on U^2, where $S[A,B]$ is the isometric image of the interval $[a,b]$ of real numbers under f. We assert that $S[A,B] =$ $\widehat{AB}$, where $f(a) = A$, $f(b) = B$, and $\widehat{AB}$ is the shortest arc joining A to B on the great circle through A and B. If A and B are antipodal, $\widehat{AB}$ is the arc passing through some fixed third point of $S[A,B]$. To see this let $X \varepsilon \widehat{AB}$. Then $\alpha(A,X) + \alpha(X,B) = \alpha(A,B)$. Let r divide the interval $[a,b]$ in the same ratio that X divides $\widehat{AB}$, that is, $\alpha(A,X)/\alpha(A,B) =$ $|a - r|/|a - b|$. If $f(r) = R$, it follows that $\alpha(A,R) + \alpha(R,B) = \alpha(A,B)$. From spherical trigonometry we know that the sum of two sides of a spherical triangle is always greater than the third (see Exercise 28.5). It follows that $R = X$ and $X \varepsilon S[A,B]$. On the other hand, suppose $X \notin \widehat{AB}$. Then $\alpha(A,X) + \alpha(X,B) > \alpha(A,B)$ and $X \notin S[A,B]$. Therefore $S[A,B] = \widehat{AB}$, and our proof is complete.

We notice that if P and Q are antipodal points of S^2, there are infinitely many segments joining them in U^2.

---

[1] See Kells, Kern, and Bland, "Plane and Spherical Trigonometry," 3d ed., McGraw-Hill Book Company, New York, 1951.

28.12 Let M be a subset of E^n and $P \varepsilon E^n$. A **cone** $C_p(M)$ with **vertex** P and **directrix** M is the union of all rays $R[P,Q)$ such that $Q \varepsilon M$. If there is no line contained in a given cone, we call it a **strict cone**.

28.13 Theorem Each closed convex strict cone in E^3 with vertex O intersects S^2 in a proper closed convex subset of U^2, and each proper closed convex subset of U^2 is the directrix of a closed convex strict cone in E^3 with vertex O.

PROOF We shall use s to stand for segments in U^2 and S for segments in E^3. First we note that $C_0(K)$ is closed iff K is closed whenever K is a subset of S^2. For suppose K is closed and B is a boundary point of $C_0(K)$. Let $R[O,B)$ intersect S^2 in B'. If N is an arbitrary small neighborhood of B in E^3, then $N_\alpha = C_0(N) \cap S^2$ is a neighborhood of B' in U^2. Since K is closed, $B' \varepsilon K$ and therefore $B \varepsilon C_0(K)$. On the other hand, suppose $C_0(K)$ is closed and B is a boundary point of K. Since $K \subset C_0(K)$, B is also a boundary point of $C_0(K)$, or $B \varepsilon C_0(K)$. Therefore $B \varepsilon C_0(K)$. Since $B \varepsilon S^2$, it follows that $B \varepsilon K$ and K is closed.

Suppose K is a closed convex subset of U^2, $K \neq S^2$. We assert that $C_0(K)$ is a convex strict cone. Let P', $Q' \varepsilon C_0(K)$. Then $P' \varepsilon R[O,P)$ and $Q' \varepsilon R[O,Q)$ for some P, $Q \varepsilon K$. Let $R' \varepsilon S(P',Q')$. The ray $R[O,R')$ intersects $s(P,Q)$ in some point R. Since K is convex, $R \varepsilon K$ and $R' \varepsilon C_0(K)$. Therefore $C_0(K)$ is convex. Suppose $C_0(K)$ contained a line L. We may assume that L passes through the origin. For, if not, let L' be the line through O parallel to L and let X be an arbitrary point of L'. Every neighborhood of X contains a point lying on some ray $R[O,P)$ where $P \varepsilon L$. Therefore X is a boundary point of $C_0(K)$. But $C_0(K)$ is closed so that

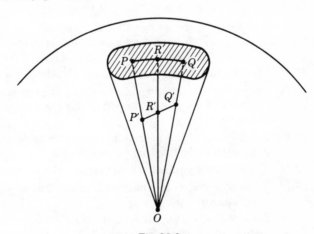

Fig. 28.2

$X \varepsilon C_0(K)$ and $L' \subset C_0(K)$. Let $L' \cap S^2 = \{P, P'\}$. P, P' lie on K and are antipodal. Since every point of S^2 lies on a segment joining P to P', and since K is convex, we have $K = S^2$, contrary to assumption. Therefore $C_0(K)$ is a strict cone.

Now suppose that $C_0(K)$ is a closed convex strict cone and $K \subset S^2$. K is a proper subset of S^2. For, if $K = S^2$, then $C_0(K)$ is the whole space E^3 and therefore is not a strict cone. Let $P, Q \varepsilon K$, then $P, Q \varepsilon C_0(K)$. If $X \varepsilon s(P,Q)$, then $R[O,X) \cap S[P,Q]$ is some point $X' \varepsilon C_0(K)$. But then $X \varepsilon K$, and K is convex.

Exercises

28.1 Prove parts (c) and (d) of Theorem 28.2.

28.2 Complete the proof of Theorem 28.10.

28.3 Show that spherical 2-space is a metric space.

28.4 Show that in spherical 2-space if P and Q are antipodal points and R is any other point, then $\alpha(P,Q) = \alpha(P,R) + \alpha(R,Q)$.

28.5 In spherical 2-space show that whenever triangle PQR has no pair of antipodal points for vertices, then $\alpha(P,Q) < \alpha(P,R) + \alpha(R,Q)$.

28.6 Let $M = R^n$ and define $\rho(X,Y) = \sum\limits_{i=1}^{n} |x_i - y_i|$. Show that (M,ρ) is a metric space.

28.7 Let M be the totality of all real-valued continuous functions on the interval $[a,b]$ and let $\rho(X,Y) = \left\{ \int_a^b [X(t) - Y(t)]^2 \, dt \right\}^{1/2}$. Show that (M,ρ) is a metric space.

28.8 Show that the axioms for a metric space can be replaced by (a) $\rho(X,Y) = 0$ iff $X = Y$, and (b) $\rho(X,Z) \le \rho(Y,X) + \rho(Y,Z)$.

28.9 In a metric space we say that X_n converges to X, written $X_n \rightharpoonup X$, iff $\rho(X_n X) \rightarrow 0$. Show that transformation f is a continuous transformation of (M,ρ) into (M',ρ') iff $f(X_n) \rightarrow f(X)$ whenever $X_n \rightharpoonup X$.

28.10 Show that the metric space in Exercise 28.6 is topologically equivalent to E_n.

28.11 Sketch the unit circle for each of the following metrics over R^2: (a) $\rho(X,Y) = 1$ if $X \ne Y$, $\rho(X,X) = 0$; (b) $\rho(X,Y) = \max\{|x_1 - y_1|, |x_2 - y_2|\}$; (c) $\rho(X,Y) = |x_1 - y_1| + |x_2 - y_2|$.

28.12 Extend each of the metrics in Exercise 28.11 to a metric space over R^3, and sketch the unit sphere for each metric.

28.13 Show that every subset of a metric space is a metric space.

28.14 If ρ_1 and ρ_2 are metrics over set M, show that $\rho_1 + \rho_2$ and $\max\{\rho_1, \rho_2\}$ are also metrics over M.

28.15 Show that whenever (M,ρ_1) and (M,ρ_2) are topologically equivalent, then all four metric spaces in Exercise 28.14 are topologically equivalent.

28.16 Prove that the motions of a metric space which leave a subset invariant (or pointwise invariant) form a group.

28.17 Make sketches of points in E^3 which describe the orthogonalization process used in the proof of Theorem 28.8.

28.18 Define the length of a curve in a metric space $\mathfrak{M}$ and show that a segment S in $\mathfrak{M}$ is a curve of shortest length connecting the end points of S.

28.19 Show that in the metric space of Exercise 28.6 there are infinitely many segments joining any pair of distinct points.

28.20 If l is a metric line in (M,ρ_1) and also in (M,ρ_2), show that l is a metric line in $(M, \rho_1 + \rho_2)$.

28.21 Define spherical 1-space. Show that it is a metric space, and describe its segments.

28.22 Show that the following subsets of S^2 are convex sets in (S^2,α):
  a. A spherical triangular region each side with length less than π
  b. An open hemisphere

28.23 Show that the following subsets of S^2 are not convex sets in (S^2,α):
  a. A spherical triangular region having a side of length π
  b. A closed hemisphere

29 THE MINKOWSKI PLANE

Consider the following figure F in E^3. F is the union of the unit circle U with center at the origin lying in the x_1x_2 plane, the x_1 and x_2 axes, and the square circumscribed to U with sides parallel to x_1 and x_2 axes. If we rotate F about the origin to F' so that the plane of F' is oblique to the x_1x_2 plane, then the orthogonal projection F'' of F' onto the x_1x_2 plane will be the union of an ellipse U' with center at the origin, a pair of oblique lines l and m through O, and a parallelogram circumscribed to U' with sides parallel to l and m. If our line of vision were parallel to the x_3 axis, the rotated figure F' would still appear to us as a circle inscribed to a square. However, if our vision were flat instead of stereographic, F' would look like F''. We can still consider F'' as containing a unit circle circumscribed by a square provided we define the distance between points of F'' to be ·equal to the distance between their preimages in F'. This can be accomplished without considering F and F'' as imbedded in E^3.

29.1 Theorem Let U be an ellipse in the euclidean plane $E^2 = (R^2,e)$ with center at the origin. If X, $Y \in R^2$, let $L_0(X,Y)$ be the line through O parallel to $L(X,Y)$ and let P be a point on $L_0(X,Y) \cap U$. We define $m(X,Y) = e(X,Y)/e(O,P)$ and call $m(X,Y)$ a **Minkowski distance** between X and Y. $M^2 = (R^2,m)$ is a metric space and M^2 is isometric to E^2.

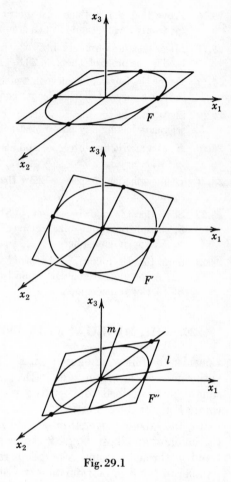

Fig. 29.1

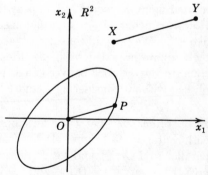

Fig. 29.2

PROOF First we show that m is a metric. $m(X,Y) = 0$ iff $e(X,Y) = 0$. Therefore the first property of a metric holds. The symmetry property follows directly from the definition of m. In order to prove the triangle inequality let P, Q, and R be any three distinct points of R^2. If they are collinear with Q between P and R, then $e(P,Q) + e(Q,R) = e(P,R)$ and $m(P,Q) + m(Q,R) = m(P,R)$. It follows that the triangle inequality holds for collinear points. Suppose P, Q, and R form a triangle with sides of length $\alpha = m(P,R)$, $\beta = m(P,Q)$, and $\gamma = m(R,Q)$. We shall show that $\alpha < \beta + \gamma$. From the definition of m it follows that the distance between two points will not change under a translation. Let $\triangle OAB$ be the image of $\triangle PQR$ under a translation sending P onto O, and let $R[O,A) \cap U = A'$ and $R[O,B) \cap U = B'$. Let $R[O,C)$ be drawn parallel to $L(R,Q)$ so that $R[O,A)$ lies in the smaller angle formed by $R[O,B)$ and $R[O,C)$, let $m(O,C) = \gamma$, and let $R[O,C) \cap U = C'$. Then

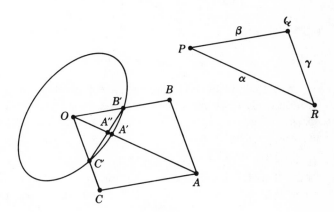

Fig. 29.3

$A = \alpha A'$, $B = \beta B'$, and $C = \gamma C'$.   The point $A'' = A/(\beta + \gamma) = (B + C)/(\beta + \gamma) = (\beta/\beta + \gamma)B' + (\gamma/\beta + \gamma)C'$ lies inside the ellipse, since an ellipse bounds a convex body, and A'' also lies on $L(O,A)$. Therefore there is a number θ, $0 < \theta < 1$, such that $A'' = \theta A'$. But then $A = \alpha A' = \theta(\beta + \gamma)A'$ and $\alpha < \beta + \gamma$. This proves that m is a metric.

It remains to show that M^2 is isometric to E^2. We may assume that the equation of U in R^2 is of the form $x^2/a^2 + y^2/b^2 = 1$. For if not, we can rotate the coordinate axes in R^2 until they coincide with the principal axes of U. Consider the linear transformation f of R^2 onto itself given by $x' = ax$, $y' = by$. f is one-to-one and maps the circle $x^2 + y^2 = 1$ onto the ellipse U. Let X, Y be arbitrary points of R^2, $OXYQ$ be a parallelogram, and $R[O,Q) \cap U = P$. If $X' = f(X)$ for $X \in R^2$, then P' lies on U

and $e(O,Q) = e(O,Q)/e(O,P) = e(O,Q')/e(O,P') = m(O,Q')$. Since f sends parallel lines onto parallel lines, $OX'Y'Q'$ is a parallelogram. Therefore $e(X,Y) = e(O,Q) = m(O,Q') = m(X',Y')$, and f is an isometry.

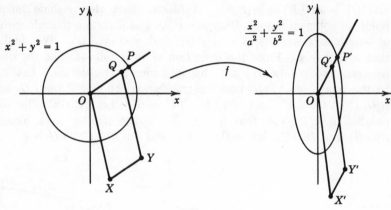

Fig. 29.4

Although we have not done so, it is possible to define perpendicularity in E^n entirely in terms of distance. We do this now for an arbitrary metric space so that the new definition agrees with our previous definition for perpendicularity in E^n.

29.2 If metric line l intersects metric line m at point X, and if for every point P of m, $\rho(P,X) = \min_{Y \in l} \rho(P,Y)$, then m is called **perpendicular** to l and we write $m \dashv l$.

Returning to our considerations at the beginning of the section we now see that F'', as a figure in M^2, consists of a unit circle inscribed to a square and a pair of perpendicular lines through its center parallel to the sides of the square. This follows from the fact that there is an isometry which sends F onto F'', namely the linear transformation which sends the circle onto the ellipse, and, since perpendicularity is defined entirely in terms of distance, perpendicular lines are mapped onto perpendicular lines.

While attempting to solve certain number theoretic problems geometrically the geometer Minkowski was concerned with "fundamental regions" of lattice points in R^2 which turned out to be convex bodies with a center. It was his idea to treat a "fundamental region" as the unit disk of a metric space over R^2.

29.3 A **Minkowski plane** $\mathfrak{M}^2$ is a metric space (R^2,m) over R^2 with metric m defined as follows. Let U be the boundary of a two-dimensional convex body in E^2 with center at the origin. If X, $Y \varepsilon R^2$, let $L_0(X,Y)$ be the line through O parallel to $L(X,Y)$ and let P be a point in $L_0(X,Y) \cap U$. We define $m(X,Y) = e(X,Y)/e(O,P)$. U is called the **unit circle** in $\mathfrak{M}^2$.

The proof that M^2 is a metric space does not use any property of an ellipse which does not hold for an arbitrary convex body with center.   This shows that $\mathfrak{M}^2$ is a metric space.

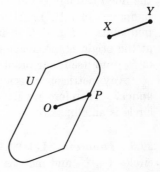

Fig. 29.5

Any ordinary line (1-flat) in R^2 is easily seen to be a metric line in $\mathfrak{M}^2$. The converse is not true. For example, if U is the parallelogram with vertices $(0,\pm 1)$ and $(\pm 1,0)$, then the curve $y = $ Arc tan x will be a metric line in $\mathfrak{M}^2$.   We can say, however, that metric lines and 1-flats coincide in $\mathfrak{M}^2$ iff U is **strictly convex**, i.e., iff no line segment is contained in U.   This follows from the proof of Theorem 29.1, where it is seen that $\alpha = \beta + \gamma$ for triangle PQR iff $A' = A''$ (see Fig. 29.3).   Whenever the word "line" is used without a qualifying adjective, it will continue to stand for a 1-flat.

We now determine necessary and sufficient conditions for two Minkowski spaces to be isometric.

29.4   Theorem   The Minkowski plane $\mathfrak{M}^2$ is isometric to E^2 iff the unit circle U of $\mathfrak{M}^2$ is the image of the unit circle C in E^2 under a linear transformation of R_2 onto itself.

PROOF   Theorem 29.1 proves one-half of the theorem.   To prove the converse we notice first that U must be strictly convex, so that the only metric lines of $\mathfrak{M}^2$ are 1-flats.   For suppose the contrary, and let f be an isometry of $\mathfrak{M}^2$ onto E^2.   Let PQR be a triangle in $\mathfrak{M}^2$ such that $m(P,Q) = m(P,R) + m(R,Q)$.   Then $L(P,Q)$ is mapped onto $L[f(P),f(Q)]$ by f since the only metric lines of E^2 are 1-flats.   It follows that $f(R) = f(X)$ for some point $X \varepsilon L(P,Q)$. This contradicts the fact that f is an isometry and therefore one-to-one.

A familiar property of an ellipse is that the midpoints of a family of parallel chords lie on a line through the center. Conversely if U bounds a convex body with center in E^2 and if the midpoints of each family of parallel chords lie on a line through the center, then U is an ellipse.[1] Now let f be an isometry of E^2 onto $\mathfrak{M}^2$ and let F be any family of parallel chords of U. $f^{-1}(F)$ is a family of parallel chords of C, and since C is a circle in E^2, the line l through O perpendicular to the chords of $f^{-1}(F)$ contains all the midpoints of $f^{-1}(F)$. It follows that $f(l)$ is a line which contains all the midpoints of F and U is an ellipse. Since every ellipse in R^2 with center at the origin is the image of the unit circle under a linear transformation of R_2 onto itself, our proof is complete.

Any metric space isometric to E^2 will naturally be called a **euclidean space.** Therefore we have just proved that $\mathfrak{M}^2$ is euclidean iff its unit circle is an ellipse.

29.5   Theorem   Let $\mathfrak{M}_1$ and $\mathfrak{M}_2$ be two Minkowski planes with unit circles U_1, U_2 and metrics m_1, m_2 respectively. $\mathfrak{M}_2$ is isometric to $\mathfrak{M}_1$ iff U_2 is the image of U_1 under a linear transformation of R^2 onto itself.

PROOF   Suppose that $\mathfrak{M}_2$ is isometric to $\mathfrak{M}_1$ under f and suppose $f(O) = O$. Let C be the locus of equation $x^2 + y^2 = 1$ in R^2, and let C' be its image under f. If U_1 and U_2 are strictly convex, then the only metric lines are 1-flats, and 1-flats are mapped onto 1-flats. If U_1 and U_2 are not strictly convex, then not all metric lines are 1-flats, but the image of a 1-flat under f is again a 1-flat (see Exercise 29.19). If F is a family of parallel chords of C and if l is the line through their midpoints, then $f(F)$ is a family of parallel chords of C' and $f(l)$ passes through their midpoints. Therefore C' is an ellipse. Let T be a linear transformation which maps C onto C'. We can assume that for at least one point $P \varepsilon C, f(P) = T(P)$. For if not, let $P \varepsilon C$ and let $f(P) = T(Q)$. If R is the rotation in R^2 which maps P onto Q, then $T' = TR$ is a linear transformation, $T'(C) = C'$, and $T'(P) = f(P)$. We now show that $f(Q) = T(Q)$ for every point Q of $L(O,P)$ when $T(P) = f(P)$. Suppose $Q = \lambda P$, $\lambda > 0$. Since f is an isometry, we have

$$\lambda = \frac{e(O,Q)}{e(O,P)} = \frac{m_1(O,Q)}{m_1(O,P)} = \frac{m_2[O,f(Q)]}{m_2[O,f(P)]}$$

$$= \frac{e[O,f(Q)]}{e[O,f(P)]}$$

[1] See H. Busemann, "Geometry of Geodesics," Academic Press Inc., New York, 1955.

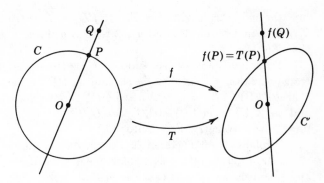

Fig. 29.6

Since T is a linear transformation, we have $T(Q) = \lambda T(P)$ and $\lambda = e[O,T(Q)]/e[O,T(P)]$. Therefore $e[O,T(Q)] = e[O,f(Q)]$ and $T(Q) = f(Q)$. If $Q = \lambda P$, $\lambda < 0$, then O is the midpoint of $S[f(Q), f(-Q)]$ and also of $S[T(Q),T(-Q)]$. Since $f(-Q) = T(-Q)$, it follows that $f(Q) = T(Q)$.

Now let X be a point on $L(O,P)$ outside C and let the tangents to C from X touch C at points Q and R. Since both T and f send tangents onto tangents, it follows that either $f(Q) = T(Q)$ and $f(R) = T(R)$ or $f(Q) = T(R)$ and $f(R) = T(Q)$. If the latter occurs, we can replace T by $T'' = TR_L$, where R_L is the reflection in R^2 about the line $L(O,P)$. We assume then that $f(Q) = T(Q)$, $Q \neq P$. As above, for every point X on $L(O,Q)$ we have $F(X) = T(X)$. Consider an arbitrary point R of C not on $L(O,P)$ or $L(O,Q)$ and let $L(O,Q) \cap C = \{Q,Q'\}$. Either $L(R,Q)$ or $L(R,Q')$ cuts $L(O,P)$ in some point inside C. Suppose the former, and let $L(R,Q) \cap L(O,P) = X$. Then $f(X) = T(X)$ lies inside C', and

$$L[f(Q),f(X)] = L[T(Q),T'(X)]$$

intersects C' in the point $f(R) = T(R)$. Again, as above, for every point X on $L(O,R)$ we have $f(X) = T(X)$. Since every point in R^2 lies on some

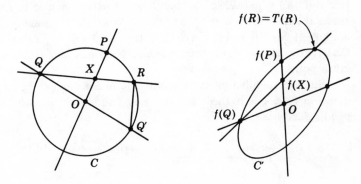

Fig. 29.7

line through the origin, $f = T$. If $f(O) = P \neq O$, then the translation T_{-P} is a motion of $\mathfrak{M}^2$, and $T_{-P}f$ is then a linear transformation T such that $T(U_1) = U_2$.

To prove the converse, suppose U_2 is the image of U_1 under a linear transformation T. Let $X, Y \in \mathfrak{M}_1$ and let $OPXY$ be a parallelogram such that $R[O,P) \cap U_1 = Q$. T maps $OPXY$ onto a parallelogram $OP'X'Y'$ and $m_1(X,Y) = e(O,P)/e(O,Q) = e(O,P')/e(O,Q') = m_2(X',Y')$. Therefore T is an isometry of $\mathfrak{M}_1$ onto $\mathfrak{M}_2$.

It follows from Theorem 29.5 that every motion of a Minkowski plane $\mathfrak{M}^2$ is the product of a nonsingular linear transformation of R^2 onto itself and a translation. It is easily seen that each translation and central reflection of R^2 is a motion of $\mathfrak{M}^2$. In general these are the only motions.[1]

The definition of $\mathfrak{M}^2$ appears to depend heavily on the underlying space E^2. Actually any euclidean space $M^2 = (R^2, e')$ isometric to E^2 could be used instead. For if $X, Y \in R^2$ and $L_0(X,Y) \cap U$ contains point W, then $m(X,Y) = e(X,Y)/e(O,W) = e'(X,Y)/e'(O,W)$, since the ratio of lengths of parallel segments is preserved under linear transformations. In general any concept which is to be a meaningful Minkowski concept must be independent of the underlying euclidean space. For example, lines, parallelism, perpendicularity, and translations are all Minkowski concepts, since they are defined in R^2 independently of the associated euclidean space.

One striking difference between euclidean geometry and Minkowski geometry is that perpendicularity, in general, is not symmetric in $\mathfrak{M}^2$, that is, if $m \dashv l$, it does not necessarily follow that $l \dashv m$.

29.6 In $\mathfrak{M}^2$ whenever $m \dashv l$, we say that l **is transversal to** m.

Suppose the unit circle U has both l_1 and l_2 supporting U at P. Then $L(O,P) \dashv l_1$ and $L(O,P) \dashv l_2$. This shows that in $\mathfrak{M}^2$ there may be more than one line transversal to a given line at a given point. Now let m be a supporting line of U parallel to $L(O,P)$. If no point X of $m \cap U$ is such that $L(O,X)$ is parallel to l_1, then l_1 is not perpendicular to $L(O,P)$. This shows that perpendicularity may not be symmetric. Finally, if U contains a segment $S[P,Q]$ and if $X \in S[P,Q]$, then $L(X,O) \dashv L(P,Q)$. This shows that there may be more than one line perpendicular to a given line at a given point.

Since perpendicularity is symmetric in a euclidean space, an obvious question to ask is if these are the only Minkowski planes for which perpendicularity is symmetric.

---

[1] See H. Busemann and P. Kelly, "Projective Geometry and Projective Metrics," Academic Press Inc., New York, 1953.

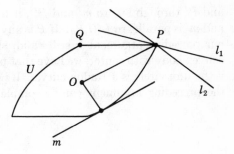

Fig. 29.8

29.7   Let C be a curve in E^2 joining $A = (0,1)$ to $B = (1,0)$ in the first quadrant so that $S[O,A] \cup S[O,B] \cup C$ bounds a convex set K contained in the square with vertices A, O, and B.   Let K^* be the polar dual of K, and rotate the part of K^* in the first quadrant $90°$ into the second quadrant to form K'.   Reflect $K \cup K'$ about the origin to get K'' and let Γ be the boundary of $K \cup K' \cup K''$.   The image of Γ under a nonsingular linear transformation is called a **Radon curve**.

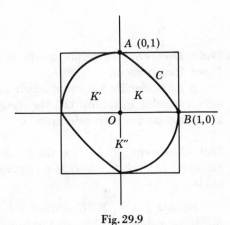

Fig. 29.9

Let P be any point on C and let l be a supporting line of K through P. Let Q be the point on $R[O,P]$ such that $e(O,Q)e(O,P) = 1$.   Let the perpendicular from O to l in E^2 intersect l in point Q' and let the perpendicular m at Q to $L(O,P)$ intersect $L(O,Q')$ in P'.   We assert that m is a supporting line of K^* at P'.   For if $X \varepsilon K$, then $P' \cdot X = e(O,P')[e(O,X) \cos \angle\ XOP'] \leq e(O,P')e(O,Q') = e(O,P)e(O,Q) = 1$. By definition of K^* we have $P' \varepsilon K^*$. But $K^* \subset H[m,O]$, therefore m is a supporting line of K^*.   If we rotate m

and P' through $90°$ to m' and P'', it follows that $L(O,P'')$ is parallel to l and m' is parallel to $L(O,P)$. If P is any point on Γ in the second quadrant, our preceding argument is still valid, since $K^{**} = K$. Since Γ bounds a convex body with center, we have that perpendicularity in $\mathfrak{M}^2$ is symmetric if the unit circle is a Radon curve. If perpendicularity in $\mathfrak{M}^2$ is symmetric, the preceding argument can be completely reversed. We therefore have

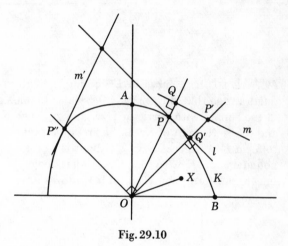

Fig. 29.10

29.8   Theorem   Perpendicularity in $\mathfrak{M}^2$ is symmetric iff the unit circle U is a Radon curve.

A particular Radon curve which has some interesting properties is the **affine regular hexagon**: i.e., the image of a regular hexagon in E^2 under a nonsingular linear transformation.

29.9   Theorem   If $L(U)$ is the Minkowski length of the unit circle U in $\mathfrak{M}^2$, then $L(U) \geq 6$. If U is a regular affine hexagon, then the equality holds.

PROOF   Let X, $Y \in U$ and let Y be the reflection of X about O. Let $S[P,Q]$ be a chord of U parallel to $S[X,Y]$ such that $e(P,Q) = e(O,X)$, and let V, W be the reflections of P, Q about O. Then X, Y, P, Q, V, and W are the vertices of a regular affine hexagon H inscribed to U, and $L(H) = 6$. Actually the equality holds iff U is a regular affine hexagon.[1]

We now consider the problem of defining area in $\mathfrak{M}^2$. We should like to have the area of a rectangle be the product of the lengths of adjacent sides. Suppose a parallelogram $\Pi = XYZW$ is circumscribed to the

[1] See C. Petty, "On the Geometry of the Minkowski Plane," Rivista di Matematica della Universita di Parma, Parma, 1955.

unit circle U and suppose that the midpoints P, Q, R, and S of the sides of Π lie on U. If P is a corner point and $L(Y,Z) \cap U = Q$, let $\Pi' = X'Y'Z'W'$ be another parallelogram circumscribed to U such that $P \varepsilon L(X',Y')$ and $Y', Z' \varepsilon L(Y,Z)$. Now $m(X,Y)m(Y,Z) = 2 \times 2 = 4$, and $m(X',Y')m(Y',Z') > m(X,Y)m(Y',Z') = 4$. It follows that we

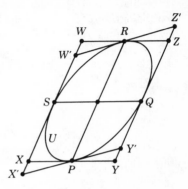

Fig. 29.11

cannot call both Π and Π' rectangles if the area of a rectangle is to be the product of lengths of adjacent sides. Although it is still not restrictive enough to give us the desired area property (see Theorem 29.13), we make the following definition.

29.10 A **rectangle** in $\mathfrak{M}^2$ is a parallelogram in which adjacent sides are mutually perpendicular, i.e., if l and m are lines containing two adjacent sides, then $l \dashv m$ and $m \dashv l$.

The first question we ask is whether rectangles exist.

29.11 Theorem   Let U bound a two-dimensional convex body K in E^2 having a center at O. Then of all parallelograms circumscribed to U there is at least one, $\beta(U)$, which has minimum area in E^2. If U is the unit circle in $\mathfrak{M}^2$, then $\beta(U)$ is a **square** (a rectangle with equal sides) in $\mathfrak{M}^2$. Of all **rhombuses** in $\mathfrak{M}^2$ (parallelograms with each side the same Minkowski length) with side length 2, at least one, $R(U)$, has maximum area in E^2. $R(U)$ is also a square.

PROOF   Let $|S|_J$ stand for the Jordan measure of set S. If $P \varepsilon U$, let $\triangle(P)$ be a triangle with maximum area having two of its vertices at O and P and the third on U. $\triangle(P)$ is defined for each P, and $|\triangle(P)|_J$ is a continuous function of P. Since P ranges over a closed bounded set, it follows that $|\triangle(P)|_J$ takes on both its maximum and its minimum.

Let $|\triangle OPQ|_J = \min_{P\varepsilon U}.|\triangle(P)|_J$, and let l and l' be supporting lines of U parallel to $L(O,P)$. Q belongs to either l or l', otherwise $|\triangle OPQ|_J \neq |\triangle(P)|_J$. Let m and m' be parallel supporting lines of U such that $P \varepsilon m$. We assert that the line through O parallel to m cuts l in a point R which lies on U. For if $R \notin U$, then $R[O,R) \cap U = R'$ would be a point for which $|\triangle(R')|_J < |\triangle(P)|_J$, contrary to the choice of P. We now claim that the parallelogram $\beta(U)$ determined by l, l', m, and m' is a minimum parallelogram circumscribed to U. Suppose parallelogram Π is circumscribed to

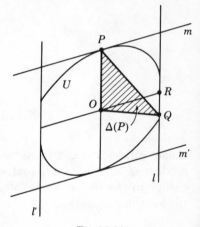

Fig. 29.12

U and two adjacent sides touch U at points P and Q. Then $|\Pi|_J \geq 8|\triangle OPQ|_J$, and equality holds iff the midpoint of a side of Π lies on U. It follows that $|\beta(U)|_J \leq |\Pi|_J$, and $\beta(U)$ is a minimum parallelogram circumscribed to U. The fact that $L(O,R) \dashv L(O,P)$ and $L(O,P) \dashv L(O,R)$ shows that $\beta(U)$ is a square.

Now let $|\triangle OPQ|_J = \max_{P\varepsilon U} |\triangle(P)|_J$, and let l and l' be supporting lines of U parallel to $L(O,P)$. Q belongs to either l or l', otherwise $|\triangle OPQ|_J \neq |\triangle(P)|_J$. Let m be the line through P parallel to $L(O,Q)$, let m' be the reflection of m about the origin, and let $R(U)$ be the parallelogram determined by l, l', m, and m'. If m is a supporting line of U, then $R(U)$ is circumscribed to U. Since $|R(U)|_J = 8|\triangle OPQ|_J$, it follows that $R(U)$ is a rhombus of side length 2 with maximum area. Since $L(O,P) \dashv L(O,Q)$ and $L(O,Q) \dashv L(O,P)$, $R(U)$ is a square. If m is not a supporting line of U, then there is some point X of U on a supporting line parallel to m separated from Q by m. But then$|\triangle OQX|_J > |\triangle OPQ|_J$, contrary to the choice of $\triangle OPQ$. This completes the proof.

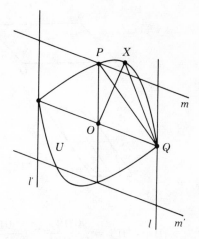

Fig. 29.13

29.12 If M is a subset of $\mathfrak{M}^2$, we define the **Minkowski area** of M to be $|M| = \sigma|M|_J = (4/|\beta(U)|_J)|M|_J$, where $\beta(U)$ is a minimum parallelogram circumscribed to U and $|S|_J$ is the Jordan measure of set S.

If $\mathfrak{M}^2 = E^2$, we notice that Minkowski area agrees with euclidean area. If M' and $\beta'(U)$ are the images of M and $\beta(U)$ under a nonsingular linear transformation of R^2 onto itself, then, since the ratio of areas is preserved,[1] $\beta'(U) = \beta(U')$, and we have $|M| = 4|M|_J/|\beta(U)|_J = 4|M'|_J/|\beta(U')|_J = |M'|$. Therefore Minkowski area is independent of the choice of the associated euclidean space. Actually we could have chosen σ to be $4/|R(U)|_J$ or any other constant such that $|M|$ is independent of the choice of the underlying euclidean space. One choice of σ that is often used is $\pi/|U|_J$.

Not all rectangles have area equal to the product of the lengths of adjacent sides. However, if we define a **minimum rectangle** to be a rectangle with sides parallel to a minimum parallelogram $\beta(U)$, then the following holds.

29.13 Theorem Let $\Pi = PQRS$ be a rectangle in $\mathfrak{M}^2$. Then $|\Pi| \geq m(P,Q)m(Q,R)$, where equality holds iff Π is a minimum rectangle.

PROOF Let $\Pi(U)$ be the parallelogram circumscribed to U with sides parallel to those of Π. Since Π is a rectangle, the midpoints of the sides of $\Pi(U)$ lie on U. Let Π' and $\Pi'(U)$ be the images of Π and $\Pi(U)$ under a linear transformation T of R^2 which sends these midpoints onto the points $(0,\pm 1)$ and $(\pm 1,0)$. Then

---

[1] See G. Birkhoff and S. Maclane, "A Survey of Modern Algebra," The Macmillan Company, New York, 1953.

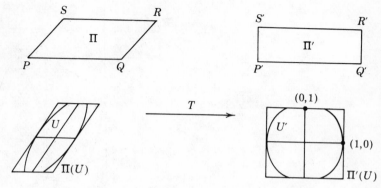

Fig. 29.14

$$|\Pi| = |\Pi'| = \frac{4|\Pi'|_J}{|\beta(U')|_J} \geq \frac{4|\Pi'|_J}{|\Pi'(U)|_J}$$

$$= e(P',Q')e(Q',R')$$

$$= m(P,Q)m(Q,R)$$

where X' is the image of X under T.   Equality holds iff $\Pi(U)$ is a minimum parallelogram circumscribed to U.

Exercises

29.1 If P, Q, and R are collinear points in E^2 and f is an affine transformation of E^2 (see Exercise 26.19), show that $f(P)$, $f(Q)$, $f(R)$ are collinear and $e(P,Q)/e(P,R) = e[f(P),f(Q)]/e[f(P),f(R)]$.

29.2 Show that every ellipse in R^2 with center at the origin is the image of the unit circle under a linear transformation.

29.3 Show that every translation and central reflection of R^2 is a motion of $\mathfrak{M}^2$.

29.4 Describe all the motions of $\mathfrak{M}^2$ when the unit circle (as a subset of E^2) is (*a*) a square; (*b*) a parallelogram; (*c*) a regular $2n$-gon.

29.5 If the unit circles of $\mathfrak{M}_1$ and $\mathfrak{M}_2$ are both parallelograms, show that $\mathfrak{M}_1$ and $\mathfrak{M}_2$ are isometric.

29.6 Using properties of an ellipse, show directly that perpendicularity is symmetric in a euclidean space.

29.7 Given any two circles in $\mathfrak{M}^2$ of radius r, show that there is a translation which maps one onto the other.

29.8 Show that perpendicularity is symmetric in $\mathfrak{M}^2$ iff any parallelogram Π circumscribed to the unit circle U has the property that whenever the midpoints of two opposite sides of Π lie on U, then the midpoints of the remaining sides also lie on U.

29.9 Give examples to show that a proper triangle ABC in $\mathfrak{M}^2$ may have the property that $m(A,B) = m(A,C) + m(C,B)$. What must be true of the unit circle for this to be possible?

29.10 Find the length of the unit circle U in $\mathfrak{M}^2$ when U is (a) a parallelogram, (b) an ellipse, (c) an affine regular octagon, (d) an affine regular $2n$-gon.

29.11 If the parallelogram Π is circumscribed to a plane convex body K with center O and if two adjacent sides of Π touch the boundary of K at points P and Q, show that $|\Pi|_J \geq 8|\triangle OPQ|_J$, where equality holds iff the midpoint of a side of Π lies on K.

29.12 Show that if $\sigma = \pi/|U|_J$ is used to define Minkowski area in Definition 29.12, then Minkowski area is independent of the choice of the associated euclidean space.

29.13 Show that every rectangle circumscribed to a Radon curve has the same euclidean area. Hence show that if perpendicularity is symmetric in $\mathfrak{M}^2$, then all rectangles have Minkowski area equal to the product of the Minkowski lengths of two adjacent sides.

29.14 Let l, m, and n be the lines which carry the sides of Minkowski length L, M, and N respectively of a given triangle $\triangle$. The **Minkowski sine** $sm(l,m)$ of the angle formed by lines l and m is defined to be $sm(l,m) = 2|\triangle|/LM$. Show that if $\mathfrak{M}^2$ is euclidean, then the Minkowski sine agrees with the ordinary sine of an angle. Also show that the law of sines holds in $\mathfrak{M}^2$.

29.15 Let $\triangle ABC$ be a given triangle and let X be a point on $S[B,C]$. Use the definition in Exercise 29.14 and show that $sm[L(A,B), L(A,C)]/m(A,X) = sm[L(A,B), L(A,X)]/m(A,C) + sm[L(A,C), L(A,X)]/m(A,B)$.

29.16 Show that $l \dashv m$ iff $sm(l',m) \leq sm(l,m)$ for every line l' through the intersection of l and m (see Exercise 29.14).

29.17 If $l \dashv m$, we define $\alpha(m) = sm(l,m)$ (see Exercise 29.16). Show that among all Minkowski planes $1 \leq \max_{l} \alpha(l) \leq 2$, where equality holds on the left if the unit circle U is a Radon curve and equality holds on the right if U is a parallelogram.

29.18 In Exercise 29.17 show that if $\max \alpha = 1$, then U is a Radon curve, and if $\max \alpha = 2$, then U is a parallelogram.

29.19 If f is an isometry of one Minkowski plane onto another, show that f maps 1-flats onto 1-flat.

30 n-DIMENSIONAL MINKOWSKI SPACE

We shall see that much of the preceding section can be generalized to higher dimensions.

30.1 A **Minkowski n-dimensional space** $\mathfrak{M}^n$ is a metric space (R^n,m) over R^n with metric m defined as follows. Let U be the boundary of an

n-dimensional convex body in E^n with center at the origin.   If X, $Y \varepsilon R^n$, let the line through O parallel to $L(X,Y)$ intersect U in a point P.   We define $m(X,Y) = e(X,Y)/e(O,P)$. U is called the **unit sphere** in $\mathfrak{M}^n$.

The proof that $\mathfrak{M}^2$ is a metric space can be carried over directly to show that $\mathfrak{M}^n$ is a metric space.

In modern analysis the idea of a normed linear space plays an important role.   We shall see that every $\mathfrak{M}^n$ is such a space.

30.2   A **linear space** $\mathfrak{L}$ is a set of points $L = \{X,Y,Z, \ldots\}$ which forms an abelian group under an operation $+$ (called addition) and has a scalar multiplication defined as follows.   Let $R = \{\alpha,\beta,\gamma, \ldots\}$ be the set of real numbers.   For each $\alpha \varepsilon R$ and each $X \varepsilon L$ the scalar product αX is an element of L such that

a. $\alpha(X + Y) = \alpha X + \alpha Y$,
b. $(\alpha + \beta)X = \alpha X + \beta X$,
c. $(\alpha\beta)X = \alpha(\beta X)$,
d. $1X = X$.

If in addition there is a function which assigns to each $X \varepsilon \mathfrak{L}$ a real number $\|X\|$ which has the following three properties, then $(\mathfrak{L}, \|X\|)$ is called a **normed linear space,** and $\|X\|$ is called the **norm** of X:

a′. $\|X\| \geq 0$, where equality holds iff $X = O$,
b′. $\|X + Y\| \leq \|X\| + \|Y\|$,
c′. $\|\alpha X\| = |\alpha| \, \|X\|$.

30.3   Theorem   If $\mathfrak{M}^n = (R^n,m)$ is a Minkowski space and if $\|X\| = m(O,X)$, then $(R^n, \|X\|)$ is a normed linear space.

PROOF   We immediately verify that if $\alpha X = \alpha(x_1, \ldots, x_n) = (\alpha x_1, \ldots, \alpha x_n)$, then R^n is a linear space.   Property (a') follows from the fact that $m(O,X) = 0$ iff $X = O$.   Next we have $\|X + Y\| = m(O, X + Y) \leq m(O,X) + m(X, X + Y) = m(O,X) + m(O,Y) = \|X\| + \|Y\|$.   Finally, for some constant k, we also have $\|\alpha X\| = m(O,\alpha X) = ke(O,\alpha X) = k|\alpha|e(O,X) = |\alpha|m(O,X) = |\alpha| \, \|X\|$.   Therefore property (c') holds, and $(R^n, \|X\|)$ is a normed linear space.

In linear algebra it is shown[1] that any finite dimensional linear space is isomorphic to R^n.   This leads to the rather strong converse of Theorem 30.3.

30.4   Theorem   If $\mathfrak{L}^n = (R^n, \|X\|)$ is any finite dimensional normed linear space and if $m(X,Y) = \|X - Y\|$, then (R^n,m) is an n-dimensional Minkowski space.

[1] See G. Birkhoff and S. Maclane, "A Survey of Modern Algebra," The Macmillan Company, New York, 1953.

PROOF   Let $U = \{X | \; ||X|| = 1\}$ and let $K = \{X | \; ||X|| \leq 1\}$.   We assert that U bounds the convex body K in E^n with center O.   If $X \varepsilon U$, then $||-X|| = |-1| \; ||X|| = 1$ and $-X \varepsilon U$.   Therefore U has center O.   If X, $Y \varepsilon K$ and $P \varepsilon S[X,Y]$, then for $0 \leq r \leq 1$ we have $||P|| = ||(1 - r)$ $X + rY|| \leq (1 - r)||X|| + r||Y|| \leq (1 - r) + r = 1$.   Therefore $P \varepsilon K$, and K is convex.   The proof that K is closed and bounded follows the same pattern as the proof of Theorem 16.6 and is left to the reader.   Now let X, $Y \varepsilon R^n$ and define $m(X,Y) = ||X - Y||$.   If $P = X - Y$ and $R[O,P) \cap U = P'$, then $m(X,Y) = ||P|| = ||\alpha P'|| = \alpha ||P'|| = \alpha = e(X,Y)/e(O,P')$, and m is a Minkowski metric with U as the unit sphere.

Although the metric properties of $\mathfrak{M}^n$ and E^n differ considerably, topologically they behave in the same way.

30.5   Theorem   Every Minkowski space $\mathfrak{M}^n = (R^n, m)$ is topologically equivalent to E^n.

PROOF   Let $X = (x_1, \ldots, x_n)$ and let E_i be the point in R^n with its ith coordinate 1 and all others 0.   From the properties of a norm it follows that

$$m(X,Y) = ||X - Y||$$

$$= ||\sum_{i=1}^{n} (x_i - y_i)E_i|| \leq \sum_{i=1}^{n} |x_i - y_i| \; ||E_i||$$

$$\leq k \sum_{i=1}^{n} |x_i - y_i| \leq kne(X,Y)$$

where $k = \max ||E_i||$.   Now let $k' = \max_{X \varepsilon U} e(O,X)$.   Then $m(X,Y) \geq e(X,Y)/k'$.   As in the proof of Theorem 28.5, we have $N_e(X,\epsilon/kn) \subset N_m(X,\epsilon)$ and $N_m(X,\epsilon/k') \subset N_e(X,\epsilon)$ for any real number $\epsilon > 0$. N_e and N_m stand for euclidean and Minkowski neighborhoods.   It follows that every open set in $\mathfrak{M}^n$ is open in E^n, and conversely.   By Theorem 28.4 $\mathfrak{M}^n$ is topologically equivalent to E^n.

Since topological equivalence is an equivalence relation, this implies that any two n-dimensional Minkowski spaces are topologically equivalent.

The proof that a linear transformation which maps the unit circle of one Minkowski plane onto the unit circle of a second is an isometry can be carried over directly to $\mathfrak{M}^n$ (see Theorem 29.5).   The converse is also true, but we shall not prove it here.[1]

30.6   Theorem   If U_1 and U_2 are the unit spheres of the n-dimensional Minkowski spaces $\mathfrak{M}_1$ and $\mathfrak{M}_2$, then any linear transformation of R^n which maps U_1 onto U_2 is an isometry of $\mathfrak{M}_1$ onto $\mathfrak{M}_2$.

[1] See H. Busemann, "Geometry of Geodesics," Academic Press Inc., New York, 1955.

Since central reflections map U onto itself, a central reflection is a motion of $\mathfrak{M}^n$. Translations are also motions, so that the group generated by translations and central reflections is a subgroup of the group of motions of $\mathfrak{M}^n$.

Perpendicular and transversal lines are defined in $\mathfrak{M}^n$ exactly as in $\mathfrak{M}^2$. We also make the following definition.

30.7   Line l is perpendicular to hyperplane π, $l \dashv \pi$, iff l is perpendicular to m for every line m in π through $l \cap \pi$.

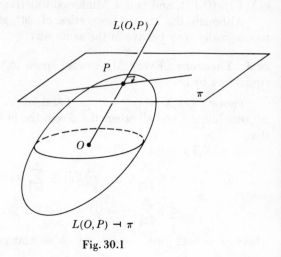

$$L(O,P) \dashv \pi$$

Fig. 30.1

If π is a supporting hyperplane to U at point P, then we see that $L(O,P) \dashv \pi$.

We now turn to a discussion of surface area and volume. Everything we discuss can be generalized to $\mathfrak{M}^n$, but we restrict ourselves to $\mathfrak{M}^3$ for simplicity.

30.8   If M is a subset of $\mathfrak{M}^3$, we define the **Minkowski volume** of M to be $|M|^3 = \sigma |M|_J^3 = (8/|\beta(U)|_J^3)|M|_J^3$, where $\beta(U)$ is a minimum parallele-piped circumscribed to the unit sphere U and $|S|_J^3$ is the three-dimensional Jordan measure of set S. If π is a plane, we define $\sigma(\pi) = 4/|\beta(\pi_0 \cap U)|_J^2$, where $|S|_J^2$ is the two-dimensional Jordan measure of set S and π_0 is the plane through O parallel to π. The **Minkowski cross-section area** of M in π is $|M \cap \pi|^2 = \sigma(\pi)|M \cap \pi|_J^2$. If Π is a polyhedron in $\mathfrak{M}^3$, then its **Minkowski surface area** is the sum of the cross-section areas of its faces.

The existence of $\beta(U)$ can be shown in a manner similar to the two-dimensional case. We notice that cross-section area agrees with area in

$\mathfrak{M}^2$. If $\mathfrak{M}^3 = E^3$, then Minkowski volume and cross-section area agree with euclidean volume and cross-section area. Both $|M|^3$ and $|M \cap \pi|^2$ are independent of the choice of the underlying euclidean space. Any other constants having these properties would serve just as well in the preceding definition. $\sigma' = 4\pi/3|U|_J^3$ and $\sigma'(\pi) = \pi/|\pi_0 \cap U|_J^2$ are often used.

Suppose $l \dashv \pi$ and $l \cap \pi = P$. If m is any line through P and $S[X,Y]$ lies on m, then the projection of $S[X,Y]$ onto l parallel to π is a segment $S[X',Y']$ and $m(X',Y') \leq m(X,Y)$. This is readily seen if we translate $S[X,Y]$ and $S[X',Y']$ so that $X' = X = P$. Then Y lies on or outside of the Minkowski sphere with center P and radius $m(X',Y')$. This suggests the following definition.

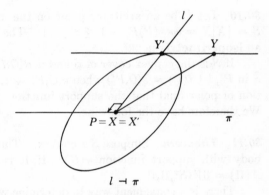

$$l \dashv \pi$$

Fig. 30.2

30.9 Line l is transversal to plane π, $l \vdash \pi$, iff for every plane π' passing through $P = l \cap \pi$ and any set M in π having cross-section area the projection M' of M onto π' parallel to l has greater or equal area, that is, $|M'|^2 \geq |M|^2$.

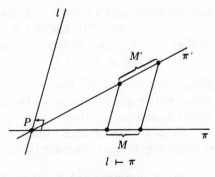

$$l \vdash \pi$$

Fig. 30.3

We now investigate the possibility of defining Minkowski surface area for arbitrary convex bodies in terms of mixed volumes. Theorem 19.15 states that $3V(K,\Pi,\Pi) = \sum\limits_{i=1}^{k} H(K,U_i)A_i$, where K is a convex body and Π is a convex polyhedron. $H(K,U_i)$ is the support function of K in the direction $\overrightarrow{OU_i}$, and $\overrightarrow{OU_i}$ is the exterior unit normal to the face F_i of Π with area A_i. If we let $A(\Pi)$ stand for the Minkowski surface area of Π, then $A(\Pi) = \sum\limits_{i=1}^{k} \sigma(U_i)A_i$, where $\sigma(U_i) = \sigma(\pi_i)$ and π_i is the plane containing the face F_i. Comparing these two equations we see that if $\sigma(U)$ is the support function of some convex body M, then $A(\Pi) = 3V(M,\Pi,\Pi)$.

30.10 Let P be an arbitrary point on the unit euclidean sphere and let $S = \{X | X = \theta\sigma^{-1}(P)P, -1 \le \theta \le 1\}$. The polar dual S^* is called an **isoperimetrix** in $\mathfrak{M}^3$.

If $\tilde{S}$ is the convex cover of S and if $R[O,P)$ intersects the boundary of $\tilde{S}$ in P', let $f(P) = e(O,P')$ when $e(O,P) = 1$. It follows from the definition of polar dual that the support function of $S^* = \tilde{S}^*$ coincides with f. We therefore have the following.

30.11 Theorem Suppose S is convex. The isoperimetrix S^* is a convex body with support function $\sigma(U)$. If Π is a convex polyhedron, then $A(\Pi) = 3V(S^*,\Pi,\Pi)$.

There is a convenient way to determine whether S is convex or not.

30.12 Theorem Let $\sigma(P) = \sigma(\pi)$ when $\overrightarrow{OP}$ is normal to π and $e(O,P) = 1$, $\sigma(O) = 0$ and $\sigma(P) = e(O,P)\sigma[P/e(O,P)]$ otherwise. Then $S = \{X | \sigma(X) \le 1\}$, and S is convex iff $\sigma(X)$ is a convex function.

PROOF Let $X \varepsilon T = \{X | \sigma(X) \le 1\}$. Then $e(O,X)\sigma[X/e(O,X)] \le 1$, and therefore $e(O,X) = \theta\sigma^{-1}(P)$, where $P = X/e(O,X)$ and $0 \le \theta \le 1$. But then $X = \theta\sigma^{-1}(P)P$ and $X \varepsilon S$. The steps are completely reversible, so that $S = T$. The theorem now follows from Theorems 16.5 and 16.6.

If $\sigma'(U) = \pi/|\pi_0 \cap U|_J^2$, where π_0 is the plane through O with euclidean unit normal $\overrightarrow{OU}$, then σ' can be defined over R^n in the same manner as σ. Both σ and σ' turn out to be convex functions. The proofs are long, however, and are omitted.[1]

So far we have defined Minkowski surface area only for polyhedra. If K is any convex body, we make the following definition (see Theorem 19.14).

---

[1] See H. Busemann and E. Straus, "Area and Normality," *Pacific Journal of Mathematics*, vol. 10, no. 1, 1960.

30.13 $A(K) = 3V(S^*,K,K) = \lim_{\epsilon \to +0} [V(K + \epsilon S^*) - V(K)]/\epsilon$ is called the **Minkowski surface area of convex body** K.

The reason we call S^* an isoperimetrix is now obvious.

30.14   Theorem   The bodies homothetic to S^* are the solutions to the isoperimetric problem in $\mathfrak{M}^3$. The convex body $I = \sigma^{-1}S^*$ is called the **normalized isoperimetrix** in $\mathfrak{M}^3$.

PROOF   Using Minkowski's inequality (see Theorem 21.8) we have $V^3(S^*,K,K) \geq (|S^*|_J^3)(|K|_J^3)^2$, where equality holds iff K is homothetic to S^*. It follows that $[A(K)/3]^3 \geq \sigma^3(|I|_J^3)(|K|_3^J)^2$ and $A(K) \geq 3(|I|^3)^{1/3}(|K|^3)^{2/3}$. Therefore of all convex bodies K with the same Minkowski volume, the one homothetic to I has the least Minkowski surface area.

We now show the close relationship between the isoperimetrix and the existence of transversals.

30.15   Theorem $\sigma(X)$ is convex iff for every plane π there is some line l such that $l \vdash \pi$. If π is a supporting plane to I at P, then $L(O,P) \vdash \pi$.

PROOF   Let π and π' be any two planes through the origin and let the euclidean normals to π and π' through O intersect S in points P and P' respectively. Let M be any set with cross-section area lying in π and let M' be the projection of M onto π' parallel to $L(O,P)$. We have $|M'|^2 = |M'|_J^2\sigma(\pi') = |M|_J^2\sigma(\pi')|\sec \angle P'OP|$. Therefore $L(O,P)$ will be transversal to π' iff $|\cos \angle P'OP|\sigma^{-1}(\pi')$ is a maximum. This occurs iff P' lies on a supporting plane of S perpendicular (in E^3) to $L(O,P)$. Since S is convex iff every boundary point of S lies on a supporting plane of S, the first part of our theorem is proved.

Now let π be an arbitrary supporting plane of I and let $\overrightarrow{OP}$ be the unit euclidean normal to π. If l is a fixed line through O, let $l \cap \pi = X$ and let $R[O,X)$ intersect the boundary of I in X'. According to the above, l will be transversal to π iff $\sigma(\pi)|\sec \angle POX|$ is a minimum. This will occur iff $\sigma^{-1}\sigma(\pi)|\sec \angle POX|$ is a minimum. Since $\sigma^{-1}\sigma(\pi)$ is the supporting function of I, it follows that $e(O,X) = \sigma^{-1}\sigma(\pi)|\sec \angle POX| \geq e(O,X')$. Since equality holds whenever $X' = X$, we have that l is transversal to the supporting plane of I at X'.

Now that we have shown the existence of transversals to planes the following generalization of the triangle inequality can be proved.

30.16   Theorem   If $\sigma(X)$ is a convex function, then the sum of the Minkowski cross-section areas of any three faces of a tetrahedron is always greater than or equal to the cross-section area of the fourth.

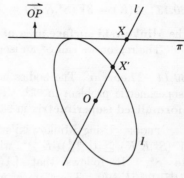

Fig. 30.4

PROOF Let F_i, $i = 1, \ldots, 4$ be the faces of a tetrahedron and let π_i be the plane containing F_i. Let l_1 be a line transversal to π_1. Since $\sigma(X)$ is convex, l_1 can always be found. Let F_i', $i = 2, 3, 4$ be the projections of F_i onto π_1 parallel to l_1. Since $F_1 \subset \bigcup\limits_{i=2}^{4} F_i'$, we have

$$\sum_{i=2}^{4} |F_i|^2 \geq \sum_{i=2}^{4} |F_i'|^2 \geq |F_1|^2$$

Everything from Definition 30.9 up to this point holds equally well in $\mathfrak{M}^2$ if we replace everywhere the word "plane" by the word "line." We notice that with this understanding Definition 30.9 agrees with our original definition of transversal lines in $\mathfrak{M}^2$. We summarize these results in the following theorem.

30.17   Theorem   Let $\mathfrak{M}^2$ be a Minkowski plane with unit circle U.

   a. The normalized isoperimetrix I is obtained by rotating U through $90°$, taking the polar dual, and then applying the homothety with center O and ratio σ^{-1}.

   b. The bodies homothetic to I are the solutions to the isoperimetric problem in $\mathfrak{M}^2$.

   c. If l is a supporting line of I at P, then $L(O,P)$ is transversal to l at P.

Many extremum problems in E^3 have their solutions determined by spheres. As we have seen, the corresponding problem in $\mathfrak{M}^3$ may or may not have its solution determined by spheres. In general, when the problem concerns finding extreme values of a quantity involving surface area, we should expect the isoperimetrix to determine the solution. If the quantity involves distance, we should expect the sphere to determine a solution. We conclude this section with two examples of this rule of thumb.

30.18   Theorem   Among all convex polyhedra in $\mathfrak{M}^3$ with parallel faces and given surface area, the one circumscribed to an isoperimetrix has maximum volume.

PROOF   Let Π' and Π be two polyhedra with parallel faces and let Π' be circumscribed to the isoperimetrix with support function $\sigma(U)$. Then $3V(\Pi',\Pi,\Pi) = \sum \sigma(U_i)|F_i|_J^2 = A(\Pi)$, where U_i is the unit exterior euclidean normal to the face F_i of Π. From Minkowski's inequality it follows that $A(\Pi) \geq 3|\Pi'|_J^3 (|\Pi|_J^3)^2$, where equality holds iff Π is homothetic to Π'.

30.19   Theorem   Among all convex bodies in $\mathfrak{M}^3$ with the same diameter D, the sphere with radius $D/2$ has the maximum volume.

PROOF   If K has diameter D, then some translation of $(D/2)U$ is circumscribed to K and $|K|^3 \leq |(D/2)U|^3$.

Exercises

30.1 Show that $\mathfrak{M}^n$ is a metric space.

30.2 Show that all one-dimensional Minkowski spaces are isometric.

30.3 Show that topological equivalence is an equivalence relation.

30.4 Prove Theorem 30.6.

30.5 Show that every translation and central reflection of R^n is a motion of $\mathfrak{M}^n$.

30.6 Show that a parallelepiped of minimum volume can be circumscribed to any three-dimensional convex body with center.

30.7 Show that Minkowski volume is independent of the choice of the underlying euclidean space.

30.8 Prove Theorem 30.17.

30.9 Show that the complex numbers can be made into a linear space.

30.10 Show that a linear space may consist of a single point.

30.11 Show how the set of all polynomials can be made into a linear space.

30.12 Show how to make each set in Exercises 30.9 to 30.11 into a normed linear space.

30.13 Let ρ be the euclidean metric of E^3 and let α be the spherical metric over S^2 (see Theorem 28.11). Show that (S^2,α) and (S^2,ρ) are topologically equivalent. Hence show that (S^2,α) and (S^2,m) are topologically equivalent for any Minkowski metric m over R^3.

30.14 Give examples to show that in $\mathfrak{M}^3$ there may be
  a. More than one line perpendicular to a given plane at a given point
  b. More than one plane π such that l is transversal to π at a given point

30.15 Show that in any euclidean space the isoperimetrix is homothetic to the unit sphere.

30.16 Show that the body S in Definition 30.10 is always convex in $\mathfrak{M}^2$.

30.17 Let Π be a parallelepiped in $\mathfrak{M}^3$ each of whose sides have Minkowski length 1. Show that if Π has the maximum volume among all such parallelepipeds and if l_1, l_2, and l_3 are the lines containing the edges of Π which meet at a vertex P, then $l_i \dashv H_i$, where H_i is the plane spanned by $l_j, j \neq i$.

30.18 Let line l intersect plane π in point P and let Π be a parallelogram in π with vertex P. If $X \neq P$ is a point on l, then we define the Minkowski sine of the angle between l and π to be $sm(l,\pi) = |\Pi'|^3/|\Pi|^2 m(P,X)$, where Π' is the parallelepiped spanned by Π and $S[P,X]$. Show that if $\mathfrak{M}^3$ is euclidean, then the Minkowski sine agrees with the ordinary sine of the angle between a line and a plane.

30.19 Show that in $\mathfrak{M}^3$ we have $l \dashv \pi$ iff $sm(l',\pi) \leq sm(l,\pi)$ for every line l' through the intersection of l and π (see Exercise 30.18).

30.20 If $l \dashv \pi$, we define $\alpha(\pi) = sm(l,\pi)$ (see Exercise 30.19). Show that $r\alpha(\pi) = 1$ is the polar equation of the normalized isoperimetrix, where r is the Minkowski length of the radius vector orthogonal to π.

30.21 Use Exercise 30.20 to show that the unit sphere coincides with the normalized isoperimetrix iff $\alpha(\pi) \equiv 1$.

LIST OF POSTULATES[1]

Postulate 1   Given any two different points, there is exactly one line which contains both of them.

Postulate 2   (The Distance Postulate).   To every pair of different points there corresponds a unique positive number.

Postulate 3   (The Ruler Postulate).   The points of a line can be placed in correspondence with the real numbers in such a way that

1.   To every point of the line there corresponds exactly one real number.

2.   To every real number there corresponds exactly one point of the line.

3.   The distance between two points is the absolute value of the difference of the corresponding numbers.

Postulate 4   (The Ruler-placement Postulate).   Given two points P and Q of a line, the coordinate system can be chosen in such a way that the coordinate of P is zero and the coordinate of Q is positive.

Postulate 5   *a.*   Every plane contains at least three noncollinear points.

   b.   Space contains at least four noncoplanar points.

Postulate 6   If two points lie in a plane, then the line containing these points lies in the same plane.

---

[1] By permission from School Mathematics Study Group, *School Mathematics Study Group Geometry Unit 13 and 14,* Yale University Press, New Haven, Conn., Copyright © 1960, 1961.

Postulate 7   Any three points lie in at least one plane, and any three noncollinear points lie in exactly one plane.   More briefly, any three points are coplanar, and any three noncollinear points determine a plane.

Postulate 8   If two different planes intersect, then their intersection is a line.

Postulate 9   (The Plane-separation postulate).   Given a line and a plane containing it, the points of the plane that do not lie on the line form two sets such that
1.   Each of the sets is convex,
2.   If P is in one set and Q is in the other, then the segment $\overline{PQ}$ intersects the line.

Postulate 10   (The Space-separation Postulate).   The points of space that do not lie in a given plane form two sets such that
1.   Each of the sets is convex.
2.   If P is in one set and Q is in the other, then the segment $\overline{PQ}$ intersects the plane.

Postulate 11   (The Angle-measurement Postulate).   To every angle $\angle BAC$ there corresponds a real number between 0 and 180.

Postulate 12   (The Angle-construction Postulate).   Let AB be a ray on the edge of the half plane H.   For every number r between 0 and 180 there is exactly one ray AP, with P in H, such that $m\angle PAB = r$.

Postulate 13   (The Angle-addition Postulate).   If D is a point in the interior of $\angle BAC$, then $m\angle BAC = m\angle BAD + m\angle DAC$.

Postulate 14   (The Supplement Postulate).   If two angles form a linear pair, then they are supplementary.

Postulate 15   (The S.A.S. Postulate).   Given a correspondence between two triangles (or between a triangle and itself), if two sides and the included angle of the first triangle are congruent to the corresponding parts of the second triangle, then the correspondence is a congruence.

Postulate 16   (The Parallel Postulate).   Through a given external point there is at most one line parallel to a given line.

Postulate 17 To every polygonal region there corresponds a unique positive number.

Postulate 18 If two triangles are congruent, then the triangular regions have the same area.

Postulate 19 Suppose that the region R is the union of two regions R_1 and R_2. Suppose that R_1 and R_2 intersect at most in a finite number of segments and points. Then the area of R is the sum of the areas of R_1 and R_2.

Postulate 20 The area of a rectangle is the product of the length of its base and the length of its altitude.

Postulate 21 The volume of a rectangular parallelepiped is the product of the altitude and the area of the base.

Postulate 22 (Cavalieri's Principle). Given two solids and a plane, if for every plane which intersects the solids and is parallel to the given plane the two intersections have equal areas, then the two solids have the same volume.

The following theorems are referred to occasionally. Since their proofs require the use of advanced calculus, we prove them here rather than in the main body of the text.

Theorem 1. If K is a convex set and Y is an exterior point to K, then there is a boundary point P of K such that $|PY| = \inf_{X \varepsilon K} |XY|$.

PROOF Let $N(Y,\delta)$ be a neighborhood of Y which contains no points of K. $|YX| > \delta$ for all $X \varepsilon K$. Therefore $r = \inf_{X \varepsilon K} |XY|$ exists, and $r \geq \delta > 0$. Choose points P_i such that $P_i \varepsilon N(Y, r + 2^{-i}) \cap K$. Sequence $\{P_i\}$ is bounded. Therefore there is a subsequence $\{P_j\}$ which converges to some point P. If P were an interior point of K, there would be a point $Q \varepsilon K$ such that $|YQ| < r$, contradicting the choice of r. Therefore P is a boundary point of K. Since $r \leq |PY| \leq r + \epsilon$ for arbitrary $\epsilon > 0$, it follows that $|PY| = r$.

Theorem 2. If K_1 is a convex body and K_2 is a closed convex set such that $K_1 \cap K_2$ is empty, then there exist points $P_1 \varepsilon K_1$ and $P_2 \varepsilon K_2$ such that $|P_1 P_2| = \min_{X_i \varepsilon K_i} |X_1 X_2|$.

PROOF Let $r(X) = \inf_{Y \varepsilon K_2} |XY|$ for each $X \varepsilon K_1$. Since $r(X)$ exists and is positive, $r = \inf_{X \varepsilon K_1} r(X)$ also exists.

Let $r(X_i) = |X_i Y_i|$, $X_i \varepsilon K_1$, $Y_i \varepsilon K_2$, be a sequence such that $r(X_i) < r + \epsilon$ for some positive ϵ and $r(X_i) \rightarrow r$. Since $X_i \varepsilon K_1$ and $Y_i \varepsilon N(K_1, r + \epsilon)$, we can pick a subsequence such that $X_j \rightarrow X \varepsilon K_1$, $Y_j \rightarrow Y \varepsilon K_2$ and $|XY| = \inf_{X_1 \varepsilon K_1} \inf_{X_2 \varepsilon K_2} |X_1 X_2| = \min_{X_i \varepsilon K_i} |X_1 X_2|$.

Theorem 3   (Helly's theorem).   Let $C = \{K_\alpha\}$ be any collection of convex bodies in E^n, and suppose that every $n + 1$ of them have a common point. Then there is a point common to all members of $\{K_\alpha\}$.

PROOF   Let K be any fixed member of C and consider the collection of sets $C' = \{K'_\alpha = K_\alpha \cap K\}$. According to Exercise 18.6, any finite number of C' have a common point. Suppose $\cap K'_\alpha$ is empty. Then every point of K lies outside of some fixed set K'_α and therefore belongs to some set of the form $K - K'_\alpha$. Therefore $K \subset \cup (K - K'_\alpha)$. Since K is compact, the Heine-Borel theorem[1] tells us that there is some finite subcollection of $\{K - K'_\alpha\}$ such that $K \subset \bigcup_{i=1}^{n} (K - K'_i)$. But then $K \subset K - \bigcap_{i=1}^{n} K'_i$ and $\bigcap_{i=1}^{n} K'_i$ is empty. This contradicts the fact that any finite number of members of C' have a common point. Therefore $\cap K'_\alpha = \cap K_\alpha$ is not empty.

[1] See R. Buck, "Advanced Calculus," McGraw-Hill Book Company, New York, 1956.

BIBLIOGRAPHY

Blasche, W.: "Kreis und Kugel," Chelsea Publishing Company, New York, 1949.

Boltyanskii, V. G.: "Equivalent and Equidecomposable Figures," D. C. Heath and Company, Boston, 1963.

Bonneson, T., and **W. Fenchel:** "Theorie der Konvexen Körper," Chelsea Publishing Company, New York, 1948.

Busemann, H.: "The Geometry of Geodesics," Academic Press Inc., New York, 1955.

Busemann, H., and **P. Kelly:** "Projective Geometry and Projective Metrics," Academic Press Inc., New York, 1953.

Coxeter, H.: "Introduction to Geometry," John Wiley & Sons, Inc., New York, 1961.

Eggleston, H.: "Convexity," Cambridge University Press, London, 1958.

Eves, H.: "A Survey of Geometry," vol. 1, Allyn and Bacon, Inc., Boston, 1963.

Fejes, Toth L.: "Lagerungen in der Ebene auf der Kugel und in Raum," Springer-Verlag, Berlin, 1953.

Hadwiger, H.: "Altes und Neues über Konvexe Körper," Birkhäuser Verlag, Basel, 1955.

————: "Vorlesungen über Inhalt, Oberfläche und Isoperimetrie," Springer-Verlag, Berlin, 1957.

254

Hadwiger, H., H. Debrunner, and **V. Klee:** "Combinatorial Geometry in the Plane," Holt, Rinehart and Winston, Inc., New York, 1963.

Karlin, S.: "Mathematical Methods and Theory in Games, Programming and Economics," vol. 1, Addison-Wesley Publishing Company, Inc., Reading, Mass., 1959.

Lyusternik, L.: "Convex Figures and Polyhedra," Dover Publications, Inc., New York, 1963.

Schreier, O., and **E. Sperner:** "Introduction to Modern Algebra and Matrix Theory," 2d ed., Chelsea Publishing Company, New York, 1959.

Sommerville, D.: "An Introduction to the Geometry of N Dimensions," Dover Publications, Inc., New York, 1958.

Valentine, F.: "Convex Sets," McGraw-Hill Book Company, New York, 1964.

Yaglom, I., and **V. Boltyanskii:** "Convex Figures," Holt, Rinehart and Winston, Inc., New York, 1961.

INDEX